GUNPOWDER TO GUIDED MISSILES -

IRELAND'S WAR INDUSTRIES

ANTRIM
torpedos

CARRICKFERGUS
tanks
parachutes

BANGOR

BELFAST incendiary
guns
bayonets
grenades
shells
tanks
armoured cars
ships
aircraft
guided missiles
ammunition

ARIGNA
cannonballs

BANBRIDGE
aircraft

WARRENPOINT
landing craft

DUNDALK
shells

NAVAN
armoured cars

GALWAY
shells
shotgun
ammunition

DUBLIN
gunpowder
guns
grenades
shells
fuses
ships

ENFIELD
blasting
explosives

CARLOW
shells

ARKLOW
high explosives

LIMERICK
fuses

WEXFORD
shells

CORK
shells

WATERFORD
shells
cases

BALLINCOLLIG
gunpowder

COBH
ships

KINSALE
ships

GUNPOWDER TO GUIDED MISSILES -
IRELAND'S WAR INDUSTRIES

George D Kelleher M.A. (N.U.I.)
1946 - 1987

BASED ON A THESIS WHICH
WAS AWARDED THE
POSTHUMOUS DEGREE OF
MASTER OF ARTS BY
UNIVERSITY COLLEGE,
CORK [NATIONAL
UNIVERSITY OF IRELAND] IN
SEPTEMBER 1989.

III

GUNPOWDER TO GUIDED MISSILES -
IRELAND'S WAR INDUSTRIES

PUBLISHED BY   JOHN F KELLEHER
1, KELLEHERS VILLAS
BUNACUMMER
INNISCARRA
CO. CORK
IRELAND

British Library Cataloguing in Publication Data
Kelleher, George D. *1946 - 1987*

       Gunpowder to Guided Missiles: Ireland's War Industries
       1361 - 1986
       1. Armaments industries, history
       I. Title
       338.476234

       ISBN 0-9514264-0-0
       ISBN 0-9514264-1-9 pbk

FIRST PUBLICATION 22nd FEBRUARY 1993

DESIGNED & PRINTED BY DATAPLUS, BELFAST

GUNPOWDER TO GUIDED MISSILES -
IRELAND'S WAR INDUSTRIES

DEDICATION

To my mother, and father's memory

GUNPOWDER TO GUIDED MISSILES -
IRELAND'S WAR INDUSTRIES

CONTENTS

CONTENTS, continued

ILLUSTRATIONS

ILLUSTRATIONS, continued

FOREWORD

George Kelleher died on 14th November 1987 before his pioneering research on the history of the gunpowder and related war industries of Ireland could be published. Fortunately however he had prepared a thesis recording the principal results of the work which had occupied him for some sixteen years. When he died his mother and his brother John were determined that the thesis should be published. This book is the result and provides a most appropriate memorial to its author.

My wife and I began to interact with George Kelleher in 1984 when we were planning the inaugural meeting of the Gunpowder Mills Study Group. He supported the new society with great enthusiasm and provided those of us who had only recently become involved in the history of the gunpowder industry with a wealth of detailed information on mills in all parts of the British Isles. His inspiration was of course the site of the former Royal Gunpowder Mills at Ballincollig, County Cork, which are near his family home. His researches into the history of this site led him to libraries and record offices at home and overseas and resulted in a vast collection of information on the British gunpowder and munition industries. This book provides an absorbing account of the most significant aspects of the research. It is particularly well documented and will provide an indispensible source book of information for all those interested in industrial, economic, military and social history over the past two centuries.

In addition to conducting meticulous historical research, George Kelleher was an ardent and determined campaigner for the surviving features of the Ballincollig gunpowder site to be recorded and conserved, so that future generations of local residents and visitors could appreciate the characteristic physical remains of this important example of a former industry. In the past few years a worthwhile start has been made in carrying out some of the necessary work but much remains to be done. Again it would be fitting tribute if the publication

GUNPOWDER TO GUIDED MISSILES -
IRELAND'S WAR INDUSTRIES

of this book results in increased activity of this kind.

Members of The Gunpowder Mills Study Group, and more generally all those interested in the history of technology, are indebted to George Kelleher for his massive contribution to our knowledge and understanding of this important industry and to his mother and brother for publishing this comprehensive account of his work.

Professor Alan Crocker, DSc, CEng,
Chairman, Gunpowder Mills Study Group.

ACKNOWLEDGEMENTS

Many persons have helped me with this project.

My gratitude goes, first and foremost, to Senator John A Murphy, Professor of Irish History, University College of Cork, for his very ready acceptance of the original, much smaller, proposal in 1974 and his constant encouragement since then.

I thank all the individuals, who assisted in the assembly of information and the institutions which provided facilities and permitted the use of copyright and other materials; these are named in the Sources if not mentioned in these Acknowledgements.

The material in Source 268, 269 and 363 appears by the gracious permission of Her Majesty Queen Elizabeth II, Sir Robin Mackworth-Young KCVO, Royal Librarian, and his staff placed every facility at my disposal in Windsor Castle.

Special acknowledgements are due to the Trustees of the National Library, the British Library and the Keeper of Public Records and the Controller of HMSO for permission to use many different documents.

I am particularly indebted to Tony Cole, Librarian and Archives Manager, ICI Millbank, London who granted the rare privilege of access to the Company's records and generously provided copies of many items and the hospitality of Imperial Chemical House; Martin Boddy and Sue J Harvey of his staff speeded the research; Roy K Shirley of the Secretary's Department smoothed the way and I enjoyed useful discussions with WJ Reader, author of the official *ICI: A History*.

Tony Moody, Assistant Public Relations Manager of IMI, Birmingham supplied copies of many documents and his colleague Alec Hutton, who was about to retire from the publicity store, unearthed from a remote corner of the huge warehouse the magnificent *illuminated address* (Source 297). As it happened when I was in Kynoch Works in 1976 large quantities of outdated advertising materials were being thrown out and had I not arrived at that time this work of art might well have perished.

In East Grinstead I had a fascinating conversation with Helen Mary Reid, the last living link with the house of Tobin, widow of the author of the family history (Source 139), grandaughter of James Aspinall and grandniece of both Sir Thomas and Lady Catherine, whom, old and widowed, she had known as a child. At the age of ninety-four she entertained me to afternoon tea with muffins and toasted crumpets, redolent of a vanished age.

In London I was assisted by GL Beech, NG Cox, FE Herme, HE Jones, N Kent, CJ Kitching, AAH Knightbridge, PR Meldrum, NAM Rodger, SGV Smith, DL Thomas, V Traylen and JL Walford at the Public Record Office. JM Backhouse and L Johnston of Manuscripts and Morna Chichester, John Goldfinch and ME Goldrick of Offical Publications helped at the British Library and HMG Baillie, Elizabeth Dunmary and Susan Willmington in the Historial Manuscripts Commission. Jack Lane, an old friend, obliged in several ways.

At the Propellants, Explosives and Rocket Motor Establishment, Sources 91-93, a chauffeured car was provided, this in the week after Derry's Bloody Sunday and the arson of the British Embassy in Dublin in January 1972 and moreover without any advance arrangement.

In Belfast I had valuable assistance from Gerry Slater, Peter Smith, Peter Houston, Geraldine Hume and Anne Hunter at the Public Records Office. Professor ERR Green, Director, Institute of Irish Studies, received me affably. H Russell, Deborah Shorley and Janet Smyth of the Irish and Local Studies Library were especially helpful. Much material was provided by Alan Hedgley, Harland and Wolff; Jim White, Short Borthers and an official of the Department of Commerce who insisted on anonymity.

In Dublin I am grateful to B Mac Giolla Choille, Deputy Keeper of Public Records and Keeper of State Papers and Philomena Connolly, Frank Corr, David V Craig, Catriona Crowe and Gay Gaynor of these Offices. At the National Library I always received the ultimate in assistance from Alf MacLochlainn, now Director, Edward Fahy, Michael Hewson, Gerard Lyne, Brian J McKenna, Donal O'Luannaigh and the ever efficient counter staff. Help was given most cordially by Brigid Dolan, Librarian, Royal Irish Academy and Oliver Snoddy, Assistant Keeper of Art and Industry and AT Lucas, former Director, National Museum. I am grateful to Dr Michael Gilheany, Registrar of the National University of Ireland (NUI), for his attention and interest and his predecessor Dr John Bourke.

In Cork I received much useful assitance from Padraig O'Maidin, County Librarian, the City Library staff and Jimmy Murphy who knows the University College Cork (UCC) Library better than anyone.

PREFACE

This thesis shows that over the period of eight hundred years many different undertakings manufactured a remarkable range of war *matériel*. Ballincollig and Arklow were as large as any in the world and most of the others were big by Irish and indeed international standards.

Many of the events and developments related are of relevance today. Industry is of immense significance in every way. The level of industrialisation is increasing very markedly and also changing profoundly in character. While many products and processes have gone out of use it is always possible that parts of the past may be of significance in the future as a few random recent examples show.

In April 1980 alder trees, which provided charcoal for gunpowder, were planted in the Bog of Allen for experiments in biomass, a system of using rapid growth vegetation as a source of alternative energy. The next year the National Board for Science and Technology began research into old hydroelectricity schemes and mills powered by water and wind.

In March 1981 the Post Office issued stamps commemorating John Philip Holland and Sir Charles Parsons (Chapter Three); Robert Boyle and Harry Ferguson (pages 202, 222, 225). Hopefully there will be a permanent seat of remembrance of the country's place in the technological world.

The study of this branch of history is a worthwhile as that of any other branch. It has the additional empirical value of practical application being a prerequisite in any exploitation of dormant systems.

In every sense, cultural, intellectual and utilitarian, industry is a fundamental feature of our lives, heritage and the future of civilisation. Its manifold aspects have scarcely yet been studied seriously in Ireland. I suggest industriology

GUNPOWDER TO GUIDED MISSILES -
IRELAND'S WAR INDUSTRIES

as a general term and trust that this example will encourage
the selective preservation of archives, photos, films, specimens
of products and machines and plans of plant which can become
obsolete within a very few years.

The basic format is by product and undertaking.

All interpretations are entirely mine.

George D. Kelleher

Spring 1982
Autumn 1987

GUNPOWDER TO GUIDED MISSILES
IRELAND'S WAR INDUSTRIES

CHAPTER ONE

GUNPOWDER COMES TO IRELAND;
THE DUBLIN MILLS

Gunpowder, in chemical terms, is a simple compound of everyday substances, saltpetre, sulphur and charcoal, which was one of the most basic advances in the history of humankind. In the obscurity of its origins and importance of its impact it is on the same plane as the other fundamental developments, fire and metal, the lever and the wheel, which form the foundations of technology.

The neutron bomb is the inevitable outcome of the relentless advance of science unleashed by the black grains which formed the world's first, and for more than six centuries, sole explosive. There is a variety of theories and views as to who invented gunpowder. Some champion the Chinese. Others advocate the Arabs. More are convinced that the Crusaders brought the explosive to Europe. In the English speaking world the cause of Roger Bacon, a friar of the Franciscan Order, has been heavily promoted down the centuries. In Germany there are two claimants, Count Albertus Magnus, Bishop of Bollstadt and one Black Berthold who is supposed to have invented both gunpowder and guns. The town of Freiburg in Baden Baden has a statue of Berthold boasting these alleged accomplishments (50).

Gunpowder could not have been invented by any friar, bishop or other individual, and it is equally certain that it was not found by any team working on a systematic research programme. It could only have evolved over a long period during which it was discovered that among numerous chemical reactions a mixture of seventy-five parts saltpetre, fifteen charcoal and ten sulphur or within a few points of these, produced a most remarkable effect when set alight. In time it was found that if a quantity was placed in a container or a crack in a rock it tended to exert a force which varied according to the purity of the mixture and the resistance involved.

Eventually it was discovered that if the powder was placed in a pipe closed at one end except for a fusehole and ignited, a lump of stone or metal was propelled, by hot gas, with speed and force such as had never been seen before. Many years must have elapsed from

1

the earliest rough and ready pipes to the first really effective guns. New techniques for working metals had to be developed and there was endless trial and error in finding the shapes and sizes for different types of weapons. It is not clear when gunpowder appeared. The first guns seem to have been used in the second quarter of the fourteenth century.

Before the introduction of weaponry, based on gunpowder, battles and sieges were slow long drawn out affairs. Cavalry charges were not at all the full tilt stampedes portrayed in countless films. The armour clad armies of the age moved, if at all, even more slowly than the proverbial tortoise. Garrisons anticipating attacks could commandeer all the livestock, granaries and other supplies for long distances, destroying any crops and stores which they could not use and behind strong walls, which were always built around at least one hopefully reliable spring, were well placed to withstand very long sieges while the attackers were a long way from home and in the midst of territory which was both barren and hostile.

During this period the principal personal weapons were swords, spears, lances and long bows, all ancient and the comparatively new crossbow. Artillery was available in a variety of forms (page 201). Also brought into the fray on rare occasions as availability of materials and technical knowledge allowed was Greek Fire or some similar compound of quicklime and such combustibles as naphta, phosphorus, bitumen and oil. These concoctions which usually burned even in water were not explosives in any sense.

Gunpower changed the entire character of battles and sieges. The previously impenetrable armour and impregnable walls were as ineffective as skin and cloth against the new weaponry. The economics of warfare changed also. The old system had been costly in its way as arms and accoutrements had not been cheap by the reckoning of the day. Guns and powder were enormously more expensive.

Gunpowder, more than any other single advantage, enabled Spain, Portugal, Britain, France, Holland, Italy, Belgium and Germany to carve out huge empires in the Americas, Africa, Asia and the Pacific as the natives with their primitive weapons had no chance against the murderous firepower of the white conquerors who in some instances exterminated entire peoples. Genocide was not invented by Adolf Hitler.

The position of Ireland in the middle and the fourteenth century, around the time that guns came into use, was that Dublin and its immediate neighbourhood, The Pale, were firmly under English control and in the remainder the extent to which the monarch's writ ran, varied. The Norman Conquest which began in 1169 was successful at first and in 1172 Pope Alexander III, sent his congratulations to King Henry II urging him to remove the abominable practices and recall the Irish to the Christian Church and exhorted the Irish to be loyal to the King (28).

Within eighty years the Irish were capable of defeating the Normans in open battle. The colony was weak, disunited and suffered from the failures of many barons to found long lasting dynasties. Many families which survived tended to intermarry with the Irish, becoming more Irish than their in-laws. Still other families were absentee landlords living in Wales and England on the rents of their estates. As the years went by and the colony had not the benefit of fresh forces, the dispossessed Irish were steadily recovering their lost lands. Even though the Kings of England had been appointed Lords of Ireland by the Pope, only one, John, visited the country in the two hundred years after Henry II.

Who first brought gunpowder and guns to Ireland? Specifically the question is who would have been in a position to do so and moreover to leave a record. Merchants, both Irish and foreign, sailors, clergymen, travellers and adventurers could very well have brought guns for their own use, for sale or barter, as gifts or novelties. It is extremely unlikely that they would have left any kind of record which even if they did would hardly have survived. Furthermore harbour authorities and customs and excise did not exist in any form resembling the present agencies.

This leaves the King of England in his capacity as Lord of Ireland as surely the party most likely to have brought the first guns to Ireland and also to have left some record.

At this time the monarch controlled all the functions of government. Parliament was still primitive. There were no cabinet ministers, departments and public boards. All aspects of administration were carried out under the control of the royal court through the Chancellor, the Chamberlain and other officers. Within the royal household, one officer, the Keeper of the King's Privy Wardrobe had, among various responsibilities, the care of the monarch's personal weapons which formed the national arsenal. In 1360 one Henry de Snayth became Keeper. While his predecessors had for nearly thirty years held quantities of powder and some guns from time to time, he was the first to keep saltpetre, charcoal and sulphur, equipment for making powder and large numbers of guns as part of the regular stock.

The first expedition under royal auspices to Ireland, after the introduction of gunpowder was in the year following de Snayth's appointment when King Edward III decided to send his son, Lionel Duke of Clarence.

In August 1361 as Lionel was about to depart, de Snayth issued him with a gun for his campaign. This lasted five years, winding up with a Parliament which passed a series of measures, the Statutes of Kilkenny (1).

These laws were intended to keep the colony together as far as possible and to hold the Irish at bay. Various restrictions were imposed. The second Statute forbade the colonists, on pain of life and limb, to sell to the Irish in time of peace and war any horse or armour or victuals in war. The sixth Statute laid down, on pain of imprisonment and fine, that the colonists were not to play hurling and instead to practice archery, lancing and other appropriate martial arts (42-3).

Guns were not mentioned and it is apparent that the weapon which Lionel brought was a mere curiosity.

Thirty years passed until the next royal visitation. In October 1394 King Richard II came bringing six large and six small cannon according to the accounts of Ranulph de Hatton, Keeper. When he returned in 1399 he had, according to Richard Lufwyk's accounts, eight large guns; two hundred round stones; two hundred charges of powder; two hundred tampions, wads for separating powder and shot; eight firpannes, charcoal braziers; sixteen touches for firing the guns; two thousand bows and six thousand sheaves of arrows. At the end of the campaign he lodged the remainder of the supplies in Dublin Castle (2,3,5).

By this time powder was coming more fully into its own and the arrangements of the Privy Wardrobe were no longer adequate for running the arsenal. Accordingly in 1414 a new office, Master of the Ordnance, was created. In time the Honourable Board of Ordnance under the Master General evolved and remained an important institution until its abolition in 1855 (4).

It seems reasonable to assume, as the first stock of firearms was in Dublin Castle, that the first powder mill was in or about the fortress also. The construction of the stronghold was ordered by King John in 1204 and it was the seat of British administration until 1922. The oldest buildings now in the Castle are from the mid-eighteenth century. The earliest mill buildings would not have been extensive or substantial, just a few sheds for storing, preparing and mixing the ingredients, a cooperage for making barrels and a magazine, no doubt in the Castle itself. The mill buildings would probably have been on the River Camac which flows, now underground, into the Liffey, conveniently close to the Castle. A document of 1248, about a century before gunpowder, refers to "the King's Mills lately erected near Dublin". Thus the practice of having mills outside the Castle would have been 150 years old at least by the time of Richard II (29,30,40).

It is not clear how long gunpowder was made in the Castle. It is apparent that by the mid-sixteenth century the Ordnance was dependent on imports. In 1560 Sir Thomas Gresham, royal agent in Antwerp who was responsible for purchasing powder and other supplies, recommended that several mills should be erected (33).

By this time the Office of Ordnance in Ireland, in theory at least separate, was well established. In 1550 the Master was called on to "declare the state of his Office". In 1617 the position was worth 6s 8d (33 1/2p) per day with an escort of eighteen horsemen and two officers (31-2).

A further indication that powder was not being made in the Castle and certainly not on a sufficient scale for the Nine Years' War is that large quantities were being imported at the end of the sixteenth century. In 1597 a cargo of 144 barrels unloaded at Wood Quay in transit to the Castle exploded causing between one and two hundred deaths and serious damage according to the subsequent official reports (34-6).

By this time the use of firearms was becoming widespread and the Castle found it necessary to place limits on the ownership of guns among the Colonists and the Irish. The earliest attempt seems to have been made by Sir Edward Poynings, Lord Deputy, who convened a Parliament chiefly famous for Poynings' Law which made the Irish Parliament subservient to that of England and passed two measures of military interest. One, "An Act that Subjects of this Realm shall have Bows and other Armour" laid down the number and type of weapons which each subject was to hold according to his wealth. Various penalties were prescribed for failure to observe the law. The other "An Act that no great Ordinance be in no fortress but by the Licence of the Deputy" was an attempt to prevent anyone having either artillery or 'handgunnes' on pain of confiscation (44-5).

This measure was mainly aimed at the colonists. It is doubtful if it had any more success than the numerous efforts directed against the Irish. In 1595 the Castle issued a long proclamation in the name of Queen Elizabeth I banning the sale of powder "to any but her

Majesty's good subjects". Offenders would suffer confiscation and indefinite imprisonment. This apparently had no effect (11).

In 1597 there was a report that sword cutlers in Birmingham and Manchester had been selling weapons to the Irish for several years. In 1599 there was a complaint that merchants in the various ports were making enormous profits smuggling powder and weapons which they sold at three times the cost to loyal subjects and six times to the insurgent Irish who were prepared to pay one bullock for a pound (0.45 kilo) of powder and six for a single musket, sword or helmet. These profits were after payment of all expenses which included "sums for stopping the searcher's mouth". A similar complaint was made the next year (37-9).

Even if powder was not being made in the Castle at this time it was certainly being produced elsewhere in the city or outskirts under the auspices of Dublin Corporation which in February 1589 voted £10 to a certain Robert Poynter, a master gunner, resolving that he would be provided with the "services of one labouring man out of every house in the city and suburbs that is thought capable of bearing the same, to labour as he shall direct, for finding out of saltpetre and making gunpowder". Apparently this meant that Poynter had to instruct a separate crew each day as there was no option to pay cash instead of doing the work. This could hardly have been an efficient arrangement even in a job which did not have the dangers inherent in powder. A contract was made under which Poynter was to supply powder at six pence ($2^{1}/_{2}$p) per pound delivered to the city warehouse.

Poynter had to provide the mills himself. It is probable that he set up his plant outside the city walls, most likely on the Camac or the Dodder on the south side. The Corporation needed quantities for their armed police force, the City Watch. In addition they sold some occasionally, for example a barrel in 1600 to the inhabitants of Thomas Street, Francis Street and James Street "for the defence of the ward". In 1603 a barrel was distributed to salute the Lord Lieutenant's departure for England. In 1608 the Mayor and Sheriffs of the Bullring, as distinct from those of the city, were fined £10 or two barrels of corn powder or a term in the Marshalsea for failing to muster on May Day which was then a traditional holiday (6-10).

Powder was made in wartime. It is doubtful if any such efforts were very productive. The Jacobites tried to do so in Limerick during the siege of 1690, "but 'tis said that the powder is so weak, it is useless; but for this they depend wholly upon the French" (677).

There was no serious system for permanent production of powder and armaments generally in Ireland and England during peacetime. Consequently when hostilities broke out factories had to be set up hastily with the heat of battle, bureaucratic no less than conventional, compounding the normal complexities of initiating industrial enterprises. When the fighting ended the mills and workshops were closed or sold and the surplus stocks disposed of.

It is possible that there were other small mills in Dublin during the sixteenth and seventeenth centuries, with or without municipal contracts. It was not until the early eighteenth century that the first was set up on a systematic and businesslike basis.

On 12 June 1716 the Irish House of Commons considered an approach from one Nicholas Grueber. A family of the name, with variant spelling, was involved in the English gunpowder industry from sometime before this and for a full century after. The firm of Curtis's & Harvey was set up in 1820 to replace the partnership of Harvey and Grueber formed apparently in the early eighteenth century with a mill at Hounslow, Middlesex. In the 1720s Francis Grueber was owner of a powdermill in Faversham, Kent. The Gruebers were Huguenots, Protestants who fled from France following the Revocation in 1685 of the 1598 Edict of Nantes which had allowed them some toleration. The Gruebers and the Pigous, also Huguenots, were among the small number of families dominant in the English gunpowder industry at the time (15, 16, 41).

Grueber described himself as a merchant, which term at the time apparently included a manufacturer, in presenting to Parliament a petition "humbly proposing to make any quantity of good and sufficient powder on reasonable terms, praying the recommendation of this House to their Excellencies the Lords Justices for that purpose".

The House agreed that the petition would be placed before the Justices by the members who also sat on the Privy Council. The matter next came before the House on 17 September 1717 when Grueber submitted another petition stating that he had "brought into this Kingdom proper artificers for making gunpowder and proposing to erect powdermills, and to furnish His Majesty's stores with such quantities as shall be requisite". The House set up a Committee to consider the petition (682).

At this point the United Company of Merchants of England Trading to the East Indies got involved. This was one of the great chartered commercial corporations of the day, ranking with the Hudson's Bay Company, the Muscovy Company, the Portuguese

Mozambique Company and others. The East India Company, set up in 1599 with a charter from Queen Elizabeth 1 as a trading house, became constituted as the actual government of India for a long period with a huge army and navy and was feared in the same way as twentieth century type multi-national companies. In the English Parliament the Company commanded extensive support amounting to a virtual party.

No doubt the Company thought they would have little difficulty with the subservient legislature in Dublin. They sent an official, one George Jackman, to place their case before the Commons. They objected to Grueber importing saltpetre into Ireland on the grounds that under their charter they had a monopoly of importing this commodity into England and as they claimed by extension, into Ireland as well. This privilege was all the more significant as India at the time had the only known mines of saltpetre.

Jackman presented a petition to the Commons against Grueber's, the House deferred consideration until the Committee's report was made. This was received and discussed on 7 October. Immediately afterwards the House heard Jackman's case pleaded by a barrister whom he had engaged. The Commons resolved to reject the Company and found in favour of Grueber. It was resolved "that the erecting of proper powdermills is highly necessary for the defence and safety of this Kingdom and will likewise increase His Majesty's revenue". The House placed a contract with Grueber for four hundred barrels a year for twenty-one years at £3-14-0 (£3.70p) per barrel. The full price for the first year was paid immediately with an advance, the amount of which was not specified, for the remaining twenty years.

On 18 December the Court of Directors of the Company resolved to send a "Humble Petition" to the King. They pointed out their privilege in regard to saltpetre which Grueber was infringing. Moreover they were under an obligation to sell five hundred tons a year to the government and to keep an equal amount in reserve, at a price much less than the going rate. There is no evidence that the King, George 1, responded (12,13).

Grueber went ahead, as well he might. Even if he had not a farthing of his own he had an advance of at least £1,500 from the Irish Parliament which must have enabled him to get into production very quickly as the machinery used at the time was not very complicated. The site of the mill is not definitely traceable. It probably was on the Camac, between Baldonnel and Clondalkin; it is believed locally that the remains of a mill worked by a pond fed from the river are those of a powdermill. Adjacent are the ruins of a strong stone building, probably a magazine (47).

On 30 September 1723 the Commons heard a petition from Grueber; he was about to build another mill and "prayed the encouragement of the House". A Committee was set up who met and reported the next day. They were fully satisfied with his case and that he deserved "encouragement from the public". The matter was referred to the Committee on Supply, that is finance, who reported in favour on 24 October. The House voted £1,000.

In 1729 there were difficulties, which were investigated by the Commons, concerning the storage of powder in the Royal Hospital, Kilmainham, a home for old soldiers, contrary to its charter. It would appear that Grueber, facing heavy competition from imports, invoked Parliament to obstruct his rivals (14).

It is not clear how long Grueber continued after this; a very brief report appeared in the *Dublin Evening Post*, Tuesday 24 November 1733, "last Sunday night the Gunpowder Mills near Clondalkin were blown up by which several persons received much damage". Presumably this was Grueber's. The original contract would have expired in 1739. It is doubtful if the house of Grueber continued in Dublin beyond the middle of the century.

A powdermill was operated on the River Camac, in the vicinity of the present Clondalkin Paper Mills, probably from sometime in the mid 1770s. The proprietor was William Caldbeck the barrister who also had a gun foundry (page 205) and a shop in Bishop Street. A William Caldbeck who was secretary to the Honourable Society of King's Inns at the time was presumably the same individual.

Caldbeck was a leading member of the Lawyers' Corps of Volunteers.

When the main aim of the Volunteers, Legislative Independence, was achieved in 1782 he apparently went into the export business. In 1785 the Irish Parliament passed "A Bill entitled an Act for granting Bounties on Gunpowder, the Manufacture of this Kingdom exported". The English Privy Council, which even after Legislative Independence had the function of examining Irish Measures before the Royal Assent, rejected the Bill on the grounds "of a mistake in the calculation of the present duties payable in Great Britain on saltpetre and brimstone" (sulphur), and that the measure was in contravention of trading arrangements between Ireland and Britain, and between Ireland and the British colonies in North America. Caldbeck took his case up with John Foster, then Chancellor of the Irish Exchequer and later the last speaker of the Commons. On 8 February 1787 and 5 February 1788 the Irish Parliament imposed duties on imports of powder other than of British manufacture.

The *Dublin Evening Post*, 26 April 1787, reported an explosion in the mills three days earlier which at first was thought to be an earthquake and then an accident on a barge drawing powder down the Grand Canal to Dublin. The explosion turned out to have been in the corning house of the mill. Reportedly, a large quantity of finished powder was stored in the loft instead of the magazine, which if true, was an extraordinarily hazardous practice. Two were killed and five or six injured. Casualties were so low because the majority of the workers, who were English, were away celebrating St George's day.

The mill was still in existence in 1798 and probably closed soon afterwards (17-24,690).

Another mill existed in Dublin in the late eighteenth century. Its location is not clear. In 1803 Henry Arabin, powder manufacturer with an address in Bridgefoot Street and a mill elsewhere wrote to Dublin Castle about some problems he had. In 1807 Henry Arabin and Richard Chenevix, licensed gunpowder manufacturers, sent a petition to The Castle requesting the removal of various restrictions which had been imposed over the previous few years. In 1822 Arabin, by then on his own again, mentioned in a letter to The Castle that he had been in the business since 1796, no longer a manufacturer he had become a wholesaler and was agent for Curtis's & Harvey of London (25-7).

So after an intermittent history of possibly four centuries from around 1400 to 1800 the manufacture of powder ceased in Dublin. There is no evidence of any mill recognised by The Castle in Belfast or the North generally. Gunpowder was one of several substances used in Ulster for dying linen which were banned by the Linen Act 1763. It does not seem that any other mill, except the great enterprise by the banks of the Lee ever existed in the country (46, 48-9).

W H E N Mr. CALDBECK fettled the Price of his P. GUN POWDER at £4. 10s. per Barrel, SALT-PETRE was at the Price of £2. 3s. 10d½. and notwithftanding a confiderable rife upon it, and alfo upon COALS, of which a great Quantity is ufed in the Manufacture, he did not raife the Price; but SALT-PETRE having rifen to £4. 11s. he is under the neceffity of adding, tho' very reluctantly, £1. 15s 8d½. to the Price of each Barrel,—making,

```
       P. . . . . . . . .£6   5   8
 Double P. . . . . . . . . . 6  10   8
    No. 3. . . . . . . . . . .7   0   2
    ——5. . . . . . . . . . .7  14   8
```

H E hopes that his Friends and Cuftomers, from whom he has received fo many Favors, will excufe this Rife, from the obvious neceffity of it; and they may depend upon it, that the Price of Powder fhall fall with that of Petre.

December 19th, 1792.

Printed by J. & J. CARRICK, Bedford-row.

Decimal Equivalents

£4 - 10 - 0	=	£4.50
£2 - 3 - 10½	=	£2.19½
£4 - 11 - 0	=	£4.55
£1 - 15 - 8½	=	£1.79

£6 - 5 - 8	=	£6.28½
£6 - 10 - 8	=	£6.53½
£7 - 0 - 2	=	£7.01
£7 - 14 - 8	=	£7.73½

BALLINCOLLIG
LESLIE FOUNDS THE MILLS;
WILKS, the BOARD OF ORDNANCE

A day in spring. Seventeen hundred and ninety-three.

A man on horseback rides up and down the banks of the Lee some distance from Cork. The stream on this stretch of its course flows in several channels which the rider surveys closely. He is not seeking foxes, hares or rabbits, nor the wild duck which have their haunts in the watery inches, nor the pheasant and partridge on the hills nearby. He crosses the old bridge of Inniscarra unmindful of the salmon and trout teeming beneath. He continues his inspection along the north bank oblivious of the fact that one hundred and ninety-three years earlier also on a day in spring, Hugh O'Neill had made camp there and received the allegiances of the clan chiefs of Munster.

That had been during the Nine Years' War. Now another conflict is beginning. This is on an international scale, which, time will tell, is to last for twenty years. Whether long or short, wars can be made to yield profits. The horseman has every intention of getting all he can extract while the opportunity is available which is why he is not interested in the customary rural sports for which the valley offers targets. He is going to build a factory which will make black powder, the only explosive of the age and the most essential single element in warfare.

The horseman goes back to the bridge and pauses for a moment as the rays of the setting sun slant across the sky. Satisfied that the site is suitable he spurs the horse for home in the Liberties of Cork.

Another day in spring. One hundred and ten years later. A group of men, some of whom have probably never seen the valley, sit around a boardroom table in the City of London and in the course of a routine meeting they decide to close the mills by the Lee.

Such were the beginning and end of one of the most remarkable industries ever to exist in the country.

When the horseman rode along the Lee the time was about halfway through the era of Grattan's Parliament, as the Irish legislature was known during its last twenty years. The Parliament was, for most of its existence, subservient to London and lacked any real power. Only a select few thousand men could vote. Seats could be bought and sold like armchairs and there were many other abuses. For example, large salaries for sinecures, positions with elaborate titles and no duties were paid regularly from the Irish Treasury to favourites of the monarch.

There was no cabinet drawn from the majority in the lower house. All authority was exercised by the Lord Lieutenant, the Chief Secretary and officials in The Castle who were answerable to London. In the mid 1770s a number of parliamentarians formed what became known as the Patriot Party. This was not a party in the sense understood today with organisational networks nationwide and a whip system in the chambers. It was composed quite loosely of a number of members in both chambers who held broadly similar views on the issues of the day. Their patriotism meant essentially the preservation of their privileges as planters. While they were in favour of easing the more serious restrictions imposed by the Penal Laws on Catholics, they did not even remotely envisage a sovereign state ruled by the majority with the consent of the minority and votes for all persons without property and income qualifications; neither of course did parliamentarians in England or anywhere else.

Though neither patriotic nor a party in any respect, the members did represent a departure in some slight way from the long standing attitudes held by the colonists and they formed a passably effective opposition in Parliament. The leaders were James Caulfield, First Earl of Charlemont and Henry Grattan, from whom the era is known, who sat for most of his career for the borough of Charlemont, Armagh which was owned, lock, stock and barrel by the Earl.

The patriots were fortunate in the circumstance of their times. Thirteen of the British colonies in North America declared themselves independent as the USA in 1776. Most of the English regiments stationed in Ireland were withdrawn for transatlantic service. Corps of Volunteers were formed in many districts to guard against the danger of invasion from France which was feared at the time. These grew into a well armed formidable force with Charlemont as commander-in-chief.

As the danger of invasion eased the Volunteers turned to other matters and compelled London to ease some of the limitations which had been placed on Irish trade after the Nine Years' War which had completed the Conquest. They followed this by demanding and bringing about the repeal of Poynings' Law and other restrictive legislation.

This was in May 1782. In September the various units in Cork held a rally reviewed by Charlemont in Ballincollig, undoubtedly at the castle which, for long a stronghold of the Barretts, was by then an abandoned ruin. Subsequently an address was presented to

Charlemont paying tribute to his "life of undeviating political virtue" which had brought about the "invaluable blessings of a free constitution". Charlemont in his reply stated that "with conscious pride I do profess that the love of Ireland is the ruling passion of my soul... such a people cannot be slaves... a country so inhabited must be free"(103- 4).

The actual position did not nearly correspond to these and the numerous other high sounding sentiments in this exchange of mutual admiration. The vast majority of the people, of whatever religious persuasion, were still effectively enslaved and had no voice. While the Parliament could in theory make laws without reference to Westminster there was still no cabinet and the lower house was still returned on the same small exclusive electorate. The offices of Lord Lieutenant and Chief Secretary continued as before with the seat of power in The Castle on Cork Hill rather than the Commons on College Green.

The time of Grattan's Parliament has come to be regarded as a golden age with various old industries reviving and new enterprises being established. This was not at all due to Grattan, leader of the opposition, or anyone else in the legislature or administration. In the period of the Industrial Revolution new machinery brought mass production thereby reducing costs and stimulating demand for manufactured goods. The Parliament did have some powers to impose duties on imports and grant subsidies on exports. In practice this could only have meant that manufacturers and merchants, commanding as they did, money and influence, were able to bring about adjustments in tariffs to suit their particular interests. William Caldbeck is a perfect example of this. As in other countries in the eighteenth century, wages were very low. There was no social security system, no holidays or other statutory entitlements for employees, no tax on capital or income, no public elementary education and no health services. Consequently little or no benefits could have flowed to the public at large from the new wealth being generated.

Years passed and most of the Corps of Volunteers disbanded. As far as the vast majority of the people were concerned, Legislative Independence might as well not have come about at all until matters began to take a different turn following developments in France. The *ancien régime* collapsed with the fall of the Bastille in July 1789.

The French Revolution was widely celebrated in Ireland. On the second anniversary of the Bastille the *Declaration of the Volunteers and Citizens of the Town and District of Belfast* rejoiced at the "breaking of the chains which held France in Civil and Religious

Bondage" noting "it is good for human nature that grass grows where the Bastille stood". The rally drank a series of 27 toasts to, among other persons and causes, the Revolution, George Washington then serving as first USA president, the King of England, George 111, Ireland, the Society for abolishing the Slave Trade, Charlemont and the Volunteers and the abolition of the Popery (Penal) laws with extension of privileges to Catholics. This last was the great issue of the age. Shortly afterwards Theobald Wolfe Tone, a Dublin barrister became organising secretary of the Catholic Committee, a body which for years had been trying to bring about an easing of the Penal Laws by appeals. As recently as February 1791 they had submitted a petition to the King seeking "such reliefs from their degraded situation as the Wisdom and Justice of Parliament may grant". Supplications of this nature, made in the absence of either some substantial support or circumstances likely to sway the seat of power are futile. Tone intended to press the case with great vigour and began to organise the Catholic Convention with delegates from every district through elaborate electoral arrangements (51-2,57).

In the autumn of 1791 the Society of the United Irishmen was formed in Belfast and in Dublin. Tone was a founding member. In December the Dublin Society issued a manifesto signed by James Napper Tandy who for long had championed Catholic Relief:

The object of this Institution is to make an United Society of the Irish Nation, to make all Irishmen Citizens - [as distinct from subjects] - all Citizens Irishmen. Peace in this island has hitherto been a peace on the principles and with the consequences of civil war. For a century past [since the Boyne] there has indeed been tranquility, but to most of our dear country men it has been the tranquility of a dungeon; and if the land has lately prospered, it has been owing to the goodness of providence and the strong efforts of Human nature resisting and overcoming the malignant influence of a miserable administration.

Already London had been noting the trend of events and in October sent instructions to the Earl of Westmoreland, Lord Lieutenant, that "such measures may be taken as may effectually counteract the union between the Catholics and Dissenters at which the latter are evidently aiming". Dissenters were members of the Presbyterian Church which had doctrinal differences with the Established Church and were persecuted under the Penal Laws. Clearly, London feared that if the Dissenters became allied with the Catholics, members of the Church of Ireland, in serious numbers, might well follow and the entire basis of British rule in Ireland, which depended on such division would collapse.

In December London sent further instructions to Westmoreland; the Irish Parliament was to remove all restrictions on Catholics respecting professions and trades, marriage with Protestants, education, use of arms, service on grand and petty juries and voting. In January 1792 the Prime Minister, William Pitt, wrote, in acknowledging Westmoreland's acceptance of the reform programme, "we have thought only of what was the most likely plan to preserve the security of a British and Protestant Interest"(53-6).

As preparations for the Catholic Convention went ahead throughout 1792, developments in the French Revolution were moving to the point at which war would break out with Britain. In April the revolutionary government declared war on Prussia and Austria and soon defeated both countries in separate battles. In September they abolished the monarchy and instituted the republic, in November they announced that they would aid any people wishing to rid themselves of monarchic tyranny and also declared that the River Scheldt, one of Europe's great international waterways, should be open to the ships of all nations, having for long been closed to suit British commercial interests.

The Catholic Convention met in the Tailors' Guildhall, Dublin in the first week of December. The delegates quickly pronounced themselves as the sole body competent to voice Catholic claims. They resolved to send a deputation led by Tone directly to the King. The audience with George III took place on 2 January 1793 and on the tenth the King's speech to the opening of the new session of the Dublin Parliament expressed the hope that "the situation of our Catholic subjects will engage your serious attention and in the consideration of this subject we rely on the wisdom and liberality of our Parliament". Despite this heavy hint the legislators contrived to water down the reform programme introduced on 4 February and passed as the Catholic Relief Act 1793. Catholics with certain property qualifications could sit on borough corporations and county grand juries, forerunners of county councils. Those with higher qualifications could vote in parliamentary elections. They could not be candidates. They could bear arms. They could not hold the higher ranks in the army and navy. Following this the Convention dissolved.

On 26 December 1792 The Castle issued a proclamation which was frequently published in the *Freeman's Journal* over the following weeks. This banned the export of gunpowder, saltpetre, arms and ammunition and transport of these around the coast. Another proclamation of the same date banned the export of foodstuffs. In 1793 an Act of Indemnification was passed to cover all actions involved in the carrying out of these measures (120).

On 21 January 1793 King Louis XVI was executed and from the moment his head rolled off the guillotine, war with Britain was inevitable, the only question was which would declare first. In the event France did on 1 February. On the fifth the Attorney-General told the Irish House of Commons that a serious situation had just arisen:

> *Considerable quantities of gunpowder and firearms had been clandestinely imported and seized as they were being conveyed to the interior parts of the Kingdom; this fact and the disturbed state of some of the northern counties gave just cause to suppose that some evil design might be entertained. Government ought to be enabled to counteract these.*

Accordingly leave was sought to bring in "A Bill entitled an Act to prevent the importation of Arms, Gunpowder and Ammunition into this Kingdom and the removing and keeping of Gunpowder, Arms and Ammunition without licence". The measure prohibited, without a licence from the Lord Lieutenant, the Chief Secretary or the Board of Ordnance of Ireland, the importation and transportation of "any cannon, mortars or ordnance, guns, pistols, gun locks or parts of gun locks, pistol locks, gun stocks, swords, sword blades, bayonets, pikes, spears, spearheads, weapons of war, cannon, musket or pistol balls, gunpowder or military accoutrements". In 1796 this list was extended to include sulphur, saltpetre and "other materials used in the making of gunpowder". Originally the Gunpowder Act was to expire at the end of the session opening in January 1794. It was renewed each year until the Act of Union and afterwards by Westminster for many years (121-8).

Powers were given to magistrates and revenue officers to enter premises and ships in search of arms suspected of being held illegally or smuggled. The general penalty for possession of any contraband was a fine of £500 and confiscation of the weapons, wagons, horses and so on. Captains of ships involved in smuggling were liable to fines of £200. The Act did not prescribe terms of imprisonment as alternatives or additions to fines. The Lord Lieutenant and the Privy Council had discretion to pay the proceeds of fines to informers and to return confiscated property. Loyal subjects were permitted to carry their personal weapons provided these were properly licenced and up to four pounds (1.81kg) of powder. The Act laid down regulations under which gunpowder, guns and other items could be bought, sold, stored and moved from place to place.

The Bill was given its first reading immediately and received the royal assent on 25 February with effect from the Twentieth. William Drennan, a United Irishman of Belfast who was practicing medicine in Dublin at the time, observed the implementation of the measure in his letters, "the Lord Lieutenant has gone to Parliament today to give the royal assent to the Gunpowder Act which will make a new law against the Volunteers". Three days later he wrote, "the military have seized the cannon of the Volunteers in the city". These were the cannon of the Liberty Corps, led by Napper Tandy. This was largely the purpose of the Act. Already on 12 December 1792 The Castle had made an estimate of the artillery held by the Volunteers and found that sixteen corps had a total of 44 pieces.

The Lawyers handed their cannon into the Castle stating that they had "associated for loyal and constitutional purposes only" and as these had been accomplished they "deemed it their duty to discontinue their meetings as members of an armed Corps". Drennan observed on 4 March that they had been "well received". On 6 March, noting the seizure of arms in Belfast, he urged that as many guns as possible should be smuggled. The homes of many United Irishmen were wrecked in Belfast and also the office of their newspaper the *Northern Star* which on 19 December 1792 had published a proposal by Drennan for an Ulster Convention. This duly met in February 1793 at Dungannon, seat of the famous '82 Volunteer Convention, and issued a call for an all Ireland Convention, obviously with a view to unification of Catholic, Protestant and Dissenter. The proposed assembly was banned. In May 1794 Drennan was prosecuted for sedition. The jury refused to find against him. The printer of the paper was found guilty. At the same time the Castle suppressed the United Irishmen and Napper Tandy and Wolfe Tone went into exile (58, 59,107-10).

In 1795 the British government found the perfect solution to the problem of keeping Catholic, Protestant and Dissenter apart. Centuries of persecution had failed to eliminate Catholicism and indeed many concessions had had to be made. Accordingly Maynooth College was founded and funded for a century, during which and for long afterwards it produced generations of priests who could be relied on to teach their parishioners to avoid Protestants and regard them as dangerous foreigners. The Protestants for their part were anxious to proclaim themselves as British. They formed the Orange Order which had a perfect target for vilification in the person of the Pope whom it was believed, as head of a rigidly authoritarian church, was constantly poised to attack the freedoms enjoyed by Protestants since the Glorious Revolution brought about by King William of Orange himself at the Boyne.

Throughout this period the Castle was preoccupied by various infringements of the Gunpowder Act. In July 1796 it was reported that there was an illegal factory near Belfast and in September that powder and saltpetre were readily available in the Belfast market. There was a report about Derry in November and an agent in Letterkenny wrote in May 1797 that he hoped to find houses in which powder was being made in Derry (60-3).

Several cases of smuggling were reported; from Dublin to Belfast in tallow casks in February 1796; from America in flaxseed casks in May and from Scotland to Belfast and Larne in January 1797. In April 1799 an anonymous letter alleged that powder was being smuggled in parcels of old clothes to Ballymena (64-8).

The other great concern in the Castle at the time was invasion from France. In May 1796 an agent in Carrickfergus, reporting activities of the Defenders - an organisation of rural Catholics, and of the United Irishmen - stated that 15,000 troops were expected from France and arms were to be landed at Cushendall. In August an official drew up a report on this possibility entitled *Thoughts on the Defence of Ireland.* In December 1796 a French fleet with the predicted number of troops appeared in Bantry Bay. Wolfe Tone was on board. They failed to land and returned to France. In the following eighteen months the country moved further and further towards war. Hostilities broke out in Wexford in the summer of '98 and another French invasion was mounted in three parts. The first landed in Killala Bay and defeated a British force at Castlebar before losing at Ballinamuck. The second came as far as Donegal with Napper Tandy and on hearing of Ballinamuck went away. The third contingent was captured at sea, including Wolfe Tone who was tried and sentenced to death. His demise took place before the date of execution (69,70,97).

The position regarding gunpowder in 1793 was that the Castle wished to control its production and use. At the same time large quantities were needed for the army and militia, an important part of the armed forces at that period. Apparently the only maker was William Caldbeck who probably could only supply small quantities, hardly enough for the normal needs of mines, quarries and sporting gun owners let alone the government. War had broken out and if it lasted any length of time the sales to the government, which were certain to be large, would pay for the outlay on setting up a large mill, leaving the cost of production afterwards very low.

All these internal, international and commerical factors prompted a man in Cork to decide on building a mill on the Lee, upstream from the city. The prospects of profits must have outweighed the plethora of problems as he surveyed his site from horseback, the only method available at the time, early in 1793. Charles Henry Leslie was a son of Charles Leslie a doctor attached to the North Infirmary apparently from its foundation in 1744. The *Cork Gazette*, 27 March 1793, reported the death of "Charles Leslie MD one of the bankers of this city". While it is not clear which bank he was involved in, it was probably Roberts' Bank which his sons later acquired. Charles Junior was admitted a freeman of Cork in November 1784. If this took place soon after his twenty-first birthday it indicates that he was born in 1763 and would have been thirty when he founded the mills. Neither Leslie seems to have taken a very active part in municipal politics. They were substantial property owners and were very much involved in parliamentary elections as agents for the family of Hely Huchinson, Earls of Donoughmore, who sat for Cork from 1761 to 1829 (105,113-14).

The year 1793 was bad for trade in Ireland in general and Cork in particular. In March the Mayor wrote to the Castle complaining of the high cost of coal and that ships plying to the city from British ports were not protected and insurance was four times the premium on vessels sailing to Dublin.

In June 1793 a deputation of Cork merchants and traders appeared before the Commissioners for Lending Money to Manufacturers, appointed by the Lord Lieutenant earlier in the year. The deputation pleaded that "from the general stagnation of trade and want of demand we cannot make good our engagements and keep in occupation the persons heretofore usually employed without the aid of the Board". If a large sum was not made available immediately in Cork "very serious consequences might be apprehended from commotion among the manufacturing poor". Eventually the Commissioners agreed:

> to grant relief only to such persons in trade as are possessed of funds ultimately more than adequate to answer all demands upon them, but who have not the means of converting those funds into money in time to meet the pressure of the moment, and that they have been particularly instructed by His Excellency to bend their chief attention to the relief of those persons on whom employment of the greatest number of working people depends.

The sum of £40,000 was provided. In 1797 the merchants approached the Commissioners again and a similar arrangement was made. In an age when there were hardly any taxes nor any laws governing conditions of employment and service to customers, it is apparent that merchants and manufacturers, on running into what would nowadays be called cash flow problems, were unable to carry on business without assistance from public funds (74-6).

Leslie does not seem to have been involved in any of this. No doubt he had adequate resources of his own. In setting up an industry of a type which had never existed in the area before, certainly not on any significant scale, he had to find a suitable site, a source of power, workers with several different skills and also acquire technical knowledge.

A powdermill obviously could not be built in the city. At this time flowing water was the only source of power available apart from the energy of horses or other animals. The steam engine had not yet come into its own and when it did it had, like the ancient windmill, no application in powdermills. Gas, electricity and other forms still lay in the future.

A riverside location was therefore essential. The various streams flowing into Cork Harbour and their tributaries provided waterpower for numerous industries as the Ordnance Survey maps show. The Owenaboy, Owencurra, Curraheen, Tramore, Dungourney, Blackpool, Glasheen, North Bride, South Bride, Dripsey, Martin, Blarney, Owenagearagh and others had breweries, distilleries, tanneries; plants for various stages of textile making; flour, grist and starch works; potteries, brick and tile yards; ironworks and paper mills. The Monard Ironworks, Blarney, established before the powdermills worked on old-style waterpower until its closure in 1960.

These rivers offered the advantage of a size which could be harnessed conveniently. Some industries, as surviving sites show, took power directly from the river without separate head and tail races. The principal river itself had comparatively few industries; in the city Beamish and Crawford's brewery on the south channel; the Lee Maltings and Wyse's North Mall Distillery served by a single weir sanctioned by the Harbour Commissioners in 1834 on the north channel and Watergate Flourmills at Carrigrohane, just downstream from Ballincollig, were the only undertakings of any consequence on the Lee (175).

The site of a mill had to be reasonably remote from any well populated areas and at the same time not too far from a port for the import of saltpetre and for despatching any exports and consignments sent coastways to other parts of the country as was common before railways. It would also be of considerable advantage if the soil was suitable for growing alder and sally used in charcoal and apple trees used for mortice gears in certain parts of the machinery.

Ballincollig, situated some six miles (9.6km) from the city centre and port was an ideal distance and in a thinly populated area. The intervening countryside was level. The soil was right for the trees and two orchards were planted. The site had in addition one outstanding, if not unique feature which made it peculiarly suitable for Leslie's purpose. From here downstream the valley is very wide and the stream carved out several channels. Water may have flowed in some only in times of flood. These channels could be readily converted to canals. The normal pattern is to draw water from the river through a canal known as the head-race and return it through the tail-race. Ballincollig differed in having a very extensive system of internal canals which ultimately totalled four miles (6.4km), the only network of its kind in Ireland. It was, like all riversides, subject to flooding. This was overcome by the use of embankments and by constructing buildings a little higher than normal. At this point the river could provide about 350 horsepower which must have been ample for even a very large mill (137).

The site had one further advantage for Leslie. It is apparent from the various title deeds that he owned most of the land before he began the mills. He had a partner, one John Travers, who owned the remainder and who seems to have taken a sleeping rather than an active part in the business. In May 1795 they leased a plot of land on the north bank of the Lee, a little way downstream from the bridge. Here they built the Inniscarra Weirs which provided the waterpower (86,102).

In hiring workers Leslie could have had little difficulty. As Cork at the time had flourishing trades in exporting butter and bacon packed in barrels, there must have been many coopers capable of making the particular types and sizes used for powder. Millwrights, masons, carpenters and other building artisans were no doubt numerous. For skilled powdermakers Leslie could probabley have enticed workers from Caldbeck in Dublin, most of whose employees were English, or from mills in England, by paying over the going rate.

As far as technical knowledge was concerned a very comprehensive account of powdermaking had been published in 1788. The author of this was George Napier who had been Comptroller of the Royal Laboratory in 1782-83, with responsibility for the quality of powder used in the public service. Napier had carried out hundreds of experiments in preparing the ingredients and making powder. Sulphur was refined by boiling in an iron vessel over a low coal fire and straining through a double linen sieve, repeating as often as necessary. Many merchants, particularly of the cutprice variety, tried to make their stocks go further by adding flour. In hot climates this tended to ferment thus ruining the powder. For the second ingredient charcoal, alder and dogwood trees were best. Though Napier tried many tests he could find no chemical reason for this. He had recently heard of a new method of producing charcoal "in a kind of oven which while admitting the extreme application of heat, the wood within is more equally charred and its volatile parts more completely evaporated". This process had indeed been developed a short time before Napier wrote his paper. The inventor was a remarkable individual, Richard Watson, who was Professor of both Chemistry and Divinity at Cambridge and also Bishop of Llandaff, Wales being appointed to these chairs without any knowledge of the subjects as he freely admitted in his autobiography in which he also described his charcoal system.

In 1786 the Board of Ordnance approached Watson, who presumably had learned some chemistry, with a view to finding improvements in the production of powder. He concentrated on charcoal. In the age old pit process, the wood, cut into lengths known as cords, was arranged in a mound which was covered in straw and earth with some holes for ventilation. The cords were burned slowly until the wood was fully charred, a long, tedious and not entirely efficient method. In the distillation process which Watson developed the cords were placed in a cylinder fully closed, with spaces for two pipes. One took gas to the furnace as extra fuel and the other extracted tar or creosote which was sold. These are early examples of full utilisation or recycling waste products. Shortly after this Watson retired from Cambridge claiming that his technology improved the quality of powder by sixty percent and saved the Board a six figure sum each year (100,115-16).

The third ingredient, saltpetre, presented more problems than the others. In Leslie's time the bulk still came from India's huge natural deposits. This substance, which is also known as nitre, is potassium nitrate in chemical terms. In 1857, Lammot du Pont, who visited Ballincollig the next year (page 55) invented a process in which sodium nitrate could be used. This is better known as guano, bird manure from Chile, which was long a popular fertiliser. It is doubtful if this was ever used in Ballincollig. Potassium nitrate occurs in underground situations such as caves, cellars, tunnels and overground in stables, cattle sheds, fowlhouses, latrines and other places where septic matter accumulates. There were great practical difficulties in collecting and concentrating worthwhile quantities. A tonne of dung would yield only a fistful of saltpetre which would not necessarily be of good quality.

Napier did not dwell at any length on the question of saltpetre, assuming that manufacturers would use the Indian product. He noted the laws which had been passed in the reign of Charles II under which the Crown was entitled to the dung of slaughter houses, stables and other buildings and "directing magistrates to have tubs placed in the streets of populous towns for the collection of urine". Napier was evidently unaware that even earlier Charles I had in 1624 and '34 issued proclamations empowering the Lords Commissioners for Saltpetre and Gunpowder to dig in stables and other buildings and ordering owners not to pave floors with stone or brick (111-12).

Saltpetre was of great strategic importance. It was the equivalent of heavy water or fissionable material. Indeed it is thought that the activities of the saltpetriers in France were so extreme as to be a contributory factor in the Revolution. The learned institutions of Europe attacked the problem of producing large quantities of high quality saltpetre at low cost; the Berlin Academy, the Paris Academy of Sciences, the Royal Society in England and similar seats of learning offered cash prizes and other inducements.

In Ireland the matter was taken up by the Royal Dublin Society which was founded in 1731 with a strong interest in agriculture and applied sciences. It might be thought that the RDS would be more interested in the food preservative and other ancillary agricultural applications of the chemical than its place in powder; the Society also promoted improvements in firearms (page 206). In December 1767 the RDS "ordered that a premium of £10 be given to Mr John Stordy of Grafton Street [Dublin] for upwards of 30 pounds weight of good merchantable saltpetre lately made by him". The search continued and in March 1794 the Society considered another method which became available in convenient time for Leslie, if he needed it (87-90).

This was developed by John Mantel who was described at a meeting of the Society in March 1788 as a native of Hungary who had been long resident in Flanders. On that occasion he had submitted a formula for a fertiliser for which they sent him two guineas (£2.10). In February 1783 the Society awarded Mantel a premium of £100 for the saltpetre method which had been sealed until his death:

*Receipt [sic] for making the mother for growing saltpetre
of materials, the greater part thereof to be found in Ireland;
Take one ton of quicklime and one ton of common salt, put
the salt on the lime, and pour water thereon to slack it, and
when slaken form it into balls; burn them together; when cold
pound them and put them into a large tub, pour boiling water
thereon and save the caput mortuam. After you have with
boiling water extracted the salt thereout, then take the same
weight of fresh quicklime as the salt so extracted; mix them as
before, slack them and burn them again, then pour the whole,
first and last into a large tub and add thereto all sorts of offals,
pigeons' dung, sheeps' dung, urine and all sorts of animal and
vegetable refuse, let it stand a while to macerate together, then
it is prepared to lay down on the earth.*

It is not clear if Leslie had to resort to this concoction so redolent
of medieval alchemy. Napier recommended that when quantities of
the ingredients had been prepared a small charge should be tested
before making the regular batches. Finally he put forward proposals
for improvements in the edge runner mills used for incorporating the
ingredients. He suggested cast-iron wheels and troughs instead of
granite or marble, with a series of grooves on the working surfaces of
the wheels. This does not seem to have been used widely if at all,
certainly all the surviving wheels at Ballincollig are of plain stone such
as *ILLUSTRATION 6.* In the early days of gunpowder the ingredients
were simply mixed together in a bucket with a pounder on the pestle
and mortar principle still used, if rarely, by pharmacists in
compounding prescriptions. In time this was enlarged to a sizeable
machine, in various forms, in which the ingredients were pounded by
a hammer or beater in a tub type vessel (27,87-90).

These mechanisms, known as stamping mills, could be operated
by the power of man or horses, donkeys, mules and even bullocks.
Stamping mills were quite dangerous in use and were banned as a
general rule in Britain by the Gunpowder Act 1772. The stamping mill
was replaced by the edge runner, a rather elaborate system which was
far more efficient and had a higher ouput. It was also expensive and
difficult to rebuild. The stamping mill was simple, cheap and easily
replaced after an explosion. It is probable that Leslie used this type
while constructing the weirs, canals and buildings (233).

When the Gunpowder Act was renewed in 1795 an extra clause
was inserted enabling "makers of gunpowder in Cork to send powder
to their offices or His Majesty's stores in Dublin". Clearly by then
Leslie had a warehouse in Dublin and the Castle wanted to facilitate

him in sending consignments to it and to their own premises. Otherwise the Castle seem to have taken little notice of Leslie. The official who wrote the memo *Thoughts on the Defence of Ireland* did not mention the mills. Neither did Major General Charles Vallencey, chief military engineer, who in 1796 made a *"Military Survey of the South of Ireland"* in particular Cork, Kinsale and Ballinhassig, a district between these towns and Ballincollig. This is certainly strange as the mills, by then well established, must have been of strategic importance (96).

Following the suppression of the '98 Rising, London decided to do away with the Dublin Parliament altogether. The proposal found great favour with the merchants of Cork. In January 1799 the Corporation passed a resolution enthusiastically in favour of the proposed Union which came into operation on the first day of 1801 (106).

As part of the administrative adjustments which followed, the Irish Board of Ordnance was replaced by the "Respective Officers for Conducting the Civil and Military Business of His Majesty's Ordnance in that Part of the United Kingdom called Ireland" (130).

Whether this involved any great changes in personnel and day to day practice may be doubted because the Irish Board could have had little real discretion. There was one immediate change as far as Leslie was concerned. The Irish Board had a system of buying their supplies of guns, powder, ammunition, saddlery, wagons, clothing, tents, tools and other equipment through an agent. In 1797 one Richard Spear who had held the position submitted a statement of his contracts over the previous few years. He had bought powder in England and:

> *I thought it essential to encourage the Powder Mill of Leslie and Travers at Cork as it appeared to me that the importation of gunpowder might become too hazardous and precarious a matter for the government to depend on for the safety of Ireland; this company have acted admirably well.*

The British Board abolished the agency arrangements and the Respective Officers purchased directly from the manufacturers (673).

In March 1801 an official in Dublin Castle wrote a memo reviewing proposals which he had put forward four years previously for controlling the sale and distribution of powder recalling that in 1796 he had come to the conclusion that "the Rebel Party were forming a depot of ammunition in the North". The memo noted that there were two mills in Dublin, clearly Caldbeck's and Arabin's, and another in Cork with a warehouse in Dublin. By 1801 one of the

Dublin mills, evidently Calbeck's, had closed. The official suggested a scheme under which the manufacturers, dealers and carbrokers, presumably wagon hire firms, would have to keep full records of all transactions and movements of powder. All orders, receipts and invoices were to be kept and copies sent to the Castle regularly. It was hoped that by comparing the returns it would be possible to trace all consignments from production to final use and thus find anyone who was attempting to accumulate large quantities (77).

In September 1801 Leslie submitted a detailed statement of all sales over the previous twelve months. This showed a total of 1,584 barrels of which 184 full barrels, 45 halves and seven quarters were local sales in Cork. Thirteen barrels and sixty halves had been sold in Dublin. The government bought 1,132 barrels. Very significantly in view of developments over thirty years later, two hundred barrels had been "exported to Liverpool for the African Trade". Most of the local sales were to captains of yeomanry in various parts of Munster and an occasional quantity directly to industries mainly the Hibernian Copper Mines, Wicklow and an iron foundry. In a letter with this return Leslie, trading as Leslie, Travers and Company, Royal Irish Gunpowder Mills, near Cork, said that the mills had been set up with "our principal object being the supply of His Majesty's Government" (77).

At this time Leslie was obviously dissatisfied with the amounts which the government were buying. In July 1801 he approached the Earl of Donoughmore for whose family he had long been election agent. He in turn wrote to the Respective Officers at Dublin asking them to place larger orders with Leslie. They replied that they could only act on instructions from London. After some further correspondence they agreed to take 500 barrels, seemingly as a trial (78).

At the same time Leslie sent a petition to the Castle observing that as "the circumstances of the times make it necessary to place restrictions on the removal of gunpowder from one part of the country to another" and as "the quantities ordinarily consumed in sporting make it necessary to provide a constant supply for persons legally qualified and licenced in the metropolis" he requested permission to build a magazine in the Pigeon House or the Phoenix Park or elsewhere in Dublin. The Respective Officers gave permission for a magazine alongside their own in the Park (79).

Apparently the Board continued to buy quantities regularly because correspondence concerning an order in April 1804 for 1,000 barrels indicates that this was of a routine nature. The Board supplied the saltpetre. By this time Leslie had obviously developed the mills into a highly productive and prosperous concern (80).

In December 1804 Leslie bought out the interest which John Travers held in the lands on which part of the mills stood. No doubt at the same time he acquired the stake which Travers had in the firm. On 18 May 1805, Leslie, as sole proprietor sold the mills to the Board of Ordnance on a lease of 999 years for £30,000 and an annual rent of £1,275 (86,101).

This kind of money would have enabled Leslie to live in luxury for the remainder of his life. He chose to go into banking. Possibly he was already involved in the firm of Sir Thomas Roberts, Baronet and Company in which his brother John was an active partner. After a few years the firm was known as Roberts, Leslie and Leslie and finally as Leslies' Bank, issuing notes for one pound, twenty-five shillings (£1.25) and other amounts. At the time banks were very different from today. Under the law as it stood then, no firm could have more than six partners. Few, if any, had more than one office or substantial resources and even the Bank of Ireland, with its royal charter, did not operate outside Dublin. Many shopkeepers and traders issued notes and tokens. The notes of banks were in many cases worth no more than those of a huckster (85).

In 1820 the Leslies were forced to close their doors. They reopened in 1822 on receiving a loan of £80,000 from the Commissioners for the Relief of Trade, set up by the government to assist firms unable to pay their way. In January 1826 the assimilation of the currencies, or parity, which the "European Monetary System" ended in March 1979, and was the last administrative aspect of the Act of Union, came into operation. Before this the ratio had been thirteen Irish pennies to the British shilling. The purchasing power of wages, inadequate at best, was severely reduced and the general effect like decimalisation in 1971 was severe inflation.

In March 1826 a rush on Leslies' Bank took place as a consequence of the death of another Cork banker and they closed their door for good, or evil as far as holders of their notes were concerned. Two years earlier the Relief of Bankers in Ireland Act, by removing the restriction on the number of partners, had paved the way for banks on the present joint stock basis with large bodies of shareholders, boards of directors, professional managements and branches nationwide. The era of the partnership type banks was over even if some did linger on a while. The Northern Bank immediately adopted joint stock status and the Provencial Bank was set up in 1825 with its first office in Cork. This, with an agency of the Bank of Ireland opened the same year and the Cork Savings Bank established in 1817 must have presented stiff competition to the Leslies (118, 129).

Winding up was the only realistic course open to the Leslies. They still owed the Commissioners £47,000. It is improbable that they could have converted to the joint stock system as this would have necessitated outside investors who would hardly have been attracted to a bank under their auspices. Neither is it very likely that they could have sold the goodwill to one of the new enterprises which could no doubt have scooped up the business by offering better terms and services. If they called in the debts due to them and paid off their note issue in coin of the realm they could have retired in good order. Even if the books did not quite balance and they had to dip into their own pockets they would have avoided the disgrace of literal bankruptcy.

The liquidation dragged on until 24 July 1834 when readers of the *Cork Constitution* must have been surprised that the assignees had arranged a final payment bringing the total to fifteen shillings and five pence (77p) in the pound. There was a postscript on 25 October when it was reported that £100 in conscience money had been remitted which the assignees decided to pay to some poor creditors living too far away to have claimed in person (81, 82, 83).

The Leslies lost most of the property which they owned. Charles Henry contrived to hold onto his home demesne at Leslies' Cross, Wilton, which remained in the family until some time before 1888 in which year it was acquired by the present owners, the Society of Missions to Africa. He died in obscurity, his will being admitted to probate in 1842 (84,138).

Thus the career of Charles Henry Leslie, large landowner and banker who in 1793 saw and seized the opportunity presented by the internal and international situations of the time and founded a great enterprise which he ran for twelve years and sold for a large capital sum and a substantial annual rental. Equally successful was the shrewd political agent who directed many election victories. In contrast was the man of money who, when conditions changed in that business, was unable or unwilling to adapt to the new circumstances and soon plummeted into the abyss of insolvency. The enterprising man who rode along the banks of the Lee in the spring of 1793 degenerated into the tired old incompetent of thirty-three years later. A sad change indeed.

A few weeks after bringing about the United Kingdom of Great Britain and Ireland in January 1801, William Pitt resigned as Prime Minister. In May 1804 he formed a new coalition in Parliament and returned to Downing Street. The War in Europe had by this time been going on for over 10 years and was to last as long again. For the greater part of this time the conflict was dominated by one man whose name indeed has been given to the era. Napoleon Bonaparte made a remarkably rapid rise to the top as a most fervent supporter of the new form of government. By 1804 he had so far abandoned his republican principles as to declare and crown himself Emperor of France.

Napoleon announced his assumption of permanent power and forthcoming coronation shortly before the return to office of Pitt who immediately set about organising a new alliance against the French dictator who was believed to be planning an invasion of England. In order to conduct the new phase of the Napoleonic wars on an appropriate scale the British government launched a massive rearmament programme. Many remains of this period are still to be seen throughout Ireland in the form of various barracks, coastal and inland forts, batteries and harbour defences. The best known structures are the Martello towers. Less known are the strings of signal towers worked on the semaphore system, similar to railway signalling, built across the country converging on Dublin, set up in 1804 and abandoned after five years (71-2).

The number of troops stationed in the country increased enormously resulting in a shortage of barrack accommodation so severe that many were billeted outside. This gave rise to a question as to the ownership of dung from horses so stabled out of barracks. After due deliberation the law officers gave forth their considered opinion that "where the innkeeper furnished stabling only and the straw and provender were provided by government the manure belongs to government". Perhaps the government wanted the dung for saltpetre (73).

It does not appear that the Board of Ordnance manufactured powder from the earliest days until 1759 when they bought the Home Works at Faversham, Kent and in 1787 the mills at Waltham Abbey, Essex, nearer London. In September 1804 the Board decided to erect six additional incorporating mills at Waltham. A month later this was inadequate and three more were ordered at Waltham and three at Faversham (91).

Even with all this additional productive capacity the Board were still apparently unable to meet the demand from the forces in the field and at sea and began to seek a mill for sale. There was indeed another mill at Faversham, the Oare Works and a third in Kent, run by Pigou & Wilks at Dartford; Sussex had the ancient Battle Abbey Mills near

Hastings; Middlesex had two, Bedfont and Hounslow which was operated by Harvey and Grueber; Surrey had Chilworth Mills. In the Lake District there were comparatively new mills at Bassingill, Sedgwick and Lowwood while still further north near Edinburgh there were mills at Roslin and Gorebridge. As there is no history of the British black powder industry it is not clear if there were any other factories at the time. Indeed the board had a choice of eleven on the mainland, six in the Home Counties, and it is difficult to accept that all were unsuitable or that they were unable to reach agreement with the owners. Whatever the reason the Board instead looked to Ireland and opened negotiations with Leslie probably in the autumn of 1804. An agreement was duly reached and the indenture was signed on 18 May 1805 with effect from the last day of the previous year. The Board appointed Charles Wilks as Superintendent on 9 March. They had probably taken possession of the premises by then. He was one of their most experienced officials having commenced his career at the age of 20 in 1780 as overseer of works at their depot in Chatham, Kent, becoming clerk of works in 1783. He was clerk of works at Faversham mills from 1794 to 1800 when he went to Waltham in the same capacity. He became clerk of works of powder mills in general in September 1804, obviously in anticipation of Ballincollig being acquired and no doubt was drawing up expansion plans while the purchase was being completed (93,101).

The expansion, on a truly tremendous scale, was put in hand immediately.   While there were various changes under later ownerships involving new buildings and removal of older structures the pattern which Wilks laid down in 1805 still stands. He apparently closed Leslie's main canal and altered some of his buildings which seemed to have consisted of at least three single incorporating mills and one double type.

Wilks developed Ballincollig in three parts, southern, eastern and western, surrounded by a high stone wall and rebuilt Inniscarra Bridge with twenty-four arches, twelve carrying the normal stream and the remainder on the powdermill side to take flood waters. The southern side was occupied by the main barracks. The village developed in the other side of the Cork-Crookstown-Killarney Road. At the West Village a group of buildings formed a small outpost, Faversham Square. Halfway between were three houses, now Oriel Court, the civil officers' quarters for the Superintendent, the Storekeeper and the Clerk of the Cheque who would nowadays be the financial controller. The barracks was laid out on a substantial scale having quarters and messes for a large garrison with stables, gunsheds, stores and workshops for farriers, cartwrights, and other artificers served by the Main Gate and the West Gate. Stone was quarried on the property and lime burned for mortar (98,99).

The East Gate led to the eastern area which was the heart of the mills with most of the process and ancillary buildings. There were separate buildings for preparing the ingredients; one for refining sulpher and another for saltpetre; for charcoal there were five, a sawmill and a sawpit which were separate, two cylinder houses for the Watson process and a mill for grinding it into fine dust. There were separate workshops for carpenters, millwrights, wheelwrights and coopers also an iron forge, carpenter's store, oil store, general store, carthouse, stable, bag drying house, weigh-house, and a water-wheel for pumping from the river. The management was carried out in the Call Office.

Living accommodation was provided in separate houses for the Mill Keeper, the foreman, the clerk of works and three clerks. The manual workers had three rows of houses, one built by Leslie which no longer stands and two others, Coopers Row and Waltham Abbey Row, some still occupied, known as "Blancotown" partly because the houses were whitewashed and partly because the girls living there wore canvas shoes bleached with army type blanco. Nearby stands the military cemetery.

The three terraces formed a rectangle with the incorporating mills running alongside the river. Wilks built eight singles and two doubles worked by low breastshot wheels driven by water drawn underground from the canal system and discharged into the river with a breakwater in the opposite bank to prevent erosion. Alongside the incorporating mills, away from the river, Wilks built a fire engine house and three charge houses with solid masonry roofs in which batches were made up for incorporating.

The western area which took up most of the 332 acres (134 hectares) of the mills had only a few of the sixty or so buildings. There were three pairs of combined dusting houses and press houses, three corning houses, the steam stove, the glazing house and the proof house for testing the finished products. There were four security buildings, the Grand Watch-house in the centre and the Round Tower Watch-house at Inniscarra Bridge, both occupied as dwellings until the mid 1950s, and two smaller watch-houses.

After preparing the ingredients on the principles laid down by Napier, batches called green charges were mixed in the charge houses and incorporated together in the edge runner mills for a number of hours which varied according to the fineness required, in general the bigger the gun the coarser the powder. During this the mix was constantly watered; for the first century or two powder was mixed dry, this was called serpentine, the ingredients tended to separate especially when moved over rough roads. Wetting enabled it to be formed into grains called corn powder.

After incorporation the mill cake was taken to a press house and formed into thin, hard wafers by hydraulic presses between copper plates. The press cake was placed in a corning house where it was passed through a series of sieves operated by cranks and broken down into grains of different sizes according to requirements. After this the grains were placed in the glazing house to be coated with black lead or graphite in rotating drums followed by a dusting off process. After all these stages there was still some moisture which was driven off by placing the grains for several hours in the steam stove, a building fitted with a series of pipes fed with steam from a large boilerhouse alongside.

The powder was weighed and packed in oak barrels. The standard size held one hundred pounds avoirdupois (45.36kg). The gunpowder industry traditionally used the short ton of 2,000 pounds as against the long ton of 2,240. Thus there were twenty barrels to the ton besides numerous small sizes of barrels and other containers. The powder was moved from one part of the mills to another by horse-drawn barges. A short horse tramway system connected the magazines. The powder was taken to Cork in wagons. As an interim measure Wilks rented a warehouse in George's Street, now Washington Street, for a year at fifty guineas (£52.50) in May 1805 and later leased a warehouse on Charlotte Quay, now Matthew Quay, for eight hundred years at two hundred guineas. A magazine designed to hold up to thirty thousand barrels was built on Rocky Island in the Harbour (101-2).

In May 1810 the Board presented to Parliament an abstract of the deeds to the Ballincollig property and an account of expenditure. Subsequent accounts give the costs in the following years. In 1805 £17,500 was spent; 1806, £33,107;1807, £18,828; 1808, £6,538; 1809, £10,008; 1810, £11,545. The amounts for the remaining years were given without segregating the sums for the barracks which itself cost £79,719 up to then. In 1811 the figure was £6,405; 1812, £15,197 and 1813, £7,700. The total for the mills was £126,931-15-0 (£126,931.75) less the costs for the barracks in the later years.

The cost of the Rocky Island magazine was £15,292 including apparently a crane and other equipment at Ordnance or King's Quay a short way upstream from Blackrock Castle. It seems that on the completion of this the Board gave up the warehouse on Charlotte Quay. In round figures therefore the factory itself cost the Board £150,000. It is of course impossible to give any equivalent for this especially in view of the inflation in the 1970s. Certainly it would run into millions (130-4).

Wilks carried on the mills, apparently without any particular difficulties or sensations until the conclusion of the Napoleonic wars at Waterloo in June 1815. The end of the conflict meant that the demand for powder was very much reduced. The Board cut back production and indeed discontinued altogether at Ballincollig and also at Faversham which they sold to John Hall and Sons. They had more powder in stock than they could use in a reasonable time and arranged to sell the surplus to a certain Mr Samuel who was financed by the well known London merchant bankers NM Rothschild and Sons. The gunpowder manufacturers were scandalised and, headed by Harvey & Grueber and Pigou & Wilks, they presented a protest memorial to the Lords of the Treasury who sent it to the Board. The reply was that the memorialists had submitted less favourable bids and the terms of Samuel's tender saved the public a large sum (119, 136).

In November 1808 the Board applied to the Castle to have Wilks appointed a magistrate and this was agreed. In 1812 he was elected a freeman of Cork which gave him the privilege of voting. In 1814 he took to print with a pamphlet based on his experiences and experiments with transport systems, *Observations on the Height of Carriage Wheels, On the Comparative Advantages of Employing One or Two Horses with One Carriage and on Repairing Roads*, in the full tradition of the long winded titles fashionable at the time. In June 1825 he was appointed Storekeeper at Waltham Abbey which was the corresponding position and carried a salary of £400, double that at Ballincollig, where he served the remainder of his career (94-5, 117).

In 1828 a detailed appraisal was carried out of the condition of each building in the mills, seemingly as part of a general review of the Board's properties. A similar survey had been made in 1822. Apparently no decision was taken on the future of the mills apart from the transfer the next year of Faversham Square to the Constabulary who used it as their training depot in Munster for some years following which it remained a district headquarters until 1922 (92, 135).

In November 1831 the Board decided to transfer some of the machinery to Waltham. The implementation of this turned into a civil service comic opera due to the rather dour diligence of the official in charge. This farce had far reaching consequences for the future of the mills. Following the departure of Wilks, responsibility for the mills was given to his second in command, the Storekeeper, one James Scarth, apparently a most cost conscious individual. Having dismantled the equipment he invited tenders for transportation to Cork. The lowest was six shillings (30p) per ton. He considered this rate so outrageous he wrote to the Respective Officers at Dublin for further orders suggesting that advertisements should be inserted in the local papers and posters placed around the district seeking new bids. The Officers responded quite sharply telling Scarth to get on with the job as the Board had sent a ship to Cork for the machinery.

The transfer was completed in March 1832 and soon afterwards the main performance started. It transpired that during the dismantling serious damage had been done to some buildings which would take a large sum to make good. The Board were unwilling to incur heavy, or indeed any expenditure and called for a report as to whether the work was really necessary. It was suggested that it was not as there was little likelihood that the mills would ever be used again and all that was needed was to secure the buildings against trespassers. A great deal of correspondence ensued between various officials some of whom held Scarth responsible. That worthy defended himself doggedly by blaming the workers he had hired. Eventually it was decided to make the bare minimum of repairs.

The work was carried out by the Royal Engineers who sent the Board a bill for £43 which caused a sensation altogether out of proportion to the amount. One officer wanted to know the average annual expenditure on the maintenance of the mills and the sum which might be realized if the buildings were demolished and the materials sold. It was estimated that the amount was £40 and after two years, on completion of certain plans in hand, even this would be reduced. It was difficult to estimate the sum which would be obtained if the buildings were demolished and in view of the low outgoings it did not seem worthwhile "to despoil the establishment".

In October the Board made a definite decision to sell the property and instructed the Respective Officers to forward any offers which might be made. The Officers, in acknowledging the order, suggested that it might be prudent to postpone the sale pointing out a clause in the lease from Leslie which might not be known to the Board. This provided that a proportion of the £30,000, a fine in law, which the Board had paid, was in respect of fixed assets comprising the mill buildings, machinery and waterways, as distinct from the land, which the Board were bound to maintain and deliver up in good order. The head lease had been acquired by the Wyses', a family of distillers in Cork, on the bankruptcy of Leslie. The Board suspended the sale and sent the papers to their solicitor who advised that the Officers' interpretation was correct. On the expiry of the lease in the fullness of time or earlier in the event of the Board ceasing to exist, or some other eventuality, the landlord, on entering premises and finding that the assets were not in accordance with the agreement would be entitled to recover damages from the Board or their successors-in-law. Under the weight of this ponderous legal opinion the Board's attempt to dispose of the property collapsed before it could get underway. This was in the Autumn of 1832. In the following summer, still in a mood to sell after the Scarth saga, the Board received an offer from a most unexpected quarter (101).

BALLINCOLLIG, VIEW, PART OF WESTERN AREA
SOURCE 211

THE TOBINS, MERCHANTS OF MERSEYSIDE

Another day in spring.

Forty-one years have passed by since the day Leslie rode along the banks of the Lee.

Now another man, even younger than Leslie, is about to set out for the Mills. As the time approaches for his departure from Liverpool he, his father, uncle and their partner leave the family firm's office in Wood Street, directly behind their home in Bold Street and go in a carriage by the Town Hall, where two of the older men have served in the supreme civic position, to the Pier Head whence the young man embarks on the steamer for its weekly sailing to Cork.

These merchants of Merseyside have just completed many months of negotiations for the purchase of the Mills and are wondering whether their five figure investment in a factory which has been out of operation for twenty years will pay off, especially as they have no previous experience of gunpowder or any other form of manufacturing. Moreover the mill will require large expenditure on renovation and new machinery before it can produce again.

As the mooring ropes slip from the shackles and the blades churn the water into foam, propelling the ship down the Mersey, the Irish Sea and the George Channel for the man's destination, he reflects on his family's history for he is going to the land of his ancestors. A certain John Tobyn left Ireland some time before 1728 and settled in the Isle of Man where he prospered as a periwig maker. His son Patrick became a wealthy merchant and property owner and had two sons, Sir John (1763-1851) and Thomas (1775-1863). Thomas had two sons who loom large in the history of the Mills, Sir Thomas (1807-81) and James Aspinall (1818-91).

Sir John went to sea as a youth, in merchant ships which then usually carried *Letters of Marque*, royal documents authorising them to attack and capture other ships. Privateers attacked and captured ships without such licences. This made no difference as far as the victims were concerned. At an early age Tobin was seized by one Kelly, an Irish American privateer who spared him only because he knew his father in the Isle of Man (139).

In time John ran up his own privateering flag. By the age of thirty he had his own vessel, the first of a fleet. In 1799 he visited Cork. Ships of the house of Tobin regularly captured other vessels and sold the cargoes, on a number of occasions they took slaving ships and sold the slaves as they would any other merchandise. From this Tobin went into the slave trade directly. In 1803 he set up headquarters under the style Tobin and Sons in Liverpool then an important centre of the slave trade and emerging as one of the premier ports of England. The house of Tobin, privateers and slave traders, flourished. In 1819 John Tobin was Mayor of Liverpool and was knighted as the accession of King George IV took place during his term. In 1821 Prince's Dock was opened with a Tobin ship having the privilege of being the first to tie up, this vessel was always exempt from port dues and town taxes as a mark of the esteem in which his contribution to the commerce of Liverpool was held. He was involved in the trade with China and was a director of the first steam packet company out of Liverpool (139).

Sir John was mainly interested in the Triangular Trade from Liverpool to West Africa, across the Atlantic to the West Indies and the Americas and back to Liverpool. Various goods were involved from time to time; salt from Cheshire and guns from Birmingham; numerous manufactured goods such as hatchets, knives, household utensils; iron bars and copper rods which functioned as money; other items of hardware; bolts of cloth, beads and so on were exchanged for slaves, ivory, hardwoods and gold dust. The slaves were taken across the Atlantic and traded for furs, molasses and other commodities which were taken to Liverpool, Bristol the other great port of western England, and so the cycle went on. It is not clear if Irish merchants were involved directly or otherwise in the slave trade.

From at least the 1740s Cork was a port of call for certainly one firm of Liverpool slave traders. William Davenport and Company regularly bought barrels of butter, bacon and tongues through an agent in the city. They seem to have specialised in aniseed, almonds, figs, raisins, lemons, oranges, olive oil and corkwood, buying some quantities in Spain and some across the Atlantic where they also obtained, in exchange for slaves, cotton, ginger, pimento, sugar and rum. They delivered consignments of these goods in Cork and Dublin on the way back to Liverpool and also traded in Irish linen (150).

Sir John Tobin seems to have carried on the greater part of his trading with Duke Ephraim, King of Old Calabar, who kidnapped people in the interior and sold them to the Liverpool and other slave traders who called on him. Tobin obviously had a high sense of what is nowadays public relations. In 1826 he sent Duke a large ornate brass armchair, a veritable throne, suitably inscribed as a gesture of appreciation for their many years of mutually profitable business. On another occasion he sent a wooden house which served as Ephraim's palace. In the 1820s and '30s Sir John was recognised as the biggest single trader on the West Coast of Africa (179,214).

Sir John's brother Thomas went to sea at an early age and presumably was a pirate for a period also. It is not clear if they traded together or separately. In 1810 he settled in Liverpool. In 1848 he was examined by the House of Commons Select Committee appointed to consider the Best Means Britain can adopt for the Final Extinction of the Slave Trade. He had first gone to Africa some fifty years before for slaves whom be bought at Bight, Bonny, Loango, the Gold Coast and elsewhere paying from £10 to £20 in trade goods and selling in Jamaica and other places for an average of £70. Against this sum were costs such as expenditure on the ships, seamen's wages, insurance and other items. The government paid a bonus to the captain and the ship's surgeon if they did not lose more than a certain number of slaves on each voyage. They got this on each of Tobin's expeditions.

Very few firms were able to make more than one voyage because "it required an immense capital" as payment was made in the form of bills which did not become cashable for up to three years. He made ten voyages before hearing while in Jamaica, of the Slave Trading Abolition Act 1807. He claimed that he stopped then and went into the palm oil business with Charles Horsfall (237, 238, 243).

It was generally accepted in Liverpool at the end of the nineteenth century that the Tobins had pioneered the palm oil trade, John from 1800 and Thomas from 1810. Some amounts had been imported for at least thirty years before. From 1772, the earliest year for which figures are available, the quantities remained small, well under one thousand tons, until 1809. Then imports increased steadily and after 1830 always exceeded ten thousand tons passing the thirty thousand ton mark in 1853. The commodity was in demand for soap and candles and for lubricating the many kinds of machinery then coming into use. After 1870 ever increasing quantities were used for margarine (245-7).

The development of the palm oil trade coincided with the decline in slave trading and slave owning especially following the 1807 Act and the Act for the Abolition of Slavery throughout the British Colonies which received the royal assent on 28 August 1833. On 3 July Thomas Tobin Junior wrote a letter, obviously in anticipation of the measure, then before Parliament, the first in a very lengthy correspondence which would lead to a change in the ownership of the mills and the production of powder again. The Tobins were always strong Tories and the letter was addressed to W Wainwright, agent of Lord Sandon, a Conservative MP for Liverpool:

The Government formerly possessed Gunpowder Mills at
a place called Ballincollig, about five miles distant from Cork,

*in the South of Ireland, for some years past these mills have
not been used and are at present unoccupied. Now if such is
the case we wish to know if the government have any intention
of parting with them since there is no chance of their being
required for making gunpowder. This scheme of ours will if we
can come to some arrangement with the government tend to
lessen the National Debt, you see how truly PATRIOTIC we
are (101).*

Patriotic indeed. Sir John had joined with Thomas, Thomas
Junior and Charles Horsfall who had been Mayor in 1832. The firm
of Charles Horsfall and Sons was reported in 1887 to be over a century
in business and to have run the Mersey Forge. This was later the
Mersey Steel and Iron Company and manufactured the Horsfall Gun,
reputedly the world's biggest in the mid-nineteenth century
(144,226,261).

It is not clear how the Tobins selected Ballincollig or whether
they had looked at any of the various mills in England and Scotland.
Cork was well established on the Liverpool-Africa-West Indies-North
America trade route. Sir John had called in 1799 and possibly other
times. There had been Leslies's sale of two hundred barrels in 1800
and probably other quantites from time to time. Wainwright sent
Tobins's letter to the Board of Ordnance who discussed it together
with a memo from a member of the staff advising that it would be
"highly advantageous" to take the opportunity of disposing of the
property. The Board reacted cautiously, replying that they were
prepared to give full consideration to any offer which Tobin might
make. Instead of making a bid, Tobin wrote on 26 July. He had made
enquiries and on finding many disadvantages in the property had
abandoned his plans.

So it must have seemed to the Board that this possibility of getting
rid of the premises had vanished as suddenly as it had come, before
serious negotiations could even begin. Not for long. In September
Tobin wrote again. He had changed his mind and wanted permission
to inspect the mills. The Board immediately granted this and
instructed the Respective Officers to extend Tobin every assistance.
At the end of the month Tobin spent a week viewing the buildings and
land in the company of Captain MT Doyle, Barrackmaster at
Ballincollig who had become responsible for the premises after James
Scarth had been transferred, retired or otherwise removed after the
affair of the previous year.

Word of Tobin's business in Ballincollig spread quickly and the
Inspector General of the Constabulary wrote to the Lord Lieutenant

in early October. He was worried that Faversham Square would be sold over their heads. A large sum had been spent on adapting the premises to police requirements. It was situated on the mailcoach road to Kerry and was important in other ways. The Lord Lieutenant passed the letter to the Board who replied rather airily that the interests of the force would be taken fully into account.

The Board received a letter dated 23 October from Tobin through William George Barradale, a London solicitor, requesting particulars of the conditions under which the property was held, the rent payable and so on. He would be prepared to make an offer following a study of this information. This placed the Board in an embarrassing position. They could not find the papers and no one had any personal knowledge of the details. The matter was passed to the Respective Officers at Dublin who wrote back saying indignantly that they were not responsible and suggesting that "any further information can be obtained from Mr Wilks". To make matters worse the Board were unable to find a map either and sent orders to Ballincollig for a sketch to be drawn. In the meantime the deeds were found and details forwarded to Tobin. On 13 November Barradale wrote with an offer of £10,000 and £100 a year for the use of the proof house. An assessment stated that a sum of one pound per year would place a high value on the land. The customary price in Ireland was twenty years purchase. The buildings were dilapidated and the canals gone to rack and ruin. It was a very good offer. The Board did not answer and on 5 December Barradale wrote requesting a reply. The Board responded that the matter was still under consideration and apologising for not being able to supply a detailed map.

A few days later the Board sent a representative to call on Barradale with the suggestion that his clients might prefer to rent rather than buy the mills. On 20 December Barradale wrote that this was unacceptable and increased the offer to £14,000. There was no reply and on 26 December Barradale wrote again, the bid was now £15,000. For this sum they wanted the dock and other facilities at Ordnance Quay included in the deal. While the letter said no more it seems to have been intended to convey the impression that this was the final offer.

The Board replied that the question of Ordnance Quay would have to be dealt with separately. In the meantime they were giving further consideration to the bid for the mills. An official drew up an appraisal of the offer which confirmed that the land was worth little more than one pound per acre or thirty shillings (£1.50) at the very outside. The bid especially as it had been increased by fifty percent was far in excess of the value. It was most unlikely that the Board would ever make powder in the mills again as "it would be expeditious to concentrate all production at Waltham; before long the annual expenditure on maintenance would exceed the value of the mills". Taking all the factors into account the best course would be to sell the property. On 21 January the Board advised Barradale that they were accepting the offer of £15,000 and instructed their solicitor to draw up the deed of transfer, this took the two solicitors several weeks and a number of consultations. In the course of this the board tried two mean tricks on the purchasers. The first was an attempt to insert a clause reserving rights of way through the mills to the river for bringing army horses to water from the barracks. Barradale objected and after long haggling and correspondence Tobin agreed to allow the horses through on sufferance until the Board made alternative arrangements. He insisted that if the Board sold the barracks the purchasers would not be entitled to this concession.

The second stratagem involved substantial stocks of tools and equipment used in making powder which had long before been removed from the mills to the barracks for safekeeping and had been shown to Tobin by Captain Doyle the previous autumn. The Board wanted to exclude these stores from the bargain on the basis that the items were not actually in the mills and tried to obtain a supporting opinion from the Comptroller of the Royal Laboratory, Woolwich, sending him a list. He replied that he could see no article which would not be used in making powder and the Board grudgingly conceded that they would "take a liberal view of the matter".

The final draft of the deed was agreed on 24 March. The arrangement was that the purchasers would take possession on payment of half the price with the balance to be paid a year later. The term was a sub-lease of the Board's tenure of 999 years excepting the last day. The deed had to be registered first and this featured one final flicker of farce. The property being in Ireland the document had to be sent to the Dublin Land Registry. The Board used English duty stamps which were unacceptable and there was some delay until Irish stamps were provided. On 3 April Barradale paid £7,500 to the Board. Immediately afterwards Thomas Tobin Junior went to Cork, no doubt on the weekly steamer service, one of many operated to various Irish ports by the War Office with ships crewed by the Royal Navy, which were widely advertised at the time (692).

The purchasers had formed a partnership styled Horsfall, Tobin and Company which they changed two years later to the Ballincollig Royal Gunpowder Mills Company. They were as choice a crew of merchant adventurers as ever sailed out of Liverpool in search of profit whether by plundering, trading, manufacturing or otherwise.

The Tobin company, the Horsfall company and the Ballincollig company always maintained separate offices in Liverpool. In practice most business was transacted in the Liverpool Exchange, which was for long the commercial centre of the city, with a newspaper reading room and apartments for auctions and meetings as a general forum for the merchants living and trading through the port. Different interests were served by the Liverpool Chamber of Commerce, the American Chamber of Commerce and other organisations. From the 1840s Liverpool African merchants were represented by the African Association (692).

The new owners of the mills were no doubt active in the Association. It might seem that from privateering, slaving and various types of trading to manufacturing gunpowder was a major change. It could have been that they had ample cash and wanted a suitable investment. If this was the case there must surely have been many other outlets available nearer to Liverpool and better in every way than a factory which had been derelict for twenty years.

It does not appear that the Tobins had to borrow any money to get the new venture underway. In August 1850 Thomas Senior claimed that the company:

> *embarked a capital of £80,000, our works give employment to a great number of persons and have done great good in the South of Ireland. Gunpowder is an article which is essential in the carrying on of of the African trade; it is a stable article and the advantage which this legitimate trade had conferred on Africa in superseding the Slave Trade may be estimated from the fact that a slave vessel is now almost unheard of (239).*

This of course was sheer hypocrisy. The Tobins had no concern for either providing employment in Ireland or bestowing benefits on Africa. Forced out of the slave trade they had made a virtue of this in the manner of a modern company obliged to abate pollution boasting civic pride. The Tobins wanted powder for the African trade, principally in exchange for palm oil and any other markets, civil and military, which might be found.

Thomas Junior settled in Ballincollig, taking a lease on the house formerly occupied by Wilks. In July 1834, only three months after arriving, he was elected a member of the Cork County Club a very exclusive society set up six years earlier by the Earl of Donoughmore,

Charles Henry Leslie's political associate and the Earl of Shannon, John Leslie's brother-in-law, to cater for the landed gentry of the county. Tobin personally held only eleven and the company 332 acres. Moreover he belonged to the mercantile or manufacturing class whom the gentry despised. Though no doubt useful, socially and commercially, acceptance by that class did not solve all Tobin's problems (154,248-9).

From the beginning Tobin had difficulties with the garrison, particularly over the frequency with which the horses were taken to water. The Board drew up elaborate plans for a pump at the river and a pipe to the barracks. They considered sinking wells and even proposed to erect tanks on the roofs for rainwater. It is doubtful if the Board meant any of these schemes very seriously especially as they thought of selling the barracks and in 1839 went into negotiations with the Poor Law Commissioners who wanted the premises for a workhouse. The Board advertised various fields for sale or letting from time to time. They never spent any money on an alternative water system. The problem continued until 1892, long after the demise of the Board, when an arrangement was made between the War Office and the Board of Guardians for the Union of Cork for the construction of an extensive waterworks on a hill to the south of the village which gave a substantial supply at high pressure until it was replaced by a regional system in 1968. There were also difficulties over trespassing and other irritations. After a time the Board erected proper boundary stones and fences separating the properties (101,178).

These problems were incidental to the main task of restoring the mills to working order. The canals were choked with mud and trees. The fields, roads and numerous bridges were in various stages of overgrowth and decay. The buildings, from some of which the machinery had been removed, must have been in need of major overhaul. Within months, despite all these difficulties, the area was resounding to the water flowing through the canals and the rolling of the mills while the distinctive aromas of sulphur and charcoal were wafting across the vale.

The balance of the purchase price was paid promptly in April 1835 and the Board sent the deeds to Liverpool. In December Tobin felt confident enough to apply to the Cork Harbour Commissioners for a reduction in the port charges. The Commissioners agreed to this. It is not clear what the old rates were. The new rates were one penny per barrel, one halfpenny per half and a farthing per quarter and remained in force almost until the close-down of the mills (175-7).

The system which the company had was to ship the powder to a magazine on Merseyside and despatch to the various markets. They were unable to buy, lease or rent Ordnance Quay and used a part of the Lee a little way upstream from there. This stretch is now known as the Marina. Over many years the Corporation had been engaged in building a wall from a point south of the confluence of the two branches of the river as far downstream as Blackrock Castle and reclaiming the land behind. The Harbour Commissioners, founded in 1814, took over the work which was first known as the New Wall and then as the Navigation Wall (166).

On 31 January 1837 the *Constitution* reported that a meeting "requisitioned by a number of gentlemen" had been called and presided over by the Mayor, John Saunders, to protest against the transportation of powder through the city streets. It was suggested that the shipments should be made from Monkstown, further down the harbour. Thomas Tobin Junior who attended said the extra expense would mean the "total extinction of the Ballincollig establishment". He always felt the greatest anxiety for safety and the wagons were covered with horsehide.

A committee was set up and met a number of times, the members included Daniel Meagher a wine merchant, who led the attack on Tobin, and Richard Dowden a vinegar manufacturer. At the same time a memorial signed by 77 citizens was sent to the Mayor claiming that the shipments were not being carried out as carefully as when the mills had been under government officers and calling on him in his capacity as chief magistrate to order the powder ships to a remote part of the harbour (254).

Within days another memorial signed by 156 traders was delivered to the Lord Lieutenant by Daniel Meagher who was to give any further details required. The memorialists claimed they had "represented the facts to the local authorities without obtaining that protection they are entitled to, respectfully solicit your Excellency to direct an examination to be made into the general mode of conveying gunpowder through the city".

The Mayor reacted angrily to this, writing to the Lord Lieutenant on 6 February vehemently protesting that he had been "publicly and actively endeavouring as far as my limited powers extended to make such arrangements with Mr Tobin as would tend to the prevention of accidents and to allay the fears of the inhabitants". He went further and organised a public meeting at which he took the chair, sending another memorial to the Lord Lieutenant asking for a ban on the movement of powder through the city, the erection of a special public magazine and new legislation to control the gunpowder trade generally. At the request of the Mayor the Royal Engineers investigated the position as far as they could "as it has not been within our power to visit Ballincollig". The powder was brought in covered wagons holding thirty barrels drawn by four horses. Three months previously the iron axle of one had broken down in Patrick Street and it was felt that a similar accident or a collision could cause a serious explosion.

The Mayor wrote again to the Lord Lieutenant in July suggesting that a certain Constabulary barracks would be suitable for a public magazine and that the Royal Engineers had prepared plans and estimates. The Castle replied, after consultation with the Lords Justices, that apart from some doubt about the propriety of the proposal it was a "request with which the government has no power to comply, there being no funds available for such a purpose". It is truly amazing how limited are the powers of governments when they do not want to do whatever is asked.

In the meantime on 15 February the Mayor brought the matter before the Harbour Board, of which he was a member, together with a letter from the Lord Lieutenant pointing out that the Commissioners' own Ballast Act appeared to provide adequate powers. The Commissioners held a special meeting and after "mature consideration" came to the conclusion that they were "unable to name any part of the port where the shipment of powder will not be attended with serious risk" and resolved:

> that with a serious desire to promote the interest of the enterprising firm embarked in the manufacture of gunpowder, so far as is consistent with the safety of the inhabitants, A Committee be now appointed to meet Mr Tobin and report some eligible situation for making shipments and to suggest under whose management it should take place and what accommodation would be required from this Board and that the Committee be further requested to inquire into the best road for conveying gunpowder for shipment.

The Committee made a recommendation which was accepted, that from April Tobin should discontinue shipping from the downstream end of the New Wall and instead should despatch from Ordnance Quay. There was a gap between the two at the time. Tobin had already failed to obtain the use of Ordnance Quay and going there meant a longer and more roundabout route for the wagons. He had no notion of putting himself out for the Harbour Commissioners, the Corporation or anyone else and had every intention of continuing to use the New Wall. Stonewalling was to be the Tobin policy for fifty years (167).

The Harbour Commissioners at their meeting on 8 March noted that as they had made a large reduction on the dues payable, they had "a claim on Mr Tobin" to take the necessary steps for adapting to the new arrangement. A few days after the deadline Tobin applied to the Commissioners for permission to despatch two hundred barrels which he had on hand as he had not been able to make the necessary preparations on Ordnance Quay. The Commissioners agreed on the strict understanding that no further shipments would be made from the New Wall. At the same time Commissioner James Murphy gave notice that he would raise at the next meeting "the matter of Mr Tobin's intention to ship powder from the late Ordnance Quay at Blackrock; the inhabitants of that place have expressed their determination to do all in their power to oppose such shipments if attempted".

The next meeting was attended by a deputation of a "great number of the most respectable inhabitants of Blackrock and its neighbourhood". A letter from Mrs (sic) Bell head of the local Ursuline convent in which "two hundred females were resident" was read in support of the case against powder shipments from Blackrock. The Commissioners, after some discussion, postponed the decision for a week to a special meeting. At this the Mayor complained that incorrect statements had been made about his part in the issue and he moved for the admission of a reporter. This was rejected and the meeting heard Tobin. He must have been persuasive. The Commissioners allowed him to ship from a point on the New Wall subject to various restrictions including a police escort from the mills.

At the end of the year Daniel Meagher launched another attack on Tobin by proposing that the transport of powder should be from Passage West or lower in the Harbour, subject to even more stringent conditions and through a new road to be constructed skirting the south side of the city. A Committee was set up which suggested using Rocky Island through a causeway to be built which was eventually accomplished in 1966 when Irish Steel built a bridge through Rocky to Haulbowline Island. This was found to be impractical mainly because Tobin would not agree (175).

The Commissioners laid down by-laws in 1838. In the following few years various complaints were made about infringements which Tobin had no difficulty in warding off because in June 1839 he was nominated as a Commissioner representing the Mercantile Body, in effect the Chamber of Commerce, which had twenty-five seats. The Corporation had five besides the Mayor of the year. The two MPs for the city were also members. This was presumably a leavening for the appearance of public accountability. The Commissioners did not have an annual chairman until 1883. During his forty-two years Tobin regularly took the chair of the weekly meeting and the various committees. He does not seem to have taken a very active part in the Chamber itself (206).

In October 1844 Daniel Meagher returned to the attack, seeking an order from the Admiralty regulating gunpowder movements on the basis of an order they had recently made for London, claiming that the citizens stood in need of the same protection as Londoners. Nobody seconded the motion and it fell.

In April 1846, during the Famine, it was proposed again to make a special road from Ballincollig to some point on the harbour, as a measure for the relief of distress. There was also a proposal for a canal. A committee was set up. Richard Dowden told the Commissioners that a canal would avoid the dangers of concussion. Daniel Meagher riposted "but how would you get rid of percussion?" The Commissioners literally laughed Dowden out of the boardroom when he mentioned that a scheme was being proposed to make a canal from Macroom to Ballincollig. They said that they would continue the canal to Cork when the other stretch had first been made. It was apparently intended to construct the canal on the basis of the Drainage and Navigation Act 1715 which authorised the respective Justices of the Peace and Members of Parliament to act as commissioners for the construction of canals on practically all the rivers in the country (232).

While Daniel Meagher frequently tried to force the despatch of powder from the city to the lower harbour he does not seem to have gone further. Indeed on 4 February 1846 chairing the weekly meeting he found himself virtually defending Tobin against an attack by Commissioner John Beale as recounted in the following day's *Southern Reporter*. This showed a remarkably inhuman not to say unchristian attitude to the question of slavery on the part of the mercantile and municipal moguls of Cork who doubtless would have been in the slavery business if they had the opportunity.

COMMISSIONER BEALE: The Board will perceive that the horrid traffic in gunpowder and slaves is carried on to an extent that almost staggers belief; a visitor to Calabar in 1834 found the natives boasting of a predatory excursion in which they had recently engaged, they had surprised a village, killed all who resisted and carried off the remainder as slaves (LAUGHTER).

COMMISSIONER JOHN R BURKE: Oh my God!
(ROARS OF LAUGHTER).

COMMISSIONER BEALE: An African boy declared
that he had killed three himself.

COMMISSIONER BURKE: Tremendous! (CONTINUED
LAUGHTER).

COMMISSIONER BEALE: A powder ship blew up in
Calabar harbour and nobody could tell how. What brought the
vessel there? *(LAUGHTER).* To sell powder to the Calabarians
(ROARS OF LAUGHTER).

One of the chiefs said,
There are three things we want; arms, ammunition and
brandy and we give three things in barter for them; men,
women and children *(LAUGHTER).*

CHAIRMAN: But Mr Beale, we have no jurisdiction at
Calabar (LAUGHTER).

ALDERMAN JOHN HARLEY: But it is at Fernando
Poo he means [a Spanish island in the Bight of Biafra,
near Calabar].

CHAIRMAN: Nor at Fernando Poo either. If I had my
way I would throw water on the powder (ROARS OF
LAUGHTER).

COMMISSIONER BEALE: There are two towns of the
name of Calabar, Old and New, both notorious for the slave
trade.

CHAIRMAN: But we have no jurisdiction at either.

This was the end of the discussion, Tobin was not at the
meeting. No doubt he would have disregarded Beale.

Commissioner Beale then tucked his umbrella under his arm and
left the boardroom, lost in astonishment at the want of feelings of
humanity, and all the better feelings of our nature exhibited by the
Board in not putting an immediate stop to the slave trade and cutting
off the supply of powder to the barbarous Calabarians the coverage in
the *'Reporter'* concluded, echoing the raucous ribaldry, sarcasm and
cynicism of the gentlemen entrusted with the administration of the
great port of Cork.

In January 1849 Daniel Meagher launched another onslaught
against Tobin by proposing that "a more remote place for shipping
powder be appointed". As customary a special meeting was held, as

customary a committee was formed and as customary there was no change in the system. This seems to have been Meagher's last sally. While there were no further difficulties in Cork the company were about to experience a major disruption at the centre of their distribution system.

By this time, the late 1840s, James Aspinall Tobin, Thomas Junior's younger brother, was very much in command at head office. Originally intending to be a clergyman he attended Exeter College, Oxford briefly in 1836. He sat on Liverpool Corporation, 1847-65 and was Mayor in 1854. From 1851 he was on the Corporation's Dock Committee which ran the port until it was replaced by the Mersey Docks and Harbour Board in 1858 on which he served until 1875. Thomas Senior had been a member of the Dock Committee for many years (146, 147, 149).

The Gunpowder Act 1772 had a clause exempting "the storehouse now erected near Liverpool" from the regulations which applied to magazines generally. The magazines had been erected in the early 1750s in Liscard, Cheshire, across the river from Liverpool to replace a magazine at Hanover Street. The population of the area was then small. As years passed it grew and in 1836 the people complained about the danger of the magazines. The Corporation requested the Board of Ordnance to make a survey of the premises.

The Board submitted a report which showed that the buildings were in bad repair. The storage and handling system was slipshod. While the magazines were quite unsatisfactory there was no danger to Liverpool. The report suggested the construction of new buildings and the implementation of strict rules. These recommendations were duly carried out and the magazines functioned without question until August 1850 when the Commissioners for the Improvement of Wallasey sent a lengthy memorial to the Home Secretary expressing their grave disquiet with the location and operation of the magazines especially in view of the very large increase in the population since the 1836 report. This was the beginning of a long series of memorials, correspondence and conferences.

Liverpool Corporation immediately arranged with the Board of Ordnance for another survey. The report noted that the buildings were quite unsafe, not fireproof, were not fitted with lightning conductors and there was no night patrol which had been recommended by the 1836 report. It was suggested that the magazines should be closed completely and in future all powder to be stored on floating magazines.

The magazines were held jointly by Ballincollig, Curtis's & Harvey and five other firms. The leases had been renewed in 1842 for the term of forty-five years. Within days the lessees held a meeting at the Adelphi Hotel, Liverpool and appointed Thomas Tobin Senior as their representative. He chaired the meetings and conducted the correspondence with the other parties involved. The lessees pointed out that they had carefully rebuilt the magazines after 1836 "under the express direction of a government officer". They took every precaution and actually operated the magazines even more strictly than was required by the inspector whom the Corporation posted on the premises.

Tobin observed that in his own case there were twenty different types of powder "one description being quite unsuitable for other purposes". They did not keep in stock more than was required for the trade at any time.

In October, the Corporation, in the best traditions of the Cork Harbour Commissioners, appointed a Special Gunpowder Committee which sat five times. They were unable to arrange a meeting with all of the lessees at one time. The lessees seemed to have no such difficulty among themselves. The Committee noted that James Aspinall Tobin had told a Corporation meeting that the lessees would "cordially co-operate with the Special Committee in making any practical suggestions". Eventually the committee reported to the Corporation that "no arrangement for the removal of the magazines can be effected without the aid of an Act of Parliament".

After further negotiations, the government in January 1851 decided to abolish the clause concerning the Liverpool magazines in the 1772 Act and accordingly the Gunpowder Stores (Liverpool) Exemption Repeal Act was passed. The lessees were allowed one year to make alternative arrangements. The Ballincollig company bought a ship, the *Swallow*, which they anchored permanently in the Mersey as a floating magazine in accordance with the recommendation. In 1865 the Liverpool Gunpowder Regulation Act imposed further restrictions (140-2,234-5,239-41).

While James Aspinall Tobin was moving up the municipal ladder in Liverpool, Thomas Junior was involving himself in Cork's civic affairs. In the summer of 1849 he was on the Committee of Reception making arrangements for the visit of Queen Victoria which saw the opening of Queen's, now University College. By this time he was also a Justice of the Peace. In 1852 the National Exhibition was held in Cork on the lines of the Great Exhibition in the Crystal Palace, London the previous year. Tobin was secretary of the police committee and a member of the executive.

The surplus fund from the Exhibition was used to build the city's premier theatre, the Opera House, originally the Athenaeum. Tobin, as president of the board of directors was knighted by the Lord Lieutenant at the official opening in May 1855 (216-18).

A useful description of the Mills in the twenty-fifth year under the house of Tobin was given by Lammot du Pont, grandson of EI du Pont, founder of a powder company in Delaware, USA, which grew into a huge multinational concern (page 146). In April 1858 Lammot visited Ballincollig in the course of a tour of mills in Britain and Europe, having learned in London that the company boasted "the best machinery in the WORLD". Sir Thomas received him and gave some details without showing him around the buildings. All firms had their own particular techniques and trade secrets. The incorporating millstones, seven feet (over two metres) in diameter weighing some ten tons, were the largest Lammot had ever seen and worked blasting powder for two hours and sporting for six hours, continuously, day and night. Twenty-five tons of saltpetre were used each week. There were fifty-five coopers, sixty horses for drawing the barges on the canals and fourteen wagons for taking the powder to the dock. Lammot did not say whether he thought the machinery lived up to the claim. Earlier, when an English powdermaker visiting Delaware had remarked that the du Ponts "could not learn anything from the Europeans" he had noted "this was a piece of Blarney which might be interpreted into stupidity". After leaving Ballincollig, Lammot went to Blarney Castle, nearby. Regrettably he did not record if he kissed the Stone.

In November 1861 Lammot visited Liverpool and bought up all the saltpetre on the market including some still on ships bound for the port. He had an open chequebook on behalf of the Union or Northern side of the Civil War which had just broken out. From May to July 1862 Sir Thomas was in the USA. It is difficult to imagine that he went for sightseeing or to watch history in the making. He must have been trying to sell powder, to both sides if possible, in the full traditions of the trade. He visited West Point Military Academy and the du Pont powder mills in Delaware.

On at least one occasion du Ponts bought a quantity of powder in Europe for the Union side. Tobin noted calling to the War and State Departments and obtaining passes to visit the South. There is no official record of this extant. He called on the family of Patrick Cleburne, a general on the Confederate or Southern side, who emigrated from Ovens, near Ballincollig, in 1849 and settled in

Arkansas. Before this, Cleburne's father, a doctor had been on call (page 75) at the mills (151,172-4,255-6).

Another contact Tobin could have had was John Mallet, son of Robert Mallet (page 205) who had obtained degrees in Trinity College Dublin and Gottingen University, Germany before going to the USA on research for his father at the age of 21 in 1853. Remaining, he had a notable career holding chemistry chairs in the universities of Alabama, Louisiana, Philadelphia, Texas and Virginia, had numerous distinctions and a large output of papers. During the Civil War, after service in the ranks and as a lieutenant colonel of artillery he was, 1862-65, Superintendent of the Central Ordnance Laboratories of the Confederate States. A colleague of Mallet's at Alabama University, Major Caleb Huse, was Purchasing Agent for the Confederate States in Europe during the War. He transacted most of his business with Liverpool firms, buying for cash and cotton all types of military supplies and carried out all his financial arrangements through a Liverpool bank. In a brief account of his activities he did not mention any dealings with Ballincollig, nor did he name any concerns. It seems very probable that he would have bought from the firm, as one, if not the largest, in Liverpool. Moreover James Aspinall Tobin was a partner in a Liverpool house of cotton and general produce brokers, T & H Littledale (220-222).

In the early 1860s the Tobins reorganised their affairs on the basis of limited liability. Under the Companies Act 1856 it was possible to limit the liabilities of companies to specific sums and to protect the personal assets of directors and shareholders in the event of failure.

In April 1861 the Ballincollig Royal Gunpowder Mills Company Limited was registered with James Aspinall Tobin as managing director. The share capital was £100,000 in five thousand shares of £20 each, such high values were common at the time, of which £2 was paid up immediately. In the event of liquidation the shareholders could have been liable for any uncalled balance. Four members of the house of Tobin held a total of 3,500 shares. Seven other Liverpool merchants had stakes including George Henry Horsfall MP representing the old connection. The remaining ten shareholders included various gentlemen, a mine owner and the three principal railway contractors of the age, William Dargan of Dublin, and Sir Thomas Brassey and William McCormick of London. Dargan was associated with the Dublin and Kingstown (Dun Laoghaire) the first in Ireland and later the Dublin, Wicklow and Wexford; the Dublin and Drogheda; the Great Southern and Western; the Midland Great Western; the Ulster Railway and other lines. He was also involved in the Ulster Canal,

Belfast Harbour, various roads in England and Ireland and other undertakings. Brassey built some 150 railways throughout the world from minor mineral lines in Wales to Argentina's Central and Canada's Grand Trunk. He built the Enniskillen, Bundoran and Sligo and was concerned in numerous civil engineering projects. After his death in 1870 his firm continued until 1881. From then on members of the family held the shares. McCormick who was Irish, built the Londonderry and Coleraine and the Londonderry and Enniskillen lines and many more in Britain (170,171, 182, 223, 262, 678).

In 1863 the Company of African Merchants Limited was formed to take over the businesses of Tobin and Son and Frederick Huth and Company, the partners in this concern, Louis Gruning and Alfred Castellain, both Liverpool merchants, were shareholders in the Ballincollig company. In 1874 the Company of African Merchants was dissolved and reformed as the British and Continental African Company Limited (185-6,227).

In April 1864 Sir Richard Burton, the famous diplomat, explorer and author, reported to the Foreign Office that the Company of African Merchants had establishments at several ports in what is now Nigeria and other parts of British West Africa. Charles Horsfall and Sons and several other Liverpool firms were also trading, all in competition with each other. At this time the Company of African Merchants approached the government for a subsidy to develop further trading routes and stations in the Niger. The other firms, including Horsfalls, objected very strongly with a memorial to the Foreign Secretary and the government did not pay (180-1).

The *Cork Constitution*, 25 May 1872, carried a report just received in Liverpool of an explosion in the warehouse which the Company of African Merchants had in Old Calabar. Several Dronmmen died and 1,000 barrels of powder, quantities of rum, gin and other goods to the value of £9,000 were lost.

James Aspinall Tobin gave evidence to the House of Commons Select Committee on British Establishments on the Western Coast of Africa in 1865. His companies had depots in Freetown and Sherboro then the Grain Coast, now Sierra Leone; Whydah on the Slave Coast, later Dahomey, now Ouidah; Brass and Bonny in the Oil Rivers Protectorate and Old Calabar and New Calabar, now simply Calabar, Nigeria. There were also establishments at Kinsembo in Angola a Portuguese colony and in Chincoxo and Limdannah to the north of the Congo, then unclaimed territory.

Tobin told the Committee that they also had agents in the Gold

Coast, now Ghana, and traded with the Congo and other areas where
they did not have representatives. They would not be prepared to
undertake trading on the Niger without government subsidies
guaranteeing them against losses. They had a packet vessel for
maintaining contact between the various places. In his thirty years of
trading he had called on the Royal Navy for assistance more than half
a dozen times. The main product traded was palm oil which had
passed the forty thousand ton per annum mark in 1860. Some
quantities of palm kernels, not crushed for the oil and ground or
peanuts were also imported. (244,257-8).

In the period 1845-65 up to 150,000 bright barrelled flint muskets,
Birmingham made, were exported annually to Africa at a cost price
of ten shillings (50p) each. According to another contemporary
account salt bought for sixteen shillings per ton in Liverpool was sold
for £35; gin and brandy or liquors described as such, bought for six
shillings per dozen bottles were sold at similar stupendous profits. So
after seventy years Calabar was still the chief centre in Africa for the
house of Tobin and palm oil the principal import. No other
information is available on their African interests (215,225,260).

Other markets had been developed, not least in the railways. In
September 1846 James Aspinall Tobin, in a letter to Dublin Castle,
seeking, apparently without satisfaction, restrictions on imports of
powder noted "increasing use in railway operations ". The holdings
of the three main railway magnates of the day must have ensured
substantial orders as huge quantities were used in digging tunnels and
foundations and quarrying the immense tonnages of stone needed for
track ballast and buildings. The Mining Company of Ireland, which
had many mines and quarries throughout the country from 1824 to
the turn of the century, regularly bought large quantities (168-9, 219).

There must have been many more customers, large and small in
Ireland, Britain and elsewhere. A receipted invoice of 1847 noted the
sale of six half barrels to the Birkenhead Dock Committee for
excavation work. The price was forty-one shillings per full barrel.
Gunpowder was a commodity and the price varied according to the
cost of saltpetre and the demand from time to time (148).

From 1861 with the exception of '62 and '65 the annual returns
of the Cork Harbour Commissioners, whose year began in August,
give the number of barrels exported, a total of 802,733. This of course
does not take account of sales in Ireland. A reasonable estimate might
be fifteen percent, bringing the figure to 920,000. There is no
indication as to how much Leslie and the Board of Ordnance
manufactured, perhaps a maximum of 30,000 and 200,000

respectively. Neither is there any account of how many barrels the Tobins made from 1835 to '60. Lammot du Pont's figure of twenty-five tons of saltpetre per week indicates an average of 37,000, say 35,000 per annum, totalling 875,000. These amounts add up to 2,025,000. In round figures Ballincollig turned out two million barrels of powder in its ninety years of production. From 1870 the annual reports of the Inspectors of Explosives give figures of exports from Britain. These do not give quantities of Ballincollig powder sold in Britain. There is an approximate relationship between Ballincollig's shipments and Britain's exports (177,689).

The mills began in the dramatic days of the 1790s in an area with no history of the industry and with a founder who was not involved in any form of manufacturing. In this period the production was largely for the public service and the licenced domestic market which had sporting and industrial branches. Exports were probably incidental for the most part.

In the next phase, under government ownership, the plant was expanded enormously and the entire output was for the armed forces. For twenty years the works was out of production and was stripped of much of its machinery, coming close to complete dismantling and demolition.

At that juncture new owners appeared who extended the factory yet more, overcoming many difficulties with public authorities which had not affected the previous operators and reflected the increasing role of government, central and local, in the mid-nineteenth century. They developed a considerable trade in Ireland and Britain at a time when demand was increasing very much especially for civil purposes. Sales to these outlets were ancillary to the main purpose of the proprietors whose business was essentially a mercantile concern, one of the largest in its market and era.

Ballincollig, for more than half its existence, was an in-house production unit for the provision, at first cost, of a basic commodity used in exchange for another in one of the great inter-continental trades in the world economy of the time.

BARRELS EXPORTED FROM CORK (Source 177)		BARRELS EXPORTED FROM BRITAIN (Source 689)	
1861	22,208		
1862	20,000	(estimate)	
1863	18,796		
1864	17,543		
1865	18,000	(estimate)	
1866	18,620		
1867	30,649		
1868	24,962		
1869	30,565		
1870	26,049	154,979	17%
1871	31,067	164,437	19%
1872	27,769	177,586	16%
1873	29,976	₁48,452	19%
1874	25,708	133,312	20%
1875	32,533	134,336	24%
1876	27,488	127,399	22%
1877	32,140	144,241	22%
1878	27,648	126,994	22%
1879	23,482	108,926	22%
1880	29,359	133,281	22%
1881	27,594	128,241	22%
1882	25,340	126,634	20%
1883	28,912	141,361	20%
1884	20,300	142,721	14%
1885	17,500	113,963	15%
1886	15,705	103,555	15%
1887	10,305	87,397	12%
1888	13,848	120,746	11%
1889	6,100	95,354	6%
1890	12,053	92,236	13%
1891	8,949	100,218	9%
1892	10,850	70,855	15%
1893	7,310	68,440	11%
1894	8,350	74,249	11%
1895	13,505	71,846	19%
1896	6,605	72,223	9%
1897	9,350	79,648	12%
1898	3,395	77,401	4%
1899	13,610	70,816	19%
1900	10,000	62,921	15%
1901	8,600	61,301	14%
1902	9,080	60,857	15%
1903	,840	(residual quantity)	
TOTALS	802,663	3,576,926	22%

THE FENIANS, SIX THOUSAND BARRELS

In 1858, two secret oathbound organisations were formed in parallel, pledged to overthrow British rule in Ireland by force of arms. That in Ireland was styled the Irish Republican, or Revolutionary, Brotherhood and that in the USA the Fenian Brotherhood. While the members of the organisation in Ireland were, and remain, commonly known as 'Fenians' this designation is not strictly correct. Groups known as 'circles' were formed in many areas and in the British Army, presided over by 'centres' who reported through various higher officers to James Stephens, head centre. At some point in the first three years of the organisation a circle was set up in Ballincollig under the leadership of Thomas Duggan of Cloughduv, a nearby district, who was a teacher in the village national school.

On 14 February 1862 the weekly meeting of the Commissioners of National Education, attended as usual by the Lord Chancellor, the Lord Chief Justice, the Solicitor-General and other mandarins of the Castle heard a report that "information of a confidential character had been communicated that Thomas Duggan a teacher at Ballincollig National School had been in the habit of attending a Secret and Seditious Society". The head inspector for Munster, John E. Sheridan, had been instructed to investigate and his findings were before the meeting. There is no reference to the matter in Sheridan's or the Commissioners' reports for the year.

Sheridan had found that the body in question was the 'Young Men's Society'. Apparently it catered for the Catholic youth of the area. The Reverend Cahill had denounced it as "dangerous and disloyal" and the Reverend Horgan had resigned as Spiritual Director. The Commissioners instructed Sheridan to go again to Ballincollig and "afford Mr Duggan an opportunity of giving such explanation as he may wish to offer" and also to "report any further circumstances which may serve to guide the Commissioners in arriving at a decision in the case". It is improbable that the Commissioners wanted any facts which might have exonerated Duggan.

At the next meeting the Commissioners "ordered that as Mr Thomas Duggan appears to have continued a member of the Young Mens' Society after it had ceased to be a religious and became a political society, he be dismissed". Under the rules for primary schools at the time "national teachers should be persons of Christian sentiment, imbued with a spirit of obedience to the law and of loyalty to their sovereign". These qualities were more important than the "art of communicating knowledge" (271,288-9).

It is apparent that the Society had been used as a cover for the Fenian circle and may indeed have been formed specially for the purpose. Whichever the case the clergy got suspicious and informed the Castle through the Constabulary or other channel, besides publicly dissociating themselves from the Society and no doubt condemning it from the pulpit. In all probability this was sparked off by Duggan and other local Fenians attending the famous funeral of Terence Bellew MacManus which passed through Cork on its way from California to Dublin in November 1861.

Afterwards, it is believed, that Duggan went to the USA where the Civil War was being fought and that he joined the Confederate army. There is no confirmation of this. He returned in late 1864 or early '65 as the Civil War was ending. In the meantime the Fenians had gone from strength to strength and it was apparently expected generally that Stephens would call the rising in the course of 1865. Spring became summer and that season was giving way to autumn when Duggan wrote a letter signed "A Ballincollig Man" which was printed on 2 September in the *Irish People,* the Fenian weekly paper published in Dublin. The letter in effect asked Stephens to give the signal for the general uprising (286,292-3).

On 15 September the Castle raided the paper's office and seized all correspondence and other documents. The next day Sir Thomas Tobin wrote to the Castle warning of Fenianism in Ballincollig. The letter was marked "not worthwhile to take any further precautions" and formally acknowledged. On 19 November Duggan and his second in command, Jeremiah Donovan, were arrested and brought before Tobin and two other magistrates of Ballincollig Petty Sessions. The prosecutor, Philip O'Connell, solicitor, regretting that Duggan was a married man with a family, showed the court the original of the letter to the *Irish People* along with the Ballincollig school roll-book with Duggan's handwriting proving that he was the author of the letter to the "very inflammatory paper". A copy of the issue was in Donovan's house near Blarney (273).

Two soldiers gave evidence of Fenian meetings at bars in Ballincollig and Carrigrohane, nearby. Duggan had claimed that James Stephens who had been arrested on 6 November could be released at any time. Four days later Stephens made a sensational escape from Richmond Prison, Dublin. Duggan and Donovan were returned for trial at a Special Commission held in Cork on 19 and 20 December. At this William Rudd the mills manager gave evidence against Duggan which he contradicted. Duggan was sentenced to ten years and Donovan to five, the *Constitution* reported with relish. They were sent to Millbank Prison, London and later to the Penal Settlement in Western Australia. Duggan served out his time, remained in Australia and resumed his teaching career, dying in 1913. By a piquant turn of history his granddaughter, Lucy Duggan, was Professor of Education at University College Cork, retiring in 1962 just one hundred years after the Commissioners had dismissed the leader of the Ballincollig Fenians. Donovan, formerly a coachman, is believed to have returned and died in mid-Cork (294).

The Fenian rising which eventually took place in March 1867 consisted of a few skirmishes and created a scare in The Castle and London which did not ease off for several years. As Duggan and Donovan arrived in Australia in January 1868 a row already almost three years old with as long to go was coming to a head of sorts. It was long and agonising for all concerned. The lives of the villagers and the garrison were threatened and the very existence of the mills, the barracks and the western side of Cork seemed to be in doubt.

The central figure in the affair was Sir Hugh Henry Rose, first Baron of Strathnairn and Jansi. The main feature was his campaign from 1865 to '70 as Commander of the Forces in Ireland to persuade the government to take measures against the company for keeping what he considered a dangerously large quantity of powder in the magazines at the mills and against the general danger presented by the mills during the Fenian period. The epic is extensively recorded in hundreds of letters and other documents. Strathnairn wrote more and longer letters than anyone else, up to thirty-six pages at a time.

Towards the end of 1865 Strathnairn suggested to the Castle and the War Office in London that the manufacture of gunpowder in the mills should be prohibited while the Fenian danger remained. The opinion of the Law Officers was that this was not possible under the Gunpowder Act 1860 which had replaced the 1772 Act. This was because Ballincollig was neither a market town nor a borough, that is with a mayor and corporation and there was no church, presumably a branch of the Church of Ireland, which had not yet been disestablished, within a half mile (268-70).

In January 1867 Strathnairn proposed that the government might consider paying the company to suspend the manufacture for the time being. The Treasury rejected this. In February Strathnairn sought permission to remove the troops from Ballincollig. This was discussed intensively for several weeks. In March, the Ballincollig magistrates, with Tobin staying discreetly in the background, requested a special military guard for the mills. Strathnairn played for time pointedly asking "what size of guard would be required and whether any guard, even a strong one could efficiently protect..."(274).

At the end of April it was decided to evacuate the barracks and plans were made to send the various units to other posts. This does not appear to have been implemented. On 11 May a public meeting, called and chaired by the Mayor, Francis Lyons, was held and a strong protest was made against the company having six thousand barrels in the mill magazines. The protest was sent to the Chief Secretary, the Earl of Mayo, also known as Lord Naas who took the case up with the Lord Lieutenant, the Earl of Abercorn (272, 280).

They decided to appoint Captain Neil Mackay, Commanding Royal Artillery at Ballincollig, as Inspector of the mills under the Gunpowder Act. At the same time they enquired into the possibility of storing powder at Rocky Island and found that space was available for ten thousand barrels. The Castle also looked into the terms and conditions of the Act and its implementation in relation to Ballincollig. While various minimum distances were laid down between different types of buildings, Ballincollig had been exempted from the stipulation that a magazine should be 140 yards from a dusting house. One magazine was a matter of seven yards within this limit and the other forty-five (281).

Mackay reported that he had made a careful examination of the buildings; all were "well and solidly constructed of stone and entirely cased inside with wood". He had studied the Act and the tenure of the property which was a sub-lease of the War Office's interest, inherited from the Board of Ordnance, of the entire term of 999 years excepting the last day. Right of repossession was not reserved. Without a special Act it would not be possible to restrict the amount kept in store. He recommended a maximum of 360 barrels, or three days' production. The average in the magazines was five thousand barrels. He suggested that storage facilities should be made available at Rocky Island and made a number of other recommendations, the principal being that the magazines should be demolished and replaced by two new buildings as far apart as possible.

When the plan to remove the troops became known, the company in a letter from William Rudd, manager, on 29 April requested storage space on Rocky. They were prepared to pay a reasonable rent. The War Office wanted one shilling (5p) per barrel per year which the company regarded as excessive. In June the War Office considered selling the barracks and decided against in July.

During the remainder of 1867 the lightning conductors on the magazines attracted most of the attention. The installations were of an obsolete pattern and Mackay wanted the company to erect the latest type. They promised to do this immediately and delayed for several months with a series of thin excuses (281).

In the last weeks of 1867 and early '68 several events took place which increased public tension. The Manchester Martyrs were executed and the Fenians blew down part of Clerkenwell Prison, London with gunpowder which, it was revealed at the subsequent trial, they had bought in the ordinary way from Curtis's & Harvey. In Cork, William Thomas Lomasney, better known as 'Captain Mackey' raided successfully a Martello tower in the harbour and also the Fenians robbed two gun shops in Patrick Street, Allports and Richardsons.

On the night of 3 January a raid was carried out on the magazine at Gallows Green, now Greenmount, owned by TW Murray and Company, gun and powder merchants, who were local agents for Curtis's & Harvey. Three doors, iron, copper and wood were broken and a large quantity of powder taken.

A few days later a fight took place on Patrick Street in which some Greek Fire was used. Soon after raids, presumed to be for guns, took place on the Leslie and Newenham houses, which apparently were repulsed. On 21 January, Sir Thomas Tobin, in his capacity as a magistrate, wrote to Captain Neil Mackay complaining of the inadequate number of men in the local Constabulary barracks and drawing attention to the various outrages in Cork (275-279, 282).

Against this background Strathnairn went on a tour of inspection throughout the south. It is not clear if he visited Ballincollig. On 11 January he wrote to Major General G Campbell Commanding the South Western Division stating he had received a requisition from the Castle to provide an escort for the wagons taking powder from the mills to the docks.

The next day Strathnairn wrote to Mayo. He had visited many stations and found everything to his satisfaction except:

The Ballincollig Powder Mills with their three or four hundred thousand pounds of powder and magazines which are neither bomb nor splinter proof, why the Fenians have not blown them up I cannot imagine, nothing would have been easier. But if they did the garrison would have been blown up also. The proprietors have acted with extreme bad faith; your government must undertake immediate responsibility for not allowing me to withdraw the troops from Ballincollig.

Mayo's reply was:

The case is one of extreme difficulty, the original mistake made by government some years ago was the sale of these mills, they are in a situation neither favourable nor safe. I cannot think that the Treasury would sanction the large sum which would be necessary for the repurchase of the establishment on which a considerable amount has been laid out by the proprietors. The provisions of the Gunpowder Act apply to this case to a very limited extent, the buildings having been in existence prior to the passing of the statute. I have had two or three personal conversation with Sir Thomas Tobin, he called to me at the Irish Office [London] and expressed his complete readiness to comply with any reasonable request made by the Government. They are willing to sell the mills back for £60,000 which is the value they place on the premises including the improvements.

The question of military protection for the mills is one of great difficulty, it is a matter of public safety, not as regards the chance of an explosion but the Fenian conspiracy should they attempt to remove any of the powder for their own purposes. It is not therefore a duty which either in fairness or in right should be thrown on the proprietors (268).

Strathnairn reacted strongly to this, protesting against the "lives of the officers and soldiers being placed in imminent danger for the sake of a private enterprise".

On the 14 January Strathnairn wrote to the Lord Lieutenant, the Duke of Abercorn:

I beg to state that I have received no answer to the very important telegram which I sent you some days ago respecting the danger to the troops at Ballincollig and the breach of engagement on the part of the proprietors. I have received a demi-official letter from Lord Mayo, but that is entirely in favour of the commercial interests of the proprietors and does not offer any remedy whatever against the danger to the troops and their families.

I was very glad to hear from you in the conversation I had with you that you were, generally speaking, of the same opinion respecting the question. I only regret that you have exercised no influence on the Chief Secretary. I doubt the correctness of his legal opinion. I must think that the sworn depositions of competent authorities as to the danger to the Queen's subjects caused by the mills

would enable the civil authorities who are answerable
for their safety to suspend the working of the mills, in
this opinion I am by no means alone (270).

Strathnairn followed this with another letter to the Lord
Lieutenant enclosing a document showing that the Duke of
Cambridge, Commander-in-Chief of the Army, considered the mills
to be dangerous and ordering him to remove the troops and another
with the opinion of his, Strathnairn's, legal adviser, the judge advocate
general, stating that the mills were a "a dangerous nuisance" at
common law. Strathnairn suggested to Abercorn that the opinions of
the Lord Chancellor and Attorney-General of England should be
obtained. Getting no satisfaction he wrote again to Abercorn saying
he intended to take the matter up directly with the Duke of Cambridge
and requesting permission to send copies of Abercorn's letters.
Abercorn wrote back apparently misunderstanding deliberately. He
asked if Strathnairn wanted permission to write to Cambridge.
Strathnairn replied rather testily that he was merely seeking leave to
send copies of Abercorn's letters, adding in a superior tone:

> *It is always difficult to make a civilian, however*
> *intellectual, to understand purely military matters and I have*
> *therefore not succeeded in making you understand that the*
> *Ballincollig Powder Mills are, with any means at my disposal,*
> *perfectly indefensible and that therefore while I will do my best*
> *to protect them and the powder wagons on their passage*
> *through Cork it is impossible that I can be responsible for either*
> *one or the other against either explosion or attack. I am afraid*
> *that one shot would send the powder in the air. The Fenians,*
> *even supposing that they might not destroy the mills from*
> *recklessness might do it through ignorance. An explosion from*
> *accident would be almost a certainty if the mills or escorts were*
> *attacked and shots fired. Fancy a combat around a magazine*
> *or wagon?*

On 23 January, acting on Cambridge's instructions, Strathnairn
ordered the evacuation of the barracks and patrols to protect the mills
against explosion and robbery as far as possible. Strathnairn
considered the possibility of Mackay bringing an action in his private
capacity against the company on the grounds of nuisance. They did
not go ahead with this.

In a letter to Abercorn the same day he pointed out that by all
military practices and precedents he could not be held responsible for
the safety of the mills. As regards explosions like that at Clerkenwell
it was quite impossible to guard adequately with the forces at his

disposal or any reinforcements he could send. Escorting of the wagons would be as dangerous:

> The possibility of combat in narrow crowded streets encumbered by a long train of carriages and horses, a separated escort, one horse killed by a shot from a window, a couple of cars turned upside down would stop and throw into confusion the line of men and the blowing up of the wagons with the powder would be a most natural consequence of the use of firearms whether accidental or intentional.

In other letters to Abercorn, Cambridge, Mayo and Sir Thomas Larcom the Under Secretary, Strathnairn described Cork as "the most seditious and disloyal city in Ireland. It is well known that numbers of the worst characters live in the vicinity of the river and that Fenians are on board many of the ships, particularly American, in the harbour". On 11 January, when in Cork, Strathnairn ordered General Campbell to tell the Mayor that he was responsible for the mills. Three days later Campbell reported that the Mayor had no jurisdiction, a fact which should have been obvious as the village was well outside the borough boundary (282).

Some hint of the possibility of the government buying the mills leaked out. On 1 February 1868 the *Freeman's Journal*, a Dublin morning paper, published a report that the government had completed arrangements for the purchase. The government undoubtedly discussed the question of the mills from time to time. No record survives as regular cabinet records were not kept until 1916 (269).

On 28 January 1868 Captain Mackay noted that the property was so large and open with numerous hiding places that it was impossible to protect and in any case many of the mill and farm workers living in houses on the grounds were Fenians. A Constabulary report a week later observed that some 140 men had organised themselves into night patrols under the manager (282).

Despite Strathnairn's objections, arrangements were made for the escorts. Legal arguments continued. Strathnairn's view as drawn up by his judge advocate general was that the mills were a *dangerous nuisance* at common law, nuisances being defined as:

> Common mischiefs or offences against public order and the regimen of the state, being either the doing of a thing to the annoyance of the Queen's subjects or the neglecting to do a thing which the common good requires, encroachments on highways or rivers, offensive trades, disorderly houses; I am

clearly of the opinion that Ballincollig Powder Mills, involving as they do almost hourly danger to the lives of Her Majesty's troops and other loyal subjects, a danger aggravated by the known disloyality of many of the persons employed in the mills, come under the head of nuisance and unless the nuisance, after due warning is abated, the proprietor may be indicted for misdemeanour.

Mayo's legal opinion was:

As it appears that Ballincollig Powder Mills was a Government or Royal Manufactory prior to the passing of the Act of 1860 and all the rights were sold to the present proprietors; it must be assumed that the mills was "lawfully used" within the meaning of the Act at the time the Act was passed, and therefore was not then a nuisance. We do not think that the government could either indict or abate a nuisance so long as the regulations of the Act are observed.

Strathnairn hit back at this in a long letter seizing on the word *mill* as distinct from *magazine*. He accepted the opinion as far as it applied to the old *mill* which had been erected by the Board of Ordnance, not to the second *mill* constructed by the company after 1834 replacing one of the two earlier magazines. This new store was neither bomb nor splinter proof. Strathnairn meant of course *magazines*.

Strathnairn supported his case by submitting a report prepared by Captain Mackay which showed that the company had built, besides the notorious second magazine, a large saltpetre plant and eight incorporating mills. They had also constructed another lock from the river for extra waterpower and had deepened and widened the canals. Strathnairn maintained that these additions had doubled the capacity of the factory, which was true, and that it could no longer be considered in its original light as "the proprietors have failed in their engagements to the government" (282).

The Lord Chancellor and the Attorney General of England reported on 9 March. They had examined the 1860 Act and the exemptions granted to the company following a petition to the Lord Lieutenant in respect of the buildings which were seven and forty-five yards within the minimum distances laid down. The Act did not place any restrictions on the amount which could be held in a magazine. It only required that magazines were to be built "substantially of stone or brick". There was no power to order suspension of the manufacture(290).

In the course of the next few months an arrangement of some kind was made for the storage of powder at Rocky Island. The details are not clear. On 20 May 1868 Captain Mackay reported that he had made two inspections of the mills and had seen the company's books. One magazine was empty, the other held eight hundred barrels. The file was silent for the next year. On 15 May 1869 Mackay reported that in the meantime the company had "conducted the establishment entirely in accordance with the provisions of the Act" (283).

In March 1870 the War Office complained to Strathnairn that no more space was available at Rocky and asked "whether means cannot be adopted to reduce the store of gunpowder at the mills, so far that the barracks might be calculated upon as being safe, even if an explosion occurred". The War Office, reluctant to withdraw from the barracks, proposed to set up a board of officers including the Superintendent of Waltham Abbey to view the mills and make appropriate recommendations. Strathnairn welcomed this and suggested including the officer who had succeeded Mackay and wrote to Sir Thomas Tobin explaining the proposal. A reply was sent by Richard Briscoe, company secretary in head office, stating that all future correspondence should be sent to Liverpool.

The board of officers duly visited the mills and reported:

We do not feel in a position to state authoritatively the maximum number of barrels which might be stored without danger to the lives of the inmates of the barracks and are of opinion that the most serious danger to those inmates would consist, in the case of explosion, in the projection of the broken masses from the solid roof of the magazine and their descent upon the barracks.

The officers surmised that an explosion in one magazine would probably set off the other and the hill to the north of the mills would direct the blast southwards to the barracks and the effect "would be greater than from a light built magazine in a flat country".

Accordingly the recommendation was that the solid masonry roof on the magazine, originally built by Charles Wilks, should be removed and replaced by another of less substantial construction. This was conveyed to the company during June. In acknowledging the decision Briscoe observed "of course the proposed alterations will be entirely at the risk and expense of the government". Arrangements were made for the work to be carried out by the Royal Engineers at a cost of £150. Strathnairn objected strongly stating that a solid roof was a safeguard against lightning and pointing out the dangers presented by:

The secret organisation which has prevailed in Ireland of late years, I cannot believe that any risk which is worth mentioning is run by the troops at Ballincollig under the present arrangements whilst I am tolerably sure that if the existing solid stone roof be removed and we have renewal of the alarms that pervaded this country two years ago there will be great regret and it will be deemed necessary to withdraw the troops altogether from Ballincollig.

Holding such strong opinions on this matter I have ventured to suspend the orders to the Engineers until the wishes of the government be made known to me after reading the whole argument.

The War Office decided that the roof should be replaced and soon afterwards the masonry was removed and a timber and slate type was installed. This was dismantled along with the roofs on the other buildings in 1946 while the solid roofs on the charge houses and the steam stove still stand (253,284).

So at the end of the day, after five years of objections, Strathnairn's case was turned upside down and he was over-ruled all the way. His fears were not borne out and the Fenians did not blow up the magazines. His apprehension was grounded on fact as far as expert opinion can determine more than a century afterwards. An explosion in one magazine would certainly have set the other off. The mills, barracks and village would have been destroyed. The ground shock and airwave would have caused serious damage in the western outskirts of Cork (291).

Fenian activity continued in Ballincollig. At the Special Commission in Dublin in 1867 John Joseph Corydon gave evidence of Fenianism in the district. For several years afterwards the Constabulary sent reports of various coopers, powdermen, watchmen and others in the mills and in the area generally as known or suspected Fenians (285,287).

Strathnairn's concern for the welfare of the troops can hardly be questioned. It is clear from the whole tenor of the correspondence that he had a deep feeling of frustration. His relationships with his superiors, subordinates and other colleagues seem to have been cool at best, distant in some cases and hostile in others. Certainly he made no attempt to conceal one major grievance, a reduction of £500, representing twenty percent, in his salary on being appointed Commander of the Forces in Ireland. He wrote to the War Office complaining of this in September 1866, May 1867 and February 1868.

All his predecessors had been disgruntled about the stipend attached to the post. He took the matter up with various high figures including the Duke of Cambridge who had commanded the Dublin Division and knew of the high personal expenses involved. The responsibilities apart from military duties were quite onerous. He was obliged to attend all meetings of the Irish Privy Council and to serve frequently as a Lord Justice. In short Strathnairn was constantly out of pocket as his private means, clearly slender, did not enable him to live on the social scale which his public positions demanded (270).

It is not clear why the company had accumulated such a large quantity of powder in the first place. It certainly was far more than the usual stock in trade. Sir Thomas Tobin maintained throughout that there was no danger, pointing out that he slept on the premises every night. His house was well within the danger zone and the attendance roll of the Harbour Board shows that he was present at practically every meeting during the period in question (175).

It is significant that production as represented by exports (page 60) increased from eighteen thousand barrels in 1866 to thirty thousand the next year, fell by exactly six thousand during the crucial year of 1868 and returned to thirty thousand the following year.

So in the autumn of 1870 the whole affair fizzled out and the factory moved into the last third of its productive existence.

BALLINCOLLIG, SHOWCARD ADVERTISEMENT, MID 1890's
SOURCE 230

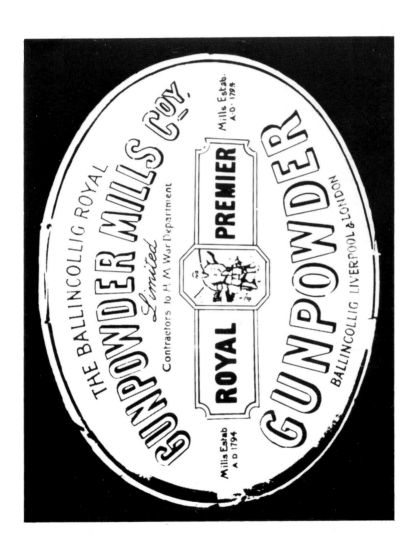

THE LAST YEARS

By the mid 1870s developments in the explosives industry, dealt with in Chapter Two, had rendered the 1860 Gunpowder Act out of date. There was no method of regulating the many individuals who were endeavouring to develop new types and who were more likely to blow themselves up than to produce usable new explosives. There was no register of factories making the new kinds let alone any control over these.

Accordingly in 1874 Parliament appointed a Select Committee on Explosive Substances. This led to the Explosives Act 1875 which came into force on the first day of 1876. The guiding light was Colonel Sir Vivian Dering Majendie who had been Inspector of Gunpowder Works under the old Act and then became Chief Inspector of Explosives with a larger department and extensive powers over the operations of explosives companies. While Majendie always acted scrupulously in the name of the Home Secretary to whom he was responsible, he was for all practical purposes the author of the Act and its administration until his death in 1898. The Act was so well drawn that it was able to deal with the many further new explosives and innumerable developments in manufacture and application and it still operates in Britain. In Ireland it was replaced by the Dangerous Substances Act 1972.

The Inspectors published annual reports giving particulars of all explosions during the year, details of factories opening and closing, new products and technical processes in Britain and abroad and other matters of interest to the industry. The reports continued in this format until the First World War when changes in policy on the part of the Inspectorate and in the production of parliamentary papers resulted in the discontinuation of most of the data. The ninety-ninth report, 1975, was the last. The Inspectorate was merged with the Department of Employment's Health and Safety Executive. Despite difficulties in identifying companies in some instances the reports from 1876 to 1914 remain a remarkable repository of information on the last years of the black powder industry and the beginnings of modern smokeless explosives (686-9).

Under the new arrangement Ballincollig became Factory Number 30 on the books of the Inspectors who were obliged to visit each works regularly and after each serious accident for which a special report was laid before Parliament. No such report was made in respect of Ballincollig from 1876 to the closure. There were indeed many minor accidents. Usually only a few boards were knocked down.

For example, in 1880 an explosion took place in an incorporating mill which "had been working for about 25 minutes on a 60 lbs charge, recently liquored". In another in 1886 "the mill had been working for about $2^1/2$ hours on a 60 lbs charge, not recently liquored, no one was injured, very little damage, merely a few covering boards displaced". There were tanks of water on the roofs to drown any fires.

While there were no deaths in the mills from 1876, despite a local legend that the mills closed because of a number of fatal accidents, several took place in the previous years and were reported in the local papers. On 29 July 1843 two men were killed in a corning house. Sir Thomas Tobin claimed in a letter to the Board of Ordnance that this was "only the second serious accident". Dr Joseph Cleburne gave evidence at the inquest. On 6 August 1859 five men were killed in a dusting house. On 23 October 1861 five died in a press house. Doubtless there were other such disasters (101).

Under the Act the function of licencing magazines was given to the magistrates who usually appointed their clerks as inspectors with the result that there were many abuses such as the instance where the owner of a magazine holding excessive stocks was himself a magistrate. "In short", Majendie reported sorrowfully to the Home Secretary, "the Act is a dead letter". He recommended that the duty of inspecting the magazines should be given to the Constabulary. This was done after long delay (190).

Under the Gunpowder Stores (Liverpool) Exemption Repeal Act 1851 responsibility for licencing the magazines floating on the Mersey was given to the Board of Ordnance in consultation with the Admiralty and the Commissioners for the Conservation of the Mersey. On the abolition of the Board their function was transferred to the War Office. In 1865 the Liverpool Gunpowder Regulation Act laid down further safety measures. In July 1881 the Admiralty appointed a Committee of Inquiry, with Majendie as a member, to review the situation. James Aspinall Tobin was interviewed at great length and evidence was also given by various other interested local parties. There was considerable anxiety as to possible damage from explosions in the magazines. As a result the Mersey (Gunpowder) Act transferred the licencing function to the Home Office (188,234-6).

In 1885 the Ballincollig company and the owners of the other floating hulks jointly formed the Liverpool Magazines Company Limited to operate the vessels. Ballincollig transferred the *Swallow* to the new agency. In April 1890 the Manchester Ship Canal Company, then building the waterway inland from the Mersey, made representations to the Home Secretary objecting to the positions of the vessels which would obstruct the canal. In June Majendie held a public inquiry replete with lawyers for the two companies and various other interested parties. Majendie, while not accepting the Canal Company's case, found that the underlying sandbanks had shifted and accordingly fixed new anchorages for the magazines (187,189,242).

This was the last major event affecting the Ballincollig Company's operations in Liverpool where they always faced far stricter regulations than in Cork with four major inquiries, 1836, 1851, 1881 and 1890 and three special acts, 1851, 1865 and 1883. In Cork the company had only to deal with isolated protests such as Daniel Meagher's occasional forays up to 1849.

In July 1877 the Cork Harbour Commissioners voted funds for a new road serving the Marina as the New Wall area was becoming known. The Corporation agreed to pay part of the cost and in October the new thoroughfare was officially named Gunpowder Road when Tobin moved the expenditure of further funds.

In 1882 Majendie advised the Commissioners to build a special shed for consignments of explosives. This was erected two years later with a door on the bankside which was closed when a wagon went in, a door on the riverside opened and there was a shielding arrangement to cover handling operations as far as possible. In 1885 the Commissioners issued a new set of regulations, still in force, under which this shed was to be used for all explosives cargoes (175-7).

So it came to pass that some years after Tobin's death the use of the New Wall became institutionalised in the solid shape of a custom built shed erected at public expense despite the history of protest by local residents. The shed has long since been removed and this part of the Marina, no longer used for wharfage, is a pleasant landscaped riverside walk.

There was one other encounter with a local authority in this period. In February 1879 the Corporation's Public Health Committee commissioned a report on an outbreak of typhoid from Charles P Cotton, chief engineering inspector of the Local Government Board, forerunner of the Department of the Environment, and author of a standard text on public health who had been president of the Institution of Civil Engineers of Ireland. He investigated all possible sources of pollution on the Lee and its tributaries from Macroom to the City and found that "that privies and cesspools at the Powder Mills were regularly cleaned and the contents used on the lands. From 15,000 to 20,000 bags [saltpetre and sulphur] are washed in the canal after being boiled, but I do not think that any harm results from this".

Obviously the company did not make saltpetre from the dung produced in the mills and instead used it for fertilising the fields on which they grew various crops (224,263).

Sir Thomas Tobin, gentleman, 73, died on 9 January 1881 and was buried in Inniscarra, near the mills. Besides being the longest serving member of the Harbour Commissioners, who paid the usual fulsome tributes, he was also the doyen of the County Club, the founder of the Victoria Hospital and was associated with the Erinville Hospital. He was also a governor of the Eglinton District Lunatic Asylum, now the Cork Psychiatric Hospital, originally called, whether in homage or humour, after the Lord Lieutenant of the day. He was also a member of the Board of Guardians for the Union of Cork and the Grand Jury, predecessors of the County Council.

Culturally Tobin was active in the Cork Literary and Scientific Society, founded in 1820 and still flourishing, which was associated with the Royal Cork Institution providing courses of lectures before the University College began. Tobin was elected to three eminent founts of learning, in 1849 the Royal Society of Northern Antiquaries, Copenhagen, in 1853 a Fellow of the Society of Antiquaries of London and in 1869 a member of the Royal Irish Academy which bought an ancient Irish ornamental gold caterpillar at the auction of his large collections a few weeks after his death.

Tobin's accomplishments deserving of these distinctions are obscure. His only written work appears to be a set of lecture notes on travels in the Middle East and the USA. Lady Catherine, his wife, appears to have been far more worthy of recognition. She translated one book from French to English, *Letters of Discoveries at Nineveh* by PE Botta the noted archaeologist, published by Longmans, London, 1850 and wrote two on her travels *Shadows of the East,* Longmans, 1855 and *The Land of Inheritance* published by Bernard Quaritch, London, 1863.

Tobin left no wealth, a few family legacies and a bequest to the Royal National Lifeboat Institution of which he had been Cork representative, endowing a lifeboat in the name of his son, Lieutenant Arthur Lionel of the Royal Welsh Fusiliers who died in Jubrolee, India in 1858. With a mere fifty shares Tobin was a minor figure in the company, a glorified works manager. Later when there were various managers in the mills he seems to have been in Ballincollig in a supernumerary capacity even though he was a director (143,145, 151-65,250).

By this time James Aspinall Tobin was apparently reducing his involvement in Ballincollig. When the company was incorporated with limited liability in 1861 he was named in the articles as the Managing Director with the usual powers of the position and also those normally discharged by the Chairman and the Secretary of a company. An extraordinary general meeting of the shareholders in September 1868 abolished the office of Managing Director. The special resolution for the purpose sent to the Registrar was signed by one Richard Briscoe, company secretary, who had evidently held the position for some time (182).

In July 1881 Tobin told the Admiralty Committee that while gunpowder was only one item "the African trade could not be carried on without it, the great bulk is used for fetes and rejoicings, it is made very weak for Africa, they fill their guns up to the muzzle and fire them off ". This powder had only one tenth the strength of military powder. The company had fifty-seven combinations of types of powder and packages from the standard 100 lbs avoirdupois barrel down to very small containers holding a kilo or less; Curtis's and Harvey had 108 and altogether in the trade there were 288.

Each market or part of a market demanded a different powder and package. The company had sales of several thousand barrels in Merseyside and in the coalfields of Lancashire, Staffordshire, Yorkshire and South Wales, the slate quarries in North Wales and in some districts of the West Country. A number of magazines served these areas. Overseas, besides Africa, there were markets in South America including Brazil and Chile and in some other parts of the world. Tobin also told the Committee that the trade to Africa was "lower than ever before". Sales to Angola, at least, continued until the end of the mills when Ballincollig powder was also being sold in Port au Prince, Haiti and possibly elsewhere in the West Indies (188,213).

The trade continued to decline in general as seen in British exports (page 60) and apparently in particular as far as Tobin was concerned with the result that he reorganised his affairs by selling Ballincollig in 1888 and the next year taking British and Continental into a merger of six Liverpool African mercantile firms with two in Glasgow and one in Bristol. This was styled the African Association Limited and despite its name was very much a commercial concern and seemingly had no connection with the African Association which had represented the interests of Liverpool African merchants from the 1840s.

The merger was brought about in opposition to the Royal Niger Company, a chartered concern. Both companies' successors ultimately formed the United Africa Company, now UAC International, the largest single subsidiary of Unilever the giant Anglo-Dutch group. The British component of this is Lever Brothers. Beginning in 1886 Levers built the world's biggest soap factory at Port Sunlight on the Mersey, used colossal quantities of palm oil and virtually created the modern soap industry. Tobin was a director of the African Association from the formation until his death in 1891 (191-2,259).

So after a century of business which began with privateering, continued with slaving, fifty-five years of manufacturing powder in Ballincollig, trading with this and other commodities for palm oil, twenty thousand transactions on the Liverpool Exchange and various involvements in public life both in Liverpool and Cork; after all this the last vestige of the house of Tobin was submerged in a slab of *Sunlight Soap*. Banal maybe. Petty perhaps. Looking at this, an item as common in the homes of Ballincollig as Merseyside it brings a realisation that sooner or later every empire, commerical as well as the more conventional kind will collapse, wither away or become absorbed by a larger unit and so the process goes on.

Several major capitalist and territorial empires mentioned in this have long since vanished and others still in existence will by unwritten and immutable laws go the way of all others. Old demands and products disappear. New needs arise or more likely nowadays are created. New patterns of manufacture and distribution emerge. Systems must be discontinued, changed or developed to meet evolving social and other circumstances.

The transition in the ownership of Ballincollig was long, very complicated and involved two companies specially formed for the purpose. In March 1888 the shareholders of the Tobin company resolved at an extraordinary general meeting to wind up the company. In September they gave consent under the Companies Act for the name to be taken by another company. The liquidation was completed in March 1889. In March 1888 as the Tobin company was going into liquidation the British and Irish Gunpowder Manufacturing Company Limited was formed with a nominal capital of ten thousand shares of £5 each of which only eight were issued without any of the money being called. The Registrar of Companies observed in May 1891 that the company was not properly formed. Nonetheless the company acquired the factory and ran it for some time. In May 1888 The Gunpowder Company Limited was formed and in October a month after the Tobin company gave consent took the title The Ballincollig Royal Gunpowder Mills Company Limited.

Under an elaborate agreement of February 1893 the British and Irish company sold to the Ballincollig company all the plant, stocks and other assets of the business for a consideration in two parts. The first was to discharge all the liabilities against the vendors and the second was to issue ten thousand ordinary shares and ten thousand cumulative preference shares all fully paid up at £5 each. Additionally an issue of debentures against British and Irish was to be replaced by a fresh issue to the same value, £17,500. This seems to have been largely a paper transaction as the eight nominal shareholders of the transitional company, British and Irish, were also shareholders in the new Ballincollig company.

The last return of the Tobin company showed thirty-nine shareholders; four Tobins, four Brasseys, four widows, four gentlemen, two clergymen, one merchant, one colonel and one solicitor in London, one Manchester merchant, one Liverpool accountant and sixteen Liverpool merchants still including George Henry Horsefall, Alfred Castellain and Louis Gruning.

The new company had nineteen shareholders all described as gentlemen in the first return, 1893. In the last, 1897, the same nineteen were registered as one bill broker, two bankers, three solicitors and five accountants while the remainder were still listed as gentlemen. The chairman lived up to this by staying permanently in the Westminster Palace Hotel. All had London addresses except two in the English provinces.

The Managing Director, John George Briscoe, was the largest single shareholder with 3,238 ordinary and 2,395 preference. The Chairman had 1,280 and 1,050 respectively. The only other substantial shareholders were the two bankers. Ernest Ruffer had 1,200 of each and John Conrad im Thurn had 2,400 each. These remain rather shadowy figures. Neither was a member of the Institute of Bankers. A Ruffer and Sons from 1886 to 1922 and the house of J C im Thurn from 1893 to '97 had establishments in the City of London where many foreign banks and firms describing themselves as bankers have always had offices (183-4, 264-5).

The ownership of the undertaking therefore changed from a Liverpool mercantile family and some other Merseyside merchants with a few small shareholders elsewhere in England to a number of individuals in London who had no particular business or other connection as far as can be seen. The change was obviously organised by John George Briscoe who had been a salaried manager in the house of Tobin. This is certainly a remarkable and probably rare example of a professional management arranging a change in the proprietorship of an enterprise from owners who no longer needed it for their business to investors who must have seen it as offering an acceptable return on capital and at the same time the management obtained a stake of one third in the new company.

In June 1890 Briscoe, erroneously named Bristow, told the Majendie Committee that he had been connected with the Ballincolig company "for five or six years". The firm of John G Briscoe & Company carried on business as gunpowder merchants from 1875 to 1883 at Old Hall Street, Liverpool. From 1884 their address was at the Ballincollig company's office, India Buildings, Water Street. He also told Majendie that competition by German gunpowder companies had increased greatly in the African trade (242,692).

In October 1890 Briscoe as Managing Director of the British and Irish company wrote to Arthur Balfour, Chief Secretary:

> *Her Majesty's Government having instituted a policy of assisting the labouring classes of Ireland, by the execution of works at the public expense, I feel justified in briefly calling your attention to the position of the Royal Gunpowder Mills, Ballincollig, County Cork. After being worked for some years at a loss, they were acquired by the present proprietors who have reorganised and improved the property, at great expense, so that the mills are now equal to any in England for the purpose of making military powders.*

> *This process of reorganisation was completed at the end of 1889 and early this year we commenced to make most successfully, the fine powder used for rifle cartridges - of 12 lots ordered we presented and passed 11, without a single rejection, the 12th lot is in the hands of the War Office officials awaiting test.*

> *I mention this to prove that we can produce with complete satisfaction to the War Office, the powder for which we ask to be favoured with further orders. We are now engaged upon pebble powder for the government, but these orders will not keep us occupied for long. An unusual demand for common powder for export to Africa had existed during 1889 and '90, enabling us to keep our hands all employed, but we are rapidly completing our contracts and as the orders are also ceasing, the proprietors find themselves approaching an early date, when from want of work for the mills they will be compelled to discharge their staff at a period of the year which will impose the greatest hardships upon the men their wives and children.*

If this unfortunately takes place these men will approach the Irish members, grievances will be made the most of, questions asked and Ministers harassed in the House for political motives, all of which we would most respectively suggest, can be avoided by the policy of Government help to the labouring classes, being carried out in Ballincollig, as well as in Galway and other places, where the light railway, Harbours etc are to be made.

I trust you will favourably consider the representation of the Company and use your influence in preventing hardship and loss to the people of Ballincollig, arising from the closing of the Mills, in consequence of want of work.

This letter is typical of a company importuning government assistance as if the welfare of the workers was the sole consideration and that the directors were worried that Ministers might be inconvenienced in the Commons. The powder which was the subject of the letter was for Martini-Henry rifles, the latest at the time. While production did increase in some years it never returned to the levels of thirty thousand barrels a year.

One of the measures of modernisation carried out at this time was the introduction of electricity for lighting and possibly some of the processes in preparing ingredients. An old switchboard with a few sockets was to be seen in one building until the early 1960s. The power house, worked on the hydro principle from a turbine on the canal system, had been demolished some years earlier. A local belief has it that this was the first electrical installation in Ireland, at least in a factory. This is difficult to ascertain as there is little or no information available on the authenticity of the earliest electrical equipment. Certainly this was a very early industrial application of the power (202, 251-3, 266).

The factory reached its centenary in 1893 and the company embarked on what must have been the only promotional campaign in its entire existence. Advertisements were placed in various newspapers, trade journals and directories. Showcards were supplied to wholesale stores and retail shops. Proudly proclaiming that they were contractors to the War Office the company offered "blasting powder of every description at market prices". The main brands for sporting guns were *Royal Premier* and *Extra Treble Strong* sold in small canisters. The advertising campaign continued into 1895. It does not seem to have been very successful as output did not really rise (228-30).

The company could hardly make money on low production and the London investors could scarcely have been satisfied with their dividends. There is no information on the profits, if any. In November 1898 Ballincollig became part of an amalgamation of all the black powder undertakings in Britain except the six mills in the Lake District and Worsboro' Dale, Yorkshire, these had been acquired earlier by Kynoch. The amalgamation was Curtis's & Harvey writ large. This firm had been formed in 1820, replacing the previous Harvey and Grueber, with a small mill at Hounslow, Middlesex. Over the following seventy years they acquired mills at Bedfont, also in Middlesex; Glenlean and Kames in Argyllshire; Glyn Neath in Wales and Tonbridge in Kent.

A new company also styled Curtis's & Harvey was formed for the merger with an issued capital of 448,000 one pound shares of which the old Curtis's & Harvey had over half. Ballincollig had 33,330 ranking behind John Hall and Son Faversham; Pigou Wilks & Lawrence, Dartford, Kent; Hay, Merricks, Roslin, near Edinburgh and ahead of the East Cornwall Gunpowder Company, Liskeard; the Midlothian Gunpowder Company and Kennal Vale Gunpowder Company, Cornwall.

This represented a considerable decline in the value of the Ballincollig business. On the transfer from the house of Tobin to the house of Briscoe it had been capitalised at £100,000 with £17,500 in debentures. On the Curtis's & Harvey reckoning it was worth only £33,330. John George Briscoe became one of several managing directors at a salary of £1,000, a high figure for the time (16, 194-6).

All the acquisitions were black powder plants. Curtis's & Harvey had no intention of relying on this which was facing competition for the first time on a serious scale as a propellant. Cordite was coming into use and the company concentrated all resources on building a smokeless explosives factory in Cliffe-at-Hoo on the Kent bank of the Thames.

On 21 April 1903 at a routine board meeting the directors decided to close Ballincollig. Glyen Lean was also closed down.

The weeks went by and the workers were dismissed as the different stages of manufacture were completed on the last batches. The sawmill cut the last cords for distillation into charcoal. The last lots of saltpetre and sulphur were refined. The last green charges were mixed and revolved under the great incorporating wheels and went through the pressing, corning, glazing and dusting houses and the steam stove. The last barrels were filled and headed up.

Finally at six o'clock on the evening of the last day in June, a Tuesday, the last workers including the women packers, were paid off. After ninety years of production in a span of one hundred and ten the industry ceased. A few workers were retained for a month or two in clearing the buildings and harvesting the crops on the lands which had always been farmed, cows had been kept to supply milk. The workers had garden allotments and some reared pigs and fowl. The last shipment of powder, a residual quantity of 840 barrels, was despatched after the beginning of the Harbour Commissioners' year in August 1903.

Some workers emigrated. Those who remained were allowed to occupy their houses at a rent of a penny per week on caretaker tenancies. Some received pensions of three shillings (15p) per week, comparing tolerably well with the state old age pension of five shillings which came a few years later. At the time there were no payments for redundancy, unemployment and so on (197-198).

The only workers in a trade union were the coopers, the best paid employees in the factory, who were members of the Cork Operative Coopers' Society. A deputation went before the executive and were told that they would have to take their places at the end of the queue of members already out of work in accordance with custom. Any who wanted to emigrate were issued with special cards. This society was affiliated to the Mutual Association of Journeymen Coopers of Great Britain and Ireland and corresponded with other unions abroad which recognised the cards (205).

There was never a strike in the mills as far as can be ascertained. The closest the workers came to industrial action was during the Cork Tailors' Strike in the summer of 1870. A long drawn out dispute in the tailoring trade involving a strike, lockout and the hiring of German scabs, spread for some weeks to a number of other employments in the city and county. The *Cork Examiner,* 30 June, reported that the powdermen in the mills had threatened to go on strike for a rise from fifteen to eighteen shillings (75-90p) per week. They agreed not to go out until the Company Secretary came from Liverpool. Apparently the matter was settled by negotiation. Thirty-three years later, exactly, the mills closed forever.

The workers made an appeal to the directors which was rejected. On 14 August the Chief Secretary's Office in The Castle received a memorial from the mill workers. George Wyndham remains one of the best remembered holders of this position because of the famous Land Purchase Act which he had just steered through Parliament and which was popularly called after him. This enabled many tenant farmers to buy out their lands and, far less known, facilitated landlords in paying off mortgages on demesne lands at tidy profits.

TO THE RIGHT HONOURABLE G WYNDHAM MP
CHIEF SECRETARY,

The Memorial of the workmen lately employed in the Royal Gunpowder Mills at Ballincollig (late Curtis's and Harvey)

HUMBLY SHEWETH,

That Memorialists are the heads or wage earners and sole support of about two hundred families who have depended for their livelihood upon the employment given in those mills, for a period extending over half a century.

That they have at all times served the different companies who worked those mills including Messrs Curtis's and Harvey, faithfully and well, and are still able and willing to do so, if again employed, and are prepared to spare no effort to make the working of the Mills under any management successful and prosperous.

That the closing of the Concern means absolute destitution to several hundred men, women and children through no fault of their own, and must result in many of them being cast a burden upon the public rates.

MEMORIALISTS, THEREFORE HUMBLY PRAY,

That the Chief Secretary whose name will be transmitted to future generations of Irishmen, as the giver of the greatest message of peace ever vouchsafed, to their country, will see his way, in some manner, in accordance with the already fostering spirit of industrial revival in Ireland, as to the re-opening of those Mills and to prevent the utter destitution which inevitably awaits a once prosperous and happy little community.

The Castle sent for a police report which confirmed that the document was genuine, one hundred persons had been thrown out of work. Twelve were still employed on the farm lands. Some had got work in the barracks where repairs were underway. A number had emigrated to England and America. Eight or ten were still out of work.

"Undoubtedly there has been and during the coming winter there will be a great deal of suffering for when the harvest is over and the barrack repairs completed a number of persons will be thrown out of work. Only black and the commoner sorts of powder were made and the plant is not suitable for the newer

improved classes of powder" (203).

The Memorial never reached Wyndham's desk. It was tossed around The Castle until someone got the bright idea of sending it to the Ɂepartment of Agriculture and Technical Instruction which had been set up three years earlier with Sir Horace Plunkett as vice-president, in effect the first minister as the presidency was a purely nominal post held by the chief secretary of the day. Plunkett had founded the modern agricultural co-operative movement a few years before and had been concerned in promoting industries in rural areas.

Plunkett's idea of a rescue was to approach Arthur Chamberlain, Chairman of Kynoch. Plunkett must certainly have known that Kynoch already had a large cordite factory in Arklow and a black powder plant in Yorkshire and consequently was unlikely to invest in Ballincollig. Chemberlain had told the House of Commons in July 1900 when Plunkett was still an MP, that he had, in 1894, contemplated using Ballincollig for his cordite factory (page 96-97). Had Plunkett made any inquiries he would have found that there was great bitterness between Kynoch and Curtis's & Harvey and that is was improbable in the extreme that the owners of Ballincollig would have sold the property to a major rival. Plunkett's letter to Chamberlain does not survive. It evidently was craven and apologetic. Chamberlain replied promptly on 11 September:

> *In reply to yours of the 8th, there is no need to apologise for putting me to any trouble in the matter of manufacturing employment for the Irish people; the subject interests me and the trouble is a pleasure.*
>
> *I am sorry to say that the Ballincollig mills would be of no use to us for the purpose of making black gunpowder. I visited them many years ago and made myself thoroughly acquainted with their possibilities. A black gunpowder factory must be either in the midst of a district having a large demand for the powder, or on a good port; or otherwise the cost of carriage which owing to the precautions which are necessary, is in the case of gunpowder very high kills the trade.*
>
> *The Ballincollig mills have neither of the foregoing requirements. As far as I could see their only advantage was a fairly large water power, and this I should say might best be utilised by some factory whose products could be sold in the district as well as exported, such, for instance, as a cloth factory or a boot and shoe factory. I fear that the carriage again would kill a manure factory.*

*When I saw the place there were only 2 dozen men and
boys and women employed. I don't for a moment believe that
anything like "hundreds" have been thrown out of employment
(203).*

Plunkett's approach to Chamberlain was naive and the
Birmingham magnate's reply was hardly honest (page 96-97).

Ballincollig would probably have survived, doubtless on a small
scale, into the 1920s when black powder finally became virtually
obsolete, if it had remained independent. Curtis's & Harvey would
almost certainly have closed the mills very soon after taking over had
the Boer War not broken out in 1899 and continued until 1902. The
age old explosive was last used for military purposes by the army of
Abyssinia, now Ethiopia, which was equipped with many ancient guns
at the time Italy invaded the country in 1935. Black powder is still used
in fuses, flares and fireworks. An early type of tractor was started with
a powder cartridge and some modern jet aircraft engines are primed
with a charge of the first explosive. Even in the 1970s a few quarries
in Ireland still used powder and some farmers did so in removing tree
stumps and other obstacles. There are gun clubs throughout the world
whose members have only old-style weapons. In Bavaria, Germany,
the Berchtesgaden Cannoneers use actual artillery at mid-summer
festivals and other local events, and inaugrated the 1972 Munich
Olympic Games, which ended in bloodshed, with a cannonade (267).

John George Briscoe was not at the meeting which decided on
the closure. He had not attended from the previous January due to ill
health and while he never appeared again he remained a Managing
Director until 1906. From time to time the company considered selling
the property. In 1904 they consulted an auctioneer. In 1907 they
received approaches from two prospective purchasers, one of whom
wanted the premises for a woollen mill. They offered to sell for £20,000
or let for £800 a year. Nothing came of these negotiations. In 1913
they disposed of the fishing rights. Occasionally items of equipment
were sold and the fields let to local farmers (195, 204).

During these years the company had mixed fortunes. They
expanded to Canada, obtained a London Stock exchange quotation
and had the indignity of a reduction in the share capital, a devaluation
of assets. The licence for Ballincollig was kept in force at least until
1914. In April 1915 the Chamber of Commerce suggested to the War
Office that the mills should be reopened. This was not done. At the
end of the War, an amalgamation, of which more in Chapter Two,
brought Curtis's & Harvey and all the other explosives companies in
Britain under the Nobel banner which in 1926 became part of Imperial

Chemical Industries. All the black powder mills, including Faversham, were closed in favour of a plant at Adeer, Nobel's main factory, which continued until 1976 (193, 206, 689).

On 17 May 1922 the British Army marched out of Ballincollig. Some weeks after, in the Civil War, a detachment of anti-treaty forces burned the barracks, the Constabulary barracks and also Oriel Lodge and House, later partly rebuilt. The military barracks was reconstructed and regarrisoned during the Second World War. In the 1937 revision of the Ordnance Survey the former factory was named simply as the Powder Mills. The full name as recorded in the surveys of 1841 and 1900 had faded from living memory (207-9).

In 1943 ICI dissolved Curtis's & Harvey and vested Ballincollig in ICI (Explosives) and in 1946 in ICI (Export). Around this time the dwelling houses were sold for nominal sums. In 1949 ICI sold all the property to the Minister for Defence except two magazines built after the closure, not the two notorious stores; these remained in use until 1971 managed by TW Murray and Company. At one time there was talk of developing the property as a resort for overstrained ICI staff. This did not come to pass (197-201, 710).

In the late 1960s a building boom began in Ballincollig with every sign of continuing indefinitely, making the village a suburb, or in modern municipal jargon, a 'satellite' town of Cork. This is a manifestation of the increasing population and prosperity of the country at large. In April 1974 the Cork County Council bought from the Minister for Defence most of the powder mill property and about half the ground attached to the barracks, some 260 acres (105 hectares) for a mere £170,000, less than one-fifth of the minimum market value at the time.

These buildings and canals could well be converted into facilities for numerous individual and collective craft, cultural, recreational and other activities. There is certainly a demonstratable need for such amenities in modern society with its numerous mental and other pressures and with the increase in educational standards and leisure time of which more is promised by new technology and threatened by largescale structural unemployment.

The mills, in line with, and indeed ahead of, the latest international museological thinking could be developed into an open air museum with the advantage of being on the main Cork-Blarney-Killarney tourist route, which would be unrivalled certainly in Ireland and Britain and possibly Europe (231).

AUTHOR AT INCORPORATING WHEEL, 1975
SOURCE 212

GUNPOWDER TO GUIDED MISSILES
IRELAND'S WAR INDUSTRIES

CHAPTER TWO

HIGH EXPLOSIVES
KYNOCH COMES TO THE VALE OF AVOCA

A day in Autumn. Nineteen hundred and seventy-three.

In the outskirts of a town on the east coast, work is in progress on the foundations for a new factory. A bulldozer roars into action and the great gleaming blade flashes in the sun as it bites deep into the ground, throwing back the masonry remaining from the factory which had previously stood on the site. At length the machine comes to a part which even its mighty metal muscles cannot move. After several attempts the inevitable conclusion is drawn. A charge of explosives is placed and the obstruction is blasted out of the way. It was the supreme irony even though it took only a few kilos. The old building was one of the earliest and longest surviving structures of a formerly flourishing factory which during twenty-three years had produced millions of kilos of explosives.

Lionel brought the first gunpowder to Ireland in 1361. Five hundred years later there was still no alternative to black powder as a propellant for guns. In 1861 Alfred Nobel, founder of the famous Prizes, commenced his career in explosives technology. The development of modern smokeless explosives began in 1845 when CF Schonbein of Basle, Switzerland impregnated wads of cotton with two acids, sulphuric and nitric. John Hall and Sons, Faversham, started production early in 1847 and stopped some months later after a disastrous explosion, for sixteen years, until Sir Frederick Abel, who was Explosives and Chemistry Advisor to the War Office, devised a method of making the compound, known as guncotton, in reasonable safety.

In 1847, Ascanio Sobrero, Professor of Chemistry at Turin University, found that nitric acid and glycerine formed a very powerful explosive, blasting oil (nitroglycerine), which was extremely dangerous in handling and was used for a time, in minute quantities, for treating heart complaints. The acids, glycerine and other chemicals which came to be used in high explosives have many industrial uses.

In this period many different experimenters were working on numerous compounds. In Ireland, Edmund W Davy, Professor of Chemistry and Agricultural Chemistry in the Royal Dublin Society, who discovered acetylene and invented the lactometer for testing milk, gave lectures in 1851 on a new explosive he had invented which was composed of potassium ferrocyanide and potassium chlorate and on improvements he had developed in the production of guncotton. It does not appear that these were used commercially (330-1).

The Nobel family made armaments for the Russian forces in St. Petersburg, now Leningrad, for many years until the end of the Crimean War when they returned to Sweden. Alfred began work on explosives and devised a safe method for the detonation of blasting oil based on mercuric fulminate. The oil itself was still dangerous and Nobel found that it could be soaked into kieselguhr, a diatomaceous earth composed of millions of tiny organisms which was capable of absorbing several times its own volume and could be moulded and cut into sticks of any size. In good condition, without excesses of heat or cold it was safe even if thrown into a fire, without a detonator. This was dynamite.

By 1866 Nobel had the world's first system of explosives for mining, quarrying and civil engineering other than black powder which continued in use for many years. The next stage was commercial production and companies were set up in many countries. In 1868 Nobel began to look at the possibilities in England. He got nowhere and went to Scotland where he met the Tennant family, proprietors of the St Rollox Chemical Works, Glasgow, with whom he set up the British Dynamite Company in 1871, changing style in 1877 to Nobel's Explosives Company Limited. The company had works in Ardeer, Ayrshire and offices in Glasgow, nearby, and remained very much a Scottish concern until the head office was transferred to London in 1920.

In 1886 the company and the Nobel companies in Germany formed the Nobel-Dynamite Trust Company Limited as a holding company registered in London with supreme control over the concerns in both countries including dividends, sharing of markets, research and technical information (302-3).

Nobel himself, in practice, had little control over the various companies bearing his name. He devoted himself to further research. Even by the time the international cartel was formed there was still no satisfactory substitute for black powder as a propellent. The other explosives, while superior for blasting could not be used in guns. Even *cocoa* or brown powder so called because of burned straw in its composition, was not completely successful. This was announced with a flourish in 1885 by the Chilworth Gunpowder Company formed that year to take over an old powdermill in Chilworth, Surrey. The managing director was Edward Kraftmeier, a German who was a director of the Nobel-Dynamite Trust throughout its existence.

In 1887 Nobel perfected his last major invention, *Ballistite.* Production soon began at the Italian Nobel factory and in May 1888 he applied for a British patent which was issued in March 1889 as Patent 6,560 of 1888. At this time the British government set up a War Office Committee with Sir Frederick Abel as Chairman, the only other member of any importance was Sir James Dewar who held chemistry chairs at Cambridge University and the Royal Institution, London. Both were consultants to Nobel's Explosives Company. Nobel provided the Committee with full details and samples of his product which was in the form of hard sheets that could be broken into grains of any size. In July 1889 Abel and Dewar applied for a patent on a product they called *Cordite,* this was accepted in May 1890 as Patent 11,664 of 1889 (335-6).

Nobel used soluble nitrocellulose while Abel and Dewar had the insoluble form. This minute molecular difference was the essence from which long legal actions are made, the sort so lucrative for lawyers. Production of cordite was put in hand immediately at Waltham Abbey. Before the Crown Proceedings Act 1947, neither the government nor any department or agency could be sued in a corporate capacity. Nobel named as defendant, William Anderson, Director General of Royal Ordnance Factories. This litigation became popularly known as the *Discordite Case* (316).

Anderson had worked as a civil engineer in Ireland in the 1850s and '60s. Returning to England he became a partner in an engineering firm, Easton and Amos, later Easton and Anderson, and worked on gunmountings for the British, Russian and USA navies. This was a period of rapid advance in naval architecture and artillery resulting in heavier ships and guns, making even more urgent the search for a new propellant explosive. Before becoming Director General in 1889, Anderson had done some work on designing cordite machinery which was continued by his son Edward (337-9).

Nobel's action was heard in the Chancery Division of the High Court over twelve days early in 1894, the writ having been issued a year earlier. The counsel for the defence opened by claiming that the government, under the Patent Act, could take over any patent for the

public service. Nobel lost. He went to the Court of Appeal and lost
again. He went to the House of Lords, the court of final appeal in
Britain, which on 28 February 1895 rejected him (316).

By this time the question of infringement of patent had been
effectively anticipated by administrative action. The government had
placed contracts with a number of companies for the manufacture of
cordite and a factory was being built in Arklow, County Wicklow.
Nobel lost the war, not quite every battle. In May 1894 there was a
serious explosion at Waltham Abbey and the government had the
mortification of having to buy pulp, an intermediate of both ballistite
and cordite, from Nobel's Explosives Company.

The government, in reply to a parliamentary question on 24 May
1894, stated that contracts for cordite would be invited by public
tender. Another reply on 6 August told the Commons that tenders
had not yet been accepted:

> The policy of the Government was to keep alive as fully as
> possible the sources of private supply and with that in view they
> had determined that a considerable part of the Service
> requirements would be obtained from private sources. At the
> same time a grave responsibility rested on the Department if it
> encouraged numerous undertakings to lay down plants so that
> while the government accepted the general principle, they would
> act as prudently as possible and confine themselves to two or
> at the most perhaps three firms. The contractors would be
> expected to follow the system used at Waltham Abbey and
> would be enabled to observe and copy the methods and
> machinery.

One of the firms hoping for an order was G Kynoch and
Company, Birmingham. George Kynoch was hewn, and in larger than
life size, from the obdurate granite of Peterhead, Aberdeen in 1834.
After stints in an insurance office and two banks he realised that he
would never become wealthy and powerful handling other people's
money. He became a partner in a small ammunition business in the
early 1850s and in time was sole proprietor. In 1862 he moved from
small premises in Birmingham city centre to Witton, then well outside,
and over the next twenty-two years built Lion Works into a huge
factory complex turning out cartridges of all types, guns, accessories
and various other products.

In 1884 the business was incorporated as G Kynoch and Company
Limited with Kynoch as Managing Director. He did not get on very
well with the other directors especially after his return to Parliament

as Unionist Member for the Aston Division of Birmingham in the 1886 general election. This arose when Joe Chamberlain, creator of modern municipal Birmingham and one of the most colourful politicians of the day, resigned from the cabinet and led a large number of MPs against the Irish Home Rule Bill proposed by the Liberal Prime Minister, W E Gladstone. The *Birmingham Post*, 3 July 1886, reported that while Kynoch's supporters were breaking up his opponent's final rally he was telling his own audience that he had ten thousand rifles and one million rounds of ammunition ready for immediate shipment to Belfast if Gladstone persisted with Home Rule.

In March 1887 the directors of the company commissioned an efficiency expert to make a survey and report. This showed many faults on the part of the Managing Director and some directors proposed that the post should be abolished. Kynoch naturally opposed this.

In August Arthur Chamberlain became a director. He and his brother Joe, whose son Neville was Prime Minister at the outbreak of the Second World War, left London where the family had been cordwainers or shoemakers and joined their cousins, the Nettlefolds, in a Birmingham screwmaking business in the 1850s.

Apart from a period as secretary of the National Radical Union or the Liberal Unionists, his brother's second party, and an intense personal interest in temperance, Arthur Chamberlain concentrated on business and was a director of several companies and a shareholder in many more. Within a month of taking his seat in the Kynoch boardroom which was in London he had formed a *Birmingham Committee*, with two other directors and himself as Chairman. This was an opposition board. In October the Committee submitted to the board a long list of complaints about the Managing Director's methods, some of which had been noted by the efficiency expert. The directors demanded Kynoch's resignation which they received and accepted two weeks later. Kynoch disappeared until he died in 1891 at Johannesburg where he had apparently been running a small gunshop, a far cry from the hugh Lion Works (332,347).

So within weeks of joining the board Chamberlain had squeezed the founder out. In April 1889 he took the chair from Lord Bury who had been merely a boardroom ornament. Soon afterwards Chamberlain began planning expansion. In April 1890 the minutes recorded, "Mr Cocking attended as proposed manager of new gunpowder manufactory possibly to be built". A month later the directors decided not to go ahead. In July 1893 they bought Shortridge and Wright's powdermill at Worsboro' Dale, Barnsley, Yorkshire. In

September the directors considered correspondence from Cocking. He reported on a visit to Cornwall seeking a site suitable for a "cordite mill" and offered to enter the company's service starting at £500 and rising by £50 annually for five years. This was the going rate for the company secretary. The engineer engaged four years previously at £250 had apparently got no rise (295).

Alan Thomas Cocking, born in Rotherham, Yorkshire in 1864 had very impressive qualifications to offer in support of such high demands by a twenty-nine year old. Apprenticed at fourteen to a consulting engineer he had worked on designing and installing many types of equipment, and from the age of nineteen held two teaching positions in Rotherham and won many prizes and distinctions in his studies at Firth College, Sheffield and the Royal School of Mines, London. Cocking also carried out commissions for the Midland Institute of Mining and Civil Engineering and the Royal Commission on Safety in Mines. At twenty-four he left the practice in which he had served his apprenticeship and as manager of the Flameless Explosives Company designed, installed and ran for three years their factory at Denaby, Doncaster. After this he took up lecturing positions at Sheffield and Derby and opened a practice as a consulting engineer with offices in Rotherham and London (348).

In the Autumn of 1893 Cocking became general manager of Kynoch, resigning this position on being elected to the board in December 1896. Though he served full-time for over twenty years he was never given the title of managing director. In December 1893 Cocking reported that the owners of the Cornwall site had increased the rent exorbitantly. In February he was instructed to conclude an agreement with the owners of another property in that county and to open negotiations with Nobel's Explosives Company for the use of their plant, adjacent to this site, to produce the ingredients of nitroglycerine.

In July 1900 Chamberlain told the House of Commons Select Committee on War Office Contracts of the position in June 1894. He had arranged to have the first refusal of two sites. The first, at Perranporth, Cornwall, was the premises of the British and Colonial Explosives Company "one of those numerous companies the Nobel-Dynamite Trust first succeeded in ruining and then drawing into their great dynamite monopoly". Extra buildings would be erected by Kynoch and Nobel's would supply glycerine from the existing factory which they would retain. The second option was "the old Royal Gunpowder Factory at Ballincollig, the return had not been sufficient to enable the company to pay its way, if it came into our possession we proposed to concentrate the black powder at one end and erect a nitroglycerine and cordite factory at the other"(361).

Apparently Chamberlain was not able to arrange satisfactory terms with John George Briscoe (page 86). Negotiations with Nobel's on the Cornwall site also fell through. Discussions continued on a possible arrangement for the supply of pulp from Ardeer and an agreement was signed on 26 November 1894 for ten years from the following March (304).

Before Kynoch could use the pulp they had to have a factory. The *Wicklow News-Letter*, 3 November 1894, reported that Cocking had inspected a site on Brittas Bay and had been so satisfied that he had asked Chamberlain by telegram to come and decide. The paper expressed the hope that the project would not be abandoned as had been the case with a similar scheme some years earlier after "one or two landlords had objected". Everyone else had been in favour.

During 1892 the paper carried several reports of this proposed undertaking. On 20 February it was announced that an application would be made to the local magistrates for a licence to erect a "gunpowder factory" and on 7 May that the promoters had purchased a large tract of land. A tramline would be built either north to Wicklow or south to Arklow which were about the same distance. A local chartered engineer had been engaged and it was expected that construction would take only three months as all the buildings would be wooden. Three hundred would be employed. The company had a similar factory near Cork already.

On 28 May the proceedings of the Tinahely Petty Sessions were reported. The company's solicitor presented a draft licence from the Home Secretary for confirmation by the magistrates under the procedure of the Explosives Act 1875. The magistrates doubted that Brittas Bay was under their jurisdiction and deferred the matter until 4 July. A formal notice was published in the paper on 4 June by the Consumers Dynamite Company Limited, Old Hall Street, Liverpool, Managing Director, R C Briscoe, stating that application would be made at the next sitting.

The magistrates refused to confirm the licence. On 30 July it was reported that the company had applied to the Queen's Bench and Exchequer Divisions, Four Courts, Dublin for a conditional order of mandamus directing the magistrates to confirm the licence. The courts were satisfied that the duty devolved on the magistrates. Legal arguments apparently continued and this intended branch of the house of Briscoe was not built. The company, registered in 1887, was wound up in 1895 (314).

The *News-Letter*, 10 November, reported that Chamberlain had come in response to Cocking's telegram and they had viewed the Brittas Bay site. Following this they had gone to Arklow and made a careful examination of an old factory in the Ferrybank area on the north side of the town.

During the autumn the government made final arrangements for the cordite contracts. On 5 September Sir Ralph Thompson, permanent under secretary in the War Office sent a memo with a schedule of *"New* Prices for Cordite from the Trade" to the Minister for War, Henry Campbell-Bannerman who had been Chief Secretary in 1884-5; "the Admiralty will have to decide as the supply is chiefly for them. You will see that the prices quoted by Chilworth and by Nobel's exclude them from any chance of an order, you will no doubt hear more of it from Sir Charles Tennant". Tennant was a director of both Nobel's Explosives Company and the Trust. Furthermore he was father-in-law of H H Asquith, Home Secretary at the time and later Prime Minister and of Lord Ribblesdale also a Trust director and Master of the Buckhounds to Queen Victoria, 1892-5. This was a political post, by then of purely ceremonial character, which was abolished some years later (363).

The British Explosives Syndicate, established in 1891, had a factory at Pitsea on the Essex bank of the Thames. The National Explosives Company, founded in 1888, had a plant at Hayle, Cornwall. Pigou & Wilks or Pigou, Wilks & Lawrence, an old established black powder firm, soon to be part of the Curtis's & Harvey merger, had a plant at Dartford, Kent.

NEW PRICES FOR CORDITE FROM THE TRADE (318)

Company	Price per pound (454 gm) 300 tons at 100 tons a year	Price per pound (454 gm) 600 tons at 200 tons a year
Nobel's	4s 6d (22^1/2p)	4s 3d (21p)
Chilworth	4s 6d (22^1/2p)	4s 3d (21p)
British Explosives Syndicate	no quotation	3s 3d (16p)
Pigou & Wilks	3s 5d (17p)	3s 3p (16p)
Kynoch	3s 3d (16p)	3s 0d (15p)
National	3s 0d (15p)	2s 10^1/2d (14p)

A memo by George Lawson, Director of Contracts in the War Office, noted that Waltham Abbey was in the neighbourhood of London and the Thames together with Pitsea and Faversham, presumably he meant Dartford; the National was in Cornwall and Nobel's in North Britain, as Scotland was also known. This left Kynoch:

> Holding a government contract, locality let open, but Cornwall named and they have verbally stated that they inclined to put factory up in the Midlands. Under these circumstances it was thought better not to have the second "trade" factory in Cornwall though it was not held of sufficient importance for us to make a binding stipulation or bargain with the company before accepting their tender. In accepting their tender I told them that the wish of the Department pointed rather to the view of the intention which they favoured themselves, of a central position for the works, than that it should be in Cornwall, but I explained that this was not a stipulation.

> They expressed themselves as desirous of meeting our wishes which agreed with their own, but recently I have been told that they experienced considerable difficulty in getting a site which would be free from objection and be suitable.

> They now ask if we would object to a site in Ireland and they name a place near the mouth of the Avoca. We have, as explained, no real right of objection to anything, but as we are asked, it may be as well to consider the matter.

> The Advantages of Ireland

> (1) ample space, in many localities, without population or danger of complaint and with abundant water supplies.
> (2) planting an industry in Ireland even though it is a small one.

> The Disadvantages are

> (3) it is separated by a considerable sea channel from the cartridge filling establishment where the cordite would be used. Under possible circumstances, i.e. when our needs were sharpest this might prove a great drawback.
> (4) would the government approve of a dangerous manufacture, on which supplies of importance to the public service depend, being carried on in Ireland, at a place where there was no garrison or special means of defence?

(5) a possible grievance might arise from the works spoiling the Vale of Avoca, but perhaps this need not be discussed here as they would not be under the Department and the objections depend on the part of the Vale that may be decided upon.

The points for decision arise, as far as the Department is chiefly interested are (3) and (4) above. Will you consider and let me know what answer should be sent. If you wish to see the company, they will come anytime.

The Adjutant General, Sir Redvers Buller, noted:

I should be inclined to attach most importance to a point not touched on, convenience of inspection and proof, it would be a great disadvantage for us to remove this from Woolwich, consequently a factory in Ireland would entail considerable delay and, I should fear, expense. I would therefore, myself be disposed to suggest to Messrs Kynoch that Wales, the Midlands or Norfolk would be preferable to Ireland.

Following this Campbell-Bannerman wrote to John Morley, Chief Secretary, for long MP for Newcastle-upon-Tyne and one of the most passionate advocates of Home Rule, known as "Honest John" a soubriquet which if given credence may say more about the believer than the bearer. Morley replied on 5 November:

I do not feel very hospitality disposed to this suggestion, of course we should have to know precisely what is to be in the Vale of Avoca. If Messrs Kynoch want to go to Kerry or Donegal, this sort of objection would not hold, on the whole, after talking it over with my best advisers, I would not be sorry if it were to be dropped.

In an undated letter a week or so later Morley wrote plaintively in a postscript "What shall I say definitely about the cordite, they are dreadfully clamorous?" He wrote yet again enclosing a letter from John Dillon MP, also "Honest John" remarking mordantly "they are very inflammable just now about the Post Office, so if they can be soothed by cordite, pray let it be so". On 24 November a memo came before Campbell-Bannerman:

The case is now materially altered and the Irish difficulties can perhaps be cleared up or at least relieved, under a letter from Messrs Kynoch which came today they propose to avoid the expense and labour attending the starting of a new nitroglycerine factory by obtaining supplies in a form incorporated with guncotton, from an existing company. This as verbally explained to me will mean that the Nobel Company will work with them.

I see no objection and have sent the papers to the Admiralty. The arrangement would also remove some of the Nobel difficulty which we felt in entirely passing by a firm of their distinction even though it arose from their own price.

The only part of the cordite process which Messrs Kynoch would have to provide is the last stage, of making cordite from the pulp of guncotton and nitroglycerine. The process and the works necessary are not so dangerous in the sense of the first two processes, guncotton and nitroglycerine, very possibly the Minister in view of Mr Morley's letter will allow them to be anywhere in the United Kingdom.

On 4 December Campbell-Bannerman wrote to the Earl of Spencer, First Lord of the Admiralty, who had been Lord Lieutenant for two periods:

At this stage I had to withdraw the papers from the Admiralty because of the Irish agitation which required some attention to ally it. Messrs Kynoch, Chairman, Arthur Chamberlain had asked us if Ireland would be objected to for their works, I consulted John Morley who said if possible this should be avoided. We did not however, make any objection to Messrs Kynoch, but told them that it was considered likely to be inconvenient to have the factory whence a supply would be drawn, separated by the sea from the place where the cordite would be delivered. This is obvious in the case of war. The Kynoch firm thereupon roused Wicklow, having had Arklow in their eye as a possible site and said that unless they obtained a promise of orders in future years they could not in the face of objections, lay out money on a factory.

A promise binding on future governments was of course, not to be thought of. Happily in the middle of this came the proposal to purchase instead of making the pulp which commended itself on grounds of speed and also of giving some part of the plunder to Nobel's Explosives Company.

This was the point in the papers communicated to the Admiralty and subsequently having to answer Tim Healy, I took it on me to say that the purchase agreement was to be adopted and therefore that the question of an Irish site did not arise. As I had to say this to him, and we have had to send our letter to Kynoch and thus your consent comes in a little after

*the fair, but as your technical advisers agreed, I felt justified in
assuming it. This is a long story and I add to it by enclosing a
copy of my letter to Healy.*

This was dated the same day. Healy was a vehement Cork anti-
Parnellite MP and later the first Governor General of the Irish Free
State. The letter noted that in view of the purchasing arrangement
Kynoch no longer needed to erect a factory in Arklow or elsewhere.
Spencer replied to Campbell-Bannerman observing "your last letter
diplomatic but ruined the susceptibilities of the Admiralty and their
new anti-Irish views"(318).

The *News-Letter*, 15 December, reported that a deputation led by
William Field, a prominent Dublin Nationalist MP and Thomas J
Troy, an Arklow auctioneer and town commissioner, had attended at
the War Office a few days before. It is clear that when the War Office
were unenthusiastic about Arklow, though recognising that they "had
no real right of objection" and the Admiralty were apparently hostile,
Kynoch induced John Dillon, Tim Healy, William Field and doubtless
other Irish members to press Dublin Castle and the War Office not
to obstruct the company in going to Arklow. At the same time
Chamberlain created the impression in the War Office that having
arranged to buy pulp from Nobel's he no longer needed Arklow or
any other site. This suited the War Office in giving Nobel's "part of
the plunder" and no longer having to make a case against Arklow on
grounds of convenience of testing and proof.

The agreement for the supply of pulp which Kynoch had signed
with Nobel's on 26 November was far too major a matter for the
Scottish company to carry through without the consent of the Trust
board of directors. On 30 November Thomas Johnston, general
manager at Glasgow sent copies of the draft agreement to the Trust
Office in London noting that he expected difficulties with Edward
Kraftmeier because of a tonnage quota sharing agreement which
Ardeer had with Chilworth (305).

The Trust Company, acknowledging Johnston's letter, raised the
question of patent right. Johnston replied that cordite was open to
all manufacturers as the type being made at Waltham for which the
government were placing contracts with the trade, differed from that
in the Abel and Dewar patent. The Trust were still not satisfied and
wrote to Johnston again. He replied that if the House of Lords
declared that cordite was an infringement of ballistite or that ballistite
was its master patent or if it was merely an improvement on ballistite,
Nobel's could prevent Kynoch manufacturing it in any of these events.
In the case of government contracts the manufacturer was protected

against the patentee by the government.

On Saturday 8 December, the day after a Trust board meeting, Johnston, himself a Trust director, had a four hour encounter with Chamberlain in Birmingham. Chamberlain refused to accept either of the alternatives which the Trust offered. The first was that the contract for the supply of pulp was to continue after the initial three years with Nobel's supplying pulp at below cost and Kynoch undertaking not to undercut prices. The second was that Nobel's would take over the Kynoch cordite factory and pay thirty percent on all orders obtained by Glasgow and Chilworth over the following seven years.

Chamberlain's response was that while he had no immediate plans for expanding his cordite interests beyond the United Kingdom he would certainly not let business go past him. He did not wish to break prices but wanted a share of the trade. He did not suppose that in such markets as Serbia, now in Yugoslavia, Turkey, Chile, Brazil, China and so on that J N Heidemann, a director of the German companies on the Trust board, or Kraftmeier, had a monopoly. If they had, they had nothing to fear from Kynoch. If they had no special hold and he saw an opportunity of doing business he would go ahead. On the other hand he was willing to negotiate, immediately or later at the convenience of Heidemann and Kraftmeier.

Chamberlain pointed out that he had given an undertaking, which was not in the formal agreement, to discuss with Nobel's all enquiries from outside sources with a view to arriving at an accommodation. He declared that if the Nobel companies in Scotland and Germany were alarmed at competition from Kynoch they should say what they considered it worth to them to get rid of the company from these markets. Chamberlain was willing to deal on the basis of a profit pooling arrangement or an exchange of Kynoch shares for Trust shares. He wanted an immediate decision. If there was no agreement forthcoming he would begin planning a factory, not just for the government contract but all other orders for cordite and dynamite he could get anywhere in the world.

Nobel's had suggested an arrangement for controlling ammunition which Chamberlain remarked was rather strange as a case of cartridges could cost £6 while the powder might cost six shillings. This would naturally increase his demands. At that time Nobel's did not manufacture ammunition.

Chamberlain concluded that a refusal by the Nobel companies to supply pulp would give him an important clue that the trade must be very profitable as they were so anxious to protect it for themselves and were afraid that Kynoch could break prices and make serious inroads in the business. He was willing to meet Heidemann but only in Birmingham.

Johnston conveyed all this in letters to the Trust Office and Kraftmeier, written immediately after the meeting. On Monday 10 December, Kraftmeier sent a telegram to Johnston who had returned to Glasgow, stating that Heidemann had gone back to Germany after the Trust board meeting. They were not afraid of Chamberlain's bluster. They would rather fight him in England with German cartridges if Chamberlain insisted on his own terms. Johnston, replying by telegram stated that he had received a wire from Chamberlain announcing that he had occasion to be in London the following day, Tuesday and possibly the Wednesday and some satisfactory arrangement might be made. Johnston said he was willing to go to London if it would help.

Kraftmeier retorted by telegram that Heidemann was not prepared to come back from Germany and would "fight Chamberlain in every direction". Chamberlain arrived in London on the Tuesday morning and booked into an hotel. At noon Johnston sent a telegram to Chamberlain pointing out that Kraftmeier's office was opposite the hotel in Charing Cross and another to Kraftmeier suggesting that they should meet. It does not appear that they did.

On the Wednesday Kraftmeier wrote to Johnston stating he would prefer to pay Chamberlain £100,000 per year on the basis that the profit on the three year contract would be £85,000, "I feel certain it would be better to pay the additional £15,000 instead of allowing the agreement to stand as it was submitted last Friday, as it would enable Messrs Kynoch to compete forthwith".

Johnston, replying, quoted a letter from Chamberlain:

> I remind you that by this agreement you secured among other advantages that we could not enter the chemical or dynamite trade. All therefore that Mr Heidemann has secured is that instead of being only free to make and sell cordite with a friendly bias in favour of yourselves and your allies we are free to make and sell everything everywhere.

Johnston concluded, "Mr Chamberlain therefore intends to order the remaining machinery required".

Kraftmeier's reponse was:

> I doubt if Messrs Kynoch would really be very anxious to go into the dynamite trade considering the disastrous results

which other competing firms have had and I am still of the opinion that they will think twice before they erect a nitoglycerine factory in consequence of the Government order they have, and I believe that they will think it a much wiser plan to purchase the pulp for this order as it was orginally discussed. Since then Mr Chamberlain has held a bigger and bigger gun at our head - if I may use such an expression - and when he sees that he cannot get all that he demands, a share in the entire business, I only hope that he will reconsider his demands, especially when he finds the difficulty is to get a site for his nitroglycerine factory; and if he ultimately succeeds in finding one, time must necessarily elapse before it is ready for working.

Kraftmeier was perfectly right in his assessment of Chamberlain's character and methods. He was wrong about his intentions regarding the dynamite trade and he was hopelessly off the mark on the question of setting up a factory. All the indications are that Chamberlain never intended to purchase pulp from Nobel's, certainly not after he and Cocking had inspected the old factory at Arklow in early November. From then on he increased his demands steadily. Johnston and the other Ardeer directors were prepared to go a long way to meet him as the supplying of pulp, which they had already sold to Waltham, was very good business.

Chamberlain, while not flamboyant in George Kynoch's way, was at least as stubborn and a far shrewder strategist. A proud, independent type of individual he was not at all prepared to rely on other companies for essential services when he could provide these himself. He had already purchased Worsboro' Dale to secure supplies of black powder and extra land at Witton on which further plants would be built for manufacturing items being bought in. As time went by he acquired several outside factories and in general made the company as self-sufficient as possible.

Chamberlain had no intention of becoming dependent on any other company and certainly not on a major potential rival. He was willing to use Nobel's as a bargaining counter and as suited his tactics made ever increasing demands, which so exasperated Kraftmeier and Heidemann, that it could hardly have been any surprise on 21 January 1895 when the Kynoch directors heard that the proposed agreement with Nobel's "had fallen through, as the foreign members of the Trust had failed to ratify it"(295).

While the minutes show no formal resolution to go ahead at Arklow the decision must have been made by mid-November. Charles

Heppenstall was appointed manager and Ralph E Brown chemist. The *News-Letter*, 29 December, carried an announcement from Cocking that they had decided on Arklow instead of Brittas Bay and construction would commence immediately.

As the new year opened, ground was broken by J McCullagh, a local contractor and a few days later a trainload of equipment arrived at Arklow station. This was not taken to the site as the company cancelled operations on the morning of Monday 7 January. Some difficulties had been experienced in obtaining all the land and easements and a remarkable exercise was held to stampede the owners and the people of Arklow generally, through the medium of a public meeting for which a cataclysmic atmosphere was whipped up by carefully inspired rumours and a printed poster placed about the district.

IN CONSEQUENCE OF OBJECTIONS HAVING BEEN RAISED TO THE PROPOSED CORDITE FACTORY, A PUBLIC MEETING WILL BE HELD IN THE COURTHOUSE ON WEDNESDAY AT 12.00 O'CLOCK, SO THAT ALL MAY HAVE A FAIR OPPORTUNITY OF EXPRESSING THEIR OPINION FOR OR AGAINST THE WORKS. MESSRS KYNOCH WILL NOT ESTABLISH THEM IN ARKLOW IN THE FACE OF OPPOSITION FROM THE INHABITANTS.

Arklow Courthouse has a large open space in front and is located on the widest part of the Main Street. The meeting was held inside with a huge throng clamouring outside. The platform was occupied by the town commissioners, harbour commissioners, poor law guardians, justices of the peace, the town clerk, the harbour master, the post master, the bank manager, merchants, shopkeepers, doctors, clergymen and all the other prominent individuals in the town. It is not recorded that the proceedings began on time.

DR. M C O'GORMAN: I move Mr Richard Kearon, Chairman of the Town Commissioners, to the chair.

J G BARLOW (Bank of Ireland Manager): I second.

HUGH BYRNE, Town Commissioner, was elected secretary to the meeting.

CHAIRMAN: Ye are all aware of the purpose for which this meeting has been called. Information has been conveyed to Messrs Kynoch that strong opposition would be given against the proposed cordite works by the inhabitants of Ferrybank and Arklow. The rumour has gone afloat that many people in the town were going to oppose it and some of the parties have come here to prove the contrary. What we want now is an expression of opinion from everyone that they are willing that the work should go ahead and that no opposition will be given in any way.

(HEAR, HEAR).

T J TROY (Town Commissioner, auctioneer, agent for Kynoch): In the absence of Mr Heppenstall, manager, it devolves on me to speak on behalf of Messrs Kynoch. I might say at the outset that the company have their choice of a number of sites to select for their works including one on the Thames and another on the Humber.

A rather grave difficulty arose at one time with the War Office, they were under contract for three years with the government and were pressed for delivery so they had to look out for another site as well as Arklow, and they fixed on a site on the Thames, everything was suitable there and the cost of the ground would be nothing more than in Arklow. They got along alright here, through the assistance of Members of Parliament of every faction, Conservative, Parnellite and McCarthyite. But the present difficulty is one that has turned up in the town. It seems very hard that they should have any difficulty in Arklow when they have been able to get over such obstacles elsewhere as seemed at times to be insurmountable. I will read just a portion of a letter that refers to what I am saying, from the Chairman of the company, Mr Chamberlain:

> *The position in Arklow has become worse it is in fact now intolerable. The opposition to fencing in the land is still more intolerable. If we are not wanted in Arklow, if there is the slightest opposition on the part of any class of the inhabitants, it will not pay us to come.*

Then the natural thing that would suggest itself to any reasonable mind is why should people with a lot of money who could get ground where they liked, come here for anybody afterwards to have anything to say to them? There is a slight misunderstanding on Mr Chamberlain's part, he seems to think the only people who can object, they cannot legally object, are the fishermen. I will read part of this letter which refers to it:

> *I suppose it is the fishermen who want the use of Lord Wicklow's land, for drying their nets, if so it is a great pity you did not warn me, I particularly asked you and you said the fishermen would be on the other side.*

I ask all fishermen here if they are on the other side *(YES, YES)*.

Mr Chamberlain also says that:

Unless all these difficultes are removed within a day or two we will be compelled finally to abandon Arklow as a possible site.

As business people they have to keep every available site open to them until they have one that is satisfactory and if Arklow fails them they fall back on the Thames. I am not to be taken as blaming any individual for having an objection to the Ferrybank site, Messrs Kynoch would not have it that I or any of their people would stand in that position. They will not come to Arklow unless the people are agreeable.

It is for ye to say if ye are agreeable. Of course ye could not go down to the sea to bathe in the summer, if ye would rather see a busy factory with a lot of people getting remunerative employment which will help to increase the population of the town and do away with poverty for years and years.

(HEAR, HEAR, WE WANT THE WORK).

In explosives work it is an absolute necessity that the grounds should be fenced in, and kept strictly private, free from trespass, the Government insists on this, as the smallest thing might cause an explosion, anyone allowed in must be under the personal conduct of an employee, if an accident occurs the company is liable. The land Messrs Kynoch are buying from the Wicklow Estate is from Ferrybank to Webb's River, including Mr Breslin's property and the old Chemical Works, down to the sea. A road will be built for the Ferrybank houses.

If anyone has any objections let them say so, they cannot prevent from a legal point of view but Kynochs do not want to go in unless the people are agreeable.They could go elsewhere, they have any amount of money and would get people to receive them with open arms in a hundred parts of Ireland where there are just as good sites as Arklow and there are dozens of places in England open to them also. I hope I have made myself perfectly clear.   I ask again if there is any objection.

No one made any objection.

CHAIRMAN: Ye have all heard Mr Troy's very full explanation. The factory would undoubtedly be a great boon to the town and would give a lot of employment, in fact there is no man in the town but it would not benefit in some way. I put it formally to the meeting if there is any objection to the proposals of the company as explained by Mr Troy.

There was no response.

A VOICE: The sooner the work goes on the better.

J W HARRISON (Church of Ireland rector, well known street preacher): It strikes me since I came into the Courthouse that a large firm like Kynochs would hardly be affected by mere rumours. It is the first I heard of mere rumours. I heard some people last evening state very strongly, they being charged with being the authors of these rumours, that they never heard of them before. I can speak for Ferrybank, I know that everyone I spoke to is in favour.

T J TROY: There is just one small matter in Mr Harrison's remarks I wish to refer to, he used the word "rumours". In justice to Kynochs it is more than rumour. It is the personal expression of a resident of Ferrybank to their manager Mr Heppenstall, in which it was stated that a number of residents of Ferrybank, including some of the wealthiest in Arklow, would oppose this thing tooth and nail and spend their last shilling on it. Probably Mr Harrison is not aware of that.

J W HARRISON: I am quite aware Mr Troy ...

T J TROY: The fact of your using the expression makes me put it in that light.

J W HARRISON: I am aware that the wealthy resident referred to has denied he ever used the words.

T J TROY: I am aware the gentleman alluded to did not use the words to the manager, but another man did say that the gentleman did use the words. In the letter the word "rumours" does occur. Mr Heppenstall learns that there would be bitter opposition to fencing in the lands.

CHAIRMAN: The parties mentioned are here to prove the contrary. We think for the good of everyone it is better to let it drop, and let us have the consent of everyone to the works going ahead.

EDWARD KEARON: Ye are all aware from what has been said that I am the person referred to principally, but I can assure ye that it would be the very last thing I would think of, to interfere, or give the works any obstruction whatever. (*HEAR, HEAR*). There were people speaking to me no doubt, about the right down to the sea. People would have their own talk, that is their way. So far from opposing it, if I had land myself I would give it in place of taking it away. Why, I would have lost my head if I had thought of giving opposition to such a thing that would give so much employment, especially now in the winter. Now I am sure ye are all satisfied I am not guilty of the charge.

JOHN BRADFORD: Mr Troy, is my name mentioned, as owner of the land in question, in any of the letters?

T J TROY: I have just received a telegram from Mr Heppenstall, in which your name occurs:

MOST IMPORTANT RESOLUTION SHOULD EXPRESS WILLINGNESS OF PEOPLE TO GIVE UP PUBLIC RIGHTS IF SUCH EXIST. I WILL NOT NEGOTIATE MORE WITH BRADFORD UNLESS HE HANDS ME LEGAL POWER WITHIN TWENTY HOURS BINDING HIMSELF TO SELL FOR £170 IF WE CHOOSE TO BUY IN ONE MONTH. I WILL CLEAR OFF.

JOHN BRADFORD: I stated on Saturday night that I am ready to sign any documents and for them to go on with the work.

JAMES DUNPHY (Catholic Parish Priest): Do you consent to that Mr Bradford?

JOHN BRADFORD: Oh yes, I do, certainly (*HEAR, HEAR*).

T G BARLOW: Will you sign the agreement within twenty hours?

JOHN BRADFORD: Within twenty minutes.

SECRETARY: There will now be a resolution submitted to ye for approval or dissent. I believe the resolution meets the case in a very ample manner and I believe it will be satisfactory to Messrs Kynochs. It is open to anyone to dissent from the resolution or to have it amended or rejected.

That we the people of Arklow, in public meeting assembled for the purpose of expressing our great satisfaction at the establishment of a cordite factory in the vicinity of our town, hereby convey to Messrs Kynoch and Company, on behalf of all classes of the community, an unanimous and genuine Irish welcome (HEAR, HEAR).

That the earnest co-operation of the public in giving every assistance to the promotion of this industry is hereby assured and guaranteed, and that we express our strong disapproval of any obstruction which would have the effect of retarding even for a day, the progress of the works, and thereby depriving the people of the locality, especially the working class, of the benefits to be derived from the outlay of so much capital on a district where the employment of labour would be such an advantage to the people.

The resolution was formally moved by James Dunphy in a very long speech which repeated all the points previously made and was garnished with a rather deferential eulogy of the business acumen and goodness of Arthur Chamberlain who had told him that Arklow was the best and most convenient site for the factory and of the Wicklow Estate and its agent, M F Beresford JP, who seconded the resolution, reiterating all the arguments already advanced and suggested that it should be sent to the company by telegram.

The resolution was adopted unanimously and was followed by rounds of cheers by the trio for Beresford and his employer, Lady Wicklow, and for Troy, Dunphy and Kynoch.

SECRETARY: In order to comply with the telegram from Mr Heppenstall, the following resolution must be moved:

> That this meeting on the part of the general public, hereby undertakes to relinquish all rights and privileges, if such ever existed, to the grounds intended to be taken over by Messrs Kynoch for the purposes of their factory.

EDWARD KEARON: I move.

T G BARLOW: I second.

The *Wicklow People*, 12 January, recorded that this was the end of the meeting and carried a postscript telegraphed just before going to press, that Heppenstall had announced he would resume operations on obtaining the signatures of the householders adjacent to the factory.

This was a truly extraordinary affair, a foray in bluff and bullying tactics in a wrapping of apparent democracy. Indeed the origin of democratic republican governance was discussion of public issues in open meetings of all the inhabitants of a particular district. Meetings of the rally type were common in Ireland at the time, mainly for land agitation and political purposes. These would normally have been held on Sundays. This meeting, on a Wednesday, was carefully organised beforehand and stage-managed while it was proceeding. The workers were dismissed on the Monday and the work ceased. The special posters were widely distributed. The atmosphere of crisis was sedulously stoked up and the tone set from the beginning with the platform speakers carefully briefed, especially the clergymen. Suitable extracts from Chamberlain's letter were read at judicious moments and the ominous telegram at exactly the right time and the resolutions, carefully drafted beforehand, were easily rushed through. No one could claim that Chamberlain, Cocking and Heppenstall exerted undue, or indeed any, influence as they were conspicuously absent.

On 21 January the Kynoch directors noted that preparations for the factory were progressing satisfactorily and that "letters of cordiality" had been exchanged with the Town Commissioners. A few more days were lost in the following weeks through snow and a very short strike. In February the directors voted £50 to T J Troy for his "trouble and expense", obviously in organising the meeting. This sum was separate from his fee and commission in handling the purchase of the property. In September the company engaged him fulltime at £200 per year. He had for some time been drawing £3 a week while "seeking a yacht". This was for the use of the management in travelling back and forth. Troy resigned the post in January 1896, no doubt because he found the condition that he was not to be involved in politics too irksome. He agreed to carry out special tasks from time to time at the £3 weekly rate.

The factory became, briefly, an issue of sorts in that most exhilarating of events in Ireland, a by-election and even more vintage nectar, in a rural constituency. This arose when the sitting member for East Wicklow, a Parnellite, resigned. Arklow was strongly Parnellite. Practically the only major industry at the time was what is still known as the Arklow Rock Parnell Quarry owned by the family and believed to have been worked at one time by Charles Stewart himself. T J Troy was the local leader of the Parnellites while James Dunphy headed the anti-Parnellites or McCarthyites. In the by-election which took place in April 1895 and the general election in July both factions were anxious to claim the credit for bringing the factory to the town. John Dillon, at a meeting in July stated that Dunphy who chaired the gathering, was mainly instrumental. The Conservative and Unionist candidate, strongly supported by the *News-Letter*, was also to the fore. The Parnellites won both contests. It would appear that the greater credit was due to Troy. In a letter to the *News-Letter*, 5 January, he stated that he had had the property on his books for over a year, offering it to every important firm in Britain and was in contact with Kynoch before they had sought a site in Ireland.

In February 1896 the directors voted £5 to J W Harrison's charities. This seems to have been an annual subscription. There is no evidence of a corresponding donation to James Dunphy. In February 1898 the company refused to give a site for a Catholic Church in Ferrybank. In 1908 they gave Dunphy an inscribed silver snuffbox marking his priestly golden jubilee. Devoted pastor he undoubtedly was, Kynoch used him as cynically as they did everyone else (327).

The local magistrates confirmed the Home Secretary's draft licence in March, without difficulty. At length all the arrangements were made and the buildings completed. Local workers were hired and senior staff, including chemists specially engaged, were brought over from Witton.

As mid-summer's day passed the Inspectors of Explosives came and thoroughly checked the equipment and systems. Finding all satisfactory they duly licenced the works as Factory 165 (689).

Supplies of cotton and other materials were landed at the port. The gas producer plant was charged with coal and electricity hummed through the wires. The great water tower filled the boilers and the steam valves built up to top pressure. Trucks bearing batches of mix rattled from one building to the next, emerging as the first finished cordite on the tenth of July as the whole mighty machine rumbled and rolled into action just one hundred and ninety-one days after the first pick and shovel had sunk into the barren sand dunes of Ferrybank, including the days lost at the outset.

Kynoch, under the house of Chamberlain, had certainly arrived in the Vale of Avoca.

ARKLOW, WOMEN AT WORK, PROBABLY FIRST WORLD WAR
SOURCE 301

MERCURY, REDMOND, GRIFFITH

The directors voted congratulations to Cocking and Heppenstall on the successful start-up of the plant. The *News-Letter*, 13 July, reported that Chamberlain had allowed three hundred yards of the beach for bathing; on 31 August that the contractor had given a dinner at which Heppenstall announced plans for doubling the size of the factory and on 5 October that Lord Ashbourne, the Lord Chancellor of Ireland, had paid a visit. These events marked the official opening.

Chamberlain did not attend the dinner although he had been in Arklow a few days previously for a meeting with the Harbour Commissioners. He was concerned that the port could not take ships of even a small size, in all weathers and tides. Travelling over in his yacht he had been disgraced by having to put in at Wicklow for shelter. Forty ship's carpenters were employed and while that was very good there could be a hundred if they would get a steam dredger. He advised them to apply to the Board of Works for a loan.

In 1900 Chamberlain told the shareholders at the annual general meeting that the company had bought a dredger which they had hired to the Commissioners. Throughout the existence of the factory there was a constant round of correspondence between the company, the Harbour Commissioners, the Commissioners of Public Works, the Department of Agriculture and Technical Instruction and the Chief Secretary's Office. The problem of dredging and the responsibility for dealing with it was never really solved.

Also in 1900, Chamberlain said that the sea facing the factory which had been retreating from the shore for the previous fifty years had turned and, encroaching on the land, had carried away the sandhills that protected the front and "seriously endangered the existence of the works". The company erected a system of walls and groins which "seriously added to the original small cost of the land" (296,321).

The *News-Letter*, 7 September, reported that a deputation of Arklow Town Commissioners, later the Urban District Council, had asked Chamberlain to provide an electricity supply for street lighting. He suggested a delay until the factory could do so "more economically". The UDC officially invited the company to tender in February 1902 and probably on other occasions also. Kynoch always refused and Arklow continued to be lit by the council's gasworks until the national electricity grid reached the town over thirty years later (340,709).

At the outset Kynoch announced that they intended to ask the

Dublin, Wicklow and Wexford Railway to build a branch line to the factory. The railway directors considered this in April and ordered a report from their engineer. In May the directors of both companies inspected the route. A spur was to be built from a point above the town, across the Avoca and along the north bank to the works. This would have involved a bridge on the river, a level crossing on the Ferrybank road and extra signalling. A private act of parliament would have been necessary as under British law all railway construction of any consequence has to be legislated separately. There need have been no difficulty about this. Thousands of railway measures had been passed without difficulty or even debate and the Irish members could easily have dealt with the matter. The line was never built. It must be concluded that this was just another part of Chamberlain's overall strategy, largely based on bluff, which he never intended to carry out. All shipments were brought in and exports despatched by sea. Sales in Ireland would scarcely have justified a spur line (325).

It does not seem that anyone in the War Office, the Admiralty, Dublin Castle nor indeed in Nobel's Explosives Company and the Nobel-Dynamite Trust realised why Kynoch were so keen to set up in Arklow. The reason was the old factory which Chamberlain and Cocking visited early in November 1894 and which T J Troy mentioned in passing at the public meeting.

This factory had been designed and built over twenty years before by John Morrison, principal of Walter Morrison and Company who besides manufacturing many chemicals in Newcastle-upon-Tyne also carried out design and installation work for other firms. In 1872 he wrote an account of his experiences in Arklow giving some interesting insights into mid-nineteenth century social conditions arising from problems when he made arrangements for the supply of building materials, in the ordinary way, as he thought. He was rudely awakened to the fact that this was not so normal a business as it might have been:

> *But stone or brick we were not destined to get in any such simple manner, for unluckily, in my ignorance of the customs and prejudices of the country, I omitted to cross the hand of a certain County Magnate, in consequence of which negligence the undertaking was denounced far and wide as one that would spread ruin and devastation on everything within a radius of at least ten miles. Hereat the agents of the two great landed proprietors of our district, Lords Carysfort and Wicklow began to make wry faces and one of them verily was not slow in favouring us with a visit for the purpose of receiving a small gratuity in return for as much of the serene light of his*

countenance as we might require; or of threatening us with the awful alternative of the furnace of his indignation, seven times heated. In other words he called to convince us that if we were able to pay for his patronage we should never be molested, but if not neither brick nor stone should be forthcoming from the estates of the two noblemen. He was politely informed that the works should be erected in spite of any opposition, at whatever cost, yea, even if necessary with marble from Kilkenny. He departed at an elevated temperature, and soon we learned that true to his threat, strict orders had been issued to the effect that no tenant on either estate should supply us with building materials of whatever kind, or assist us in any way on pain of their Lord and Master's severe displeasure.

This placed us in rather a dilemma, but there was the consolation that those more directly in power opposed us, the poorer classes, headed by the priests gave us much assistance, favouring the project in every way. The latter would allude to the undertaking at the altar on Sunday mornings, certainly from pecuniary motives, in the most glowing language, they visited the works frequently, and they seemed ever ready to do us a good turn or give us any assistance in their power; and in the most priest-ridden country in the world the moral influence of the Roman Catholic Clergy possesses immense weight. Indeed had the priests and the agents combined, perhaps they might have stopped our operations entirely.

Morrison obtained alternative supplies and built the factory with multiple facilities for the manufacture of sulphuric acid, sodium sulphate, acetone, artificial fertilisers, soap, alkali and other products. There was also a gas producer plant, a sawmill and workshops for blacksmiths, mechanics, joiners, plumbers, coopers and other artisans. The factory involved extensive reclamation on the waterfront. The harbour was owned by the Wicklow Copper Mining Company for which Morrison built the plant. This was one of several concerns which had operated the nearby Ballymurtagh Mines from 1755 and had paid dividends of up to one hundred percent in some years, employing as many as five hundred workers. The company set up a subsidiary, the Arklow Chemical Works Limited, to operate the factory using the sulphur ore and the huge quantities of waste pyrites which had accumulated for making sulphuric acid (333-4).

It is not clear how long the factory was in operation. The first company was wound up in November 1873 and at least one other undertaking used the works. The *News-Letter*, 18 July 1891, reported what was evidently just one phase in a long litigation between Edward Breslin JP of Bray, Wicklow and other directors of the Arklow Manure Company Limited which had resolved to go into liquidation in 1887. Kynoch completed the purchase in April 1895 and in 1898 made an offer for the mines which was rejected. Later they bought ore from Spain and Scandinavia (374, 675).

It is apparent that the condition of the plant was such that it could be brought into production very quickly and obviously saved Kynoch a great deal of time and trouble, no doubt to Edward Kraftmeier's chagrin. Indeed Chamberlain told the shareholders at the annual general meeting in June 1895 that the works was actually too big for immediate requirements and parts would be used for offices, stores, stables and non-danger manufacturing processes. This would have spared the necessity to erect buildings for these purposes at the beginning.

In June 1898 as the original contract was about to be completed, Chamberlain told the annual meeting:

if a further order can be secured from the government, sufficient to keep these works employed for another year, and if assurances can be obtained that an Irish industry is regarded with favour, it is the intention of the board to undertake fresh developments with a view to still further increase the amount of employment given in the neighbourhood.

This contained the first of many threats that the factory would be shut if the government did not give contracts or preferential treatment. The company did obtain an order and built several extensions. In October 1898 an acetone plant was erected in addition to the three built by Morrison; in 1899 an installation for picric acid, a compound of nitric and carbolic acids also known as lyddite and in 1900 a plant for sulphuric acid by the Kessler process. Already in 1896 a plant for nitric acid by the Vallentiner process and a guncotton works had been built followed by facilities for Kynite, a new explosive for use in certain types of coalmines, invented by Cocking.

Also in 1900 Kynoch bought 265 acres (108 hectares) of land beyond Webb's River, part of which was sold to the Arklow Brick Company "on condition they did not pollute the river". A second and larger nitroglycerine plant was constructed. The factory at its greatest, stretched three km (1 1/2 miles) from Ferrybank northwards along the shore to a maximum width of about 750m. There were several hundred buildings. Most were of wood, on concrete foundations and were mounded with earth, on which workers planted flowers picking out the numbers of the buildings. Although the workers bought the seeds the management do not seem to have given prizes for the best efforts (374).

Each building had double doors and a thermometer which could be read from outside and a motor house alongside. The floors were of sheet lead turned up around the walls which were carefully covered with smooth material so as to make the whole as dustproof as possible. The buildings were connected by tramlines on which trucks were pushed by hand or pulled by horses, donkeys and mules. In the early years there was a small canal on which a barge was used, built by John Tyrrell and Sons, well known Arklow boat builders (709).

While the manufacture of high explosives was based on chemical and engineering principles entirely different from black powder, some of the technical terms were carried over to the new processes. Cordite was a compound of 58% nitroglycerine, 37% guncotton and 5% vaseline, the only ingredient not made in Arklow. The solvent was acetone, which brought about the integration of the ingredients.

The compounding of the nitric acid and glycerine was the most dangerous process. The production of guncotton was also dangerous at the drying stage when it was cut into handsized disks and placed in trays for drying in large buildings called stoves. After this the cotton was taken in brasslined boxes to mixing houses where it was blended slowly with the nitroglycerine into pulp. Packed in rubber bags placed in small barrels it was taken to other sheds and incorporated with acetone. Following this it was moved to the press houses and extruded into cords of various lengths and thicknesses. These were placed in stoves for from three to fourteen days depending on size and were afterwards blended according to the different uses. Cordite for both military and sporting guns was sent to ammunition shops in Witton and to the government factories. Packs of blasting explosives, also called cartridges, were made up in Arklow, mainly by women. Monarkite, a powder, was wrapped in paper which was dipped in hot wax. Abbcite, a coarser powder, was wrapped the same way. Erin Gelignite was cut in sticks with a copper knife and wrapped in prewaxed paper. Red dynamite was moulded by a machine (337-8, 374-8).

The various processes involved very complicated machinery supplied by Easton and Anderson, Erith, Kent. Power and light came from dynamoes actuated by gas engines supplied by a gas producer plant distinct from that in the Chemical Works. The equipment was made by Chamberlain and Hookham, Birmingham in which Arthur Chamberlain was a partner. The manufacturing was immensely more complicated than this. Modifications were made from time to time and the Inspectors altered their regulations in the light of experience (349-353).

There was always the danger of explosions. The first took place on 4 October 1895 and was investigated by Major A Ford, Chief Inspector Majendie's assistant. Noting that the licence had been issued on 27 June and that the factory was less than four months in existence he found that the explosion had taken place in a cordite drying house which was being temporarily used for drying guncotton. One man was killed. His legs and arms were blown more than one hundred metres. Ford thought that the explosion could have been either accidental or deliberate.

An accident could have been caused because the wooden containers in which the guncotton was held while on the racks had catches and other fittings of brass. These, while not ruled out under the Explosives Act, were undesirable. Ford observed that the boxes used at Waltham Abbey which were not fitted with brass had other disadvantages. If the explosion had indeed been accidental it must have been caused by a box knocking against the tray on which it was resting, the metal parts being covered with cotton fluff.

While there was no direct evidence of malice Ford thought there were two facts which "indicated a diabolical arrangement". Nine days earlier a bottle had been placed in a covered trough taking nitroglycerine to a vat. Had it banged on the lead bottom it would have caused an explosion. It was an ordinary wine bottle which had contained beer or porter. It could hardly have been placed in the trough for concealment as it could have been hidden far more easily behind the trough, in nearby bushes or in the sand.

The second indication was that some time before the accident a lucifer, as matches were still commonly called, strictly forbidden in the factory, had been set off on the tramline by a truck wheel. Ford thought that this match had been placed to cause a scare rather than an explosion. In addition there were "rumours of a more or less shadowy character afloat in Arklow that a rise in the wages of the dangermen and the labourers would result from an explosion".

On the whole Ford thought an accident slightly the more likely. He attended the inquest which returned a verdict of accidental death, noting the point about the brass fittings. The jury absolved the management from blame and commended the deceased's family to their consideration. The jury also found that there was no evidence that the match had been placed deliberately and that there was no hostility towards the company, concluding "we are further of the opinion that the rumours referred to by the company's solicitor have no foundation in fact" (358).

Rumours indeed.

The workers went on strike seeking an increase to twenty shillings (£1) for the dangermen and sixteen shillings (80p) for the others. Cocking, in an interview with the *Irish Times,* 10 October, stated that over 260 men from the town and district were employed. Only four or five had been brought from England. The wages were based on the value of the services rendered and would rise as the workers' skills increased. A vast sum had been spent on the factory. When the workers saw the situation of the company they took advantage. It was treacherous. The firm would infinitely prefer to close the works forever than yield to unjust demands. The present intention was to bring workers from England. He could not say what increase was demanded.

Chamberlain spoke even more vehemently, issuing a statement to the newsagencies which was published widely. The matter had given the directors cause for grave concern. There had been evidence of treachery and malice of the most wicked character and carelessness and disobedience of rule almost as wicked. The workpeople had displayed characteristic Irish cowardice in not informing their superiors of what had been going on. Evidence of motive was found in the statement that an explosion would be an excuse for demanding higher wages. The company had employed many of the people in the hope of making them good workmen in time; 150 men were employed erecting new buildings. That policy was now out of the question. They would take Englishmen to Arklow and pay them higher wages rather than employ native labour at above native rates.

The company might even have to leave Arklow altogether and seek a new site elsewhere. Englishmen or old Constabulary men would be engaged for the more responsible posts. No more than one fifth of the original would be re-engaged. Any who did not apply would be permanently disqualified. The next six months would be a probationary period to see if the men could be taught self-control, discipline and to recognise the advantages of steady industry.

James Dunphy hit back at this onslaught with a letter to the *Freeman's Journal,* Tuesday, 15 October, which the previous Saturday reported that the workers had resumed "on the timely advice of the Reverend James Dunphy PP".

I fear that Mr Arthur Chamberlain must not have had

before him the sworn evidence of the witnesses at the enquiry held by the Inspector. We have it on the sworn evidence of his own Mr Wellings [a Birmingham foreman] that the bottle was at once reported. The match incident was reported immediately.

Whatever the Arklow men are they are not cowards, cowardice is incompatible with their calling. They earn as fishermen and sailors an honest livelihood at the almost constant risk of their lives, and no braver men man the English steamers and merchantmen than the Arklow sailors.

In long established industries of this kind in England, explosions have occurred through the recklessness of workmen, skilled though they be, and one has not heard them accused of malice. It is not very wonderful then that in a new industry with unskilled hands over whom there was not evidently due supervision, an explosion should have occurred.

There is a flavour of the public meeting in this exchange. Again the company used Dunphy and his influence over the people for their own purpose which was to set up and maintain the factory for as long as it suited them.

There were two further serious accidents before the First World War. In 1910 two men were killed while pushing a truck of Arkite pulp when it crashed into the points on a junction of the tramline. These, which should have opened on one branch automatically closing the other, were apparently jammed in an intermediate position. The pulp exploded setting off cotton stove 22 and damaging many other buildings. The Inspector's report made recommendations about the design of the trucks.

The next explosion which was in 1911 was very similar. Two men were killed while pushing a truck with boxes of Erin Gelignite and Arkite jelly. One or more of the boxes had brass bindings. The others were dovetailed. Some jelly got inside the metal and when the bogie crashed into a set of jammed points the boxes exploded, damaging fifteen buildings. The Inspector's report, repeating the previous advice about the bogies, recommended modifications in the points mechanism and suggested that the brass bound boxes should no longer be used. There were numerous minor accidents over the years which were duly recorded in the Inspectors' annual reports. Many of these were of ordinary industrial types such as acid splashings (359-60,689).

Despite Cocking's indication that wages would rise, the levels remained at what Chamberlain termed the "native rate" of twelve to sixteen shillings until the boom days of the First World War, even though in 1903 Chamberlain commissioned a survey into the cost of living which found that the minimum weekly sum necessary for a man, wife and three children was 21s 8d (£1.8 ^{1}/2) which he rounded up to 22s 0d. (£1.10) and paid to all workers in Witton both married and single. Chamberlain was ahead of his time in some ways. In February 1894 he introduced the 48 hour week, being one of the first to do so. At around the same time Campbell-Bannerman ordered this, which was an average of six hours shorter, in the royal factories.

Telling the annual meeting of the living wage, Chamberlain lectured at length on one of his favourite subjects, *laissez faire*. He was completely opposed to all forms of government restrictions and regulations:

> *Freedom of management, freedom for all adults in the control of their own labour, would do more to improve the conditions of labour than the most intelligent restrictions imposed from outside. The best instance of this is the factory legislation for the protection of women. Were it not for their protectors, women's wages would be on average twenty-five percent higher while their lot would in every way be infinitely improved.*

This view of how employees would stand if there were no laws limiting hours of work, prescribing minimum standards of safety, hygiene and other conditions, is of course, ludicrous. Apart from an occasional, very occasional, gesture such as a bonus or day off on the boss's wedding or some such event, employers simply did not pay any more than they possibly could help. If trade unions did not extract increased wages, paid holidays and so on there would be far less money in circulation and far less spent on goods and services, essential and otherwise. There would be no large scale entertainment trades and the community at large would be immeasurably the poorer. Even granted that improved production methods made manufactured articles available at lower costs there would have been no sales if there was not money in workers' pockets rather than employers' bank accounts. The capitalist system of itself could never have developed any channels for distribution of even a little of its vast surpluses.

Chamberlain, while advanced in some ways, was as autocratic as any employer in his day. He established a convalescent home in Llandudno, Wales run by the sick clubs which he encouraged in the factories and also provided sports and recreation facilities. In Arklow the Kynoch Social Hall, near the main gate, had a reading room and billiards tables and other games and was used regularly for card-drives, dances and other functions, some open to the general public. The building was also used every shift in searching the workers for matches, metal buttons, hair and safety pins as in all explosives factories and also for paying out wages.

Kynoch Lodge, like most of the buildings, built of wood, was used for entertaining important visitors and otherwise served as a club for the senior management. In 1897 Chamberlain told the shareholders that three houses of a "superior character" had been built for managers as well as twelve cottages with four rooms and a garden let at a half crown (12 ^{1}/2p) weekly, for foremen. Later more houses were built. A shop was opened to supply groceries to the workers which Chamberlain claimed was a co-operative. It was actually run by the company.

In time relations between the workers and the management became cordial, at least on the surface. In February 1900 the workers presented Chamberlain with a magnificent *illuminated address*, exquisitely illustrated with views of the factory, beautifully bound and contained in a box. In this, couched in rather deferential terms, they gave thanks to him for his "unvarying kindness" and pledged their "esteem and admiration" (297).

Arklow was scarcely underway when the company commenced another large factory called Kynochtown at Stanford-Le-Hope on the Essex bank of the Thames. Production began in January 1897. In March the company was reconstructed as Kynoch Limited with a capital of £500,000 which was doubled the next year. At Witton the existing enterprises were expanded and several new lines begun. The printing department was enlarged and renamed the Kynoch Press. In 1899 the *Kynoch Journal* began as a bi-monthly magazine later changing to a semi-academic quarterly and was edited for open sale by a full-time journalist. A steel foundry was installed to produce a range of ordinary bicycles and motorcycles and all types of castings. Several neighbouring firms were taken over. One was an ammunition and engineering concern. Another made artillery shells which from then on were filled with Arklow lyddite. The third made nails, tubes and wires while the fourth manufactured gas engines and producer plant. A large office on the open plan, then very new, was erected. An attempt which was not very successful was made to introduce the metric system in 1906, the directors noted "except as regards money". In this Chamberlain was some seventy years ahead of his time.

The company's first glycerine works was in Witton and this continued even after a plant was installed at Arklow. The manufacture of this chemical leaves by-products suitable for making soap and candles. This happens in many industrial instances depending on which aspect is maximised. For example gasworks based on coal produced coke of use in steelmaking while steelmills making coke have gas as a by-product. One factory's waste is another's raw material. In 1896 production of soap began at Lion Works followed by candles the next year. Glycerine of medicinal quality was also made.

Chamberlain told Arthur Griffith in 1907 that he wanted to promote all types of industries in Ireland (page 135). Perhaps there were valid reasons for not having the various metal and engineering industries in Ireland even though there must have been substantial demand for nails, wires and cycles. There could have been no reason at all for not manufacturing soap and candles in Arklow because the Chemical Works as originally designed by Morrison had been equipped for the production of soap and of alkali which is its main ingredient apart from palm oil.

The soap undertaking provides an excellent example of Chamberlain's methods. In 1905 Lever Brothers set up a scheme to amalgamate all the soap companies in Britain under the banner flying from Port Sunlight, Merseyside. Chamberlain attacked this ferociously in his annual address to the shareholders and later in the year built an entire new factory, a solid structure of brick and steel in Lion Works, in twenty-one days flat from marking the site to boiling the first bar. He proudly proclaimed that the *Soap Trust* as it was generally called, collapsed a few days later. He barely acknowledged the campaign against the proposed monopoly by Lord Northcliffe, the Dublin born press baron who founded the *Daily Mail, Daily Mirror* and other papers sold at very low prices on the basis of very heavy advertising, of which soap promotion formed a large proportion, which Levers intended to reduce (355).

Chamberlain did carry out some limited expansion in Ireland, buying in 1901 Drimnagh Paper Mills, Dublin. The price is not clear as it was part of share exchange transactions involving other acquisitions. In 1906 the company paid £20,000 cash for Clondalkin Paper Mills near Drimnagh. These provided the Kynoch Press with raw material at first cost for cartridges, catalogues, stationery and wrappings. In 1908 the directors donated a site to the Dublin Rural District Council for a library under Andrew Carnegie's scheme (354).

If Chamberlain was severe with workers he was no less so with managers. He also had a great weakness for litigation and from 1897 the company employed a solicitor full-time, being among the first to do so. Chamberlain took numerous actions to redress real or imagined grievances. One concerning Arklow was in 1896 when a certain John Kearon criticised the company's cargo handling system. This was withdrawn in 1898. In the meantime another John Kearon was appointed captain of the company's steamer at £3 per week. The factory's chief clerk was drawing £2 at the time.

As early as April 1896 the War Office rejected two batches of cordite. The directors sent severe reprimands to Ralph E Brown, chief chemist and Charles Heppenstall, factory manager. In May the War Office rejected more and the directors asked Brown for an explanation. This they found unsatisfactory and summoned him to the boardroom. They allowed him to leave their service on paying a fine of £125.

In July 1899 the War Office rejected another lot and the directors reprimanded all managers and workers, threatening dismissals if it happened again. In October the directors instructed the solicitor to investigate the hours and general conduct of the management. He reported that he had found "nothing to justify the slanderous and malicious charges brought against the Arklow management in regard to the cordite rejections".

In August 1900 the directors decided to reduce the salary of the manager, then WC Sealy, by £50 a year, this was probably a quarter, and to appoint a retired army or navy officer over his head. In September a former army officer was engaged. He was dismissed a year later. Sealy had already been discharged "on suspicion of his being connected in business" with an Arklow butcher.

The new manager was Edward W Anderson, son of the defendant in Alfred Nobel's action. Born in Dublin when his father was working as an engineer in Ireland, he received in 1898 the Crampton Prize from the Institution of Civil Engineers, London for his work on developing cordite machinery while with Easton and Anderson. Joining Kynoch in 1899 he was at first manager of the machinegun department at Lion Works. He remained only a year in Arklow before returning to Witton. In the following few years there were several changes in the position (352).

In 1904 Chamberlain told the annual meeting that sales were slack in the steel, cycle, nail and sporting ammunition departments. Military business was generally good in foreign markets. Orders from the British government were low. He complained bitterly that large sums were being spent on the royal factories at Waltham Abbey and elsewhere. In 1900 he had told the shareholders that while the Boer War had brought large orders, "your directors have not been able to satisfy themselves that any reliance can be placed on the continuance of this demand, they have therefore protected your company from future losses by charging the cost of new tools and plant to every order requiring such expenditure". This meant that Kynoch, taking advantage of the government's urgent needs, got the benefit of new machinery without cost and Chamberlain still abused the government for operating factories. In 1906 Chamberlain told the shareholders that there had been serious increases in costs which they had not been able to pass on to customers. The next year the directors dismissed a large number of managers including Anderson; discontinued the *Kynoch Journal* which they revived briefly in 1918 for internal circulation and tightened up on all expenditure. At the same time the company's most serious confrontation with the government was beginning. Already there had been a number of skirmishes and one serious clash. This was in July 1900 when the House of Commons Select Committee on War Office Contracts examined alleged irregularities in the supply of electrical equipment, hay for horses, boots for soldiers and reading stands and boxes for the War Office library (361-2).

These, it must be concluded, were merely cosmetic dressings for the real business before the Committee, cordite contracts. The explosive had been a sensitive subject from the start. Indeed allegations of inadequate arrangements for supplies of the new propellent had partly caused the defeat of the Lord Rosebery Liberal government in the 1895 general election. The Committee examined every detail of the descriptions, deliveries, quantities and prices of all contracts placed by the War Office and the Admirality from 1894 with the various firms, Kynoch, Nobel's, Chilworth, Cotton Powder, National Explosives and New Explosives.

Chamberlain was closely cross-examined. The position was very delicate as his brother was a senior minister in the Lord Salisbury Conservative government at the time. Joe Chamberlain was not just another minister. He was one of the most prominent politicians of his own or any generation and with his numerous changes in party and policy was a favourite with cartoonists. Captain AJC Donelan who later sat for East Wicklow made a proposal that contracts should not be given to any company in which a member of either House was involved. This was defeated. Chamberlain told the Committee that following the submission of the original bids in 1894 "we were then what the Government called *invited* to reduce our tenders". This is why the schedule placed before Campbell- Bannerman (page 98) was of *"New* prices for Cordite from the Trade". He said that while they had never paid bribes they had on one occasion approached Dublin Castle pointing out "the great good Kynoch were doing in Arklow" and if they did not get a further contract they would have to close the factory. Later The Castle said that their price was too high. On equal terms they could expect a share of the orders available.

Kynoch reduced their price from 3s. (15p) to 2s.10 ^{1}/2d.(14p) and later to 2s.6d. (12 ^{1}/2p). Other firms told the Committee of similarly reducing their prices.

The Director of Army Contracts, Alfred Major, gave evidence that on one occasion he had placed a contract with the company at a higher price than the other firms had quoted as "in my opinion it was absolutely necessary to give a proportion of the order to Kynochs, I would be most unwilling that Arklow should be closed".

The Committee found that better inspection was called for in the case of electrical equipment, fodder, footwear and furniture, recommending that the Public Bodies Corrupt Practices Act, which applied only to local councils, should be extended to government departments. Regarding cordite contracts the Committee were satisfied that the orders were "allocated with the single object of securing the best results to the public service" (361-2).

Chamberlain, could not, on his own terms, complain. He believed absolutely in private enterprise and was opposed to the government operating factories and playing the market. In Birmingham he frequently attacked the Corporation's undertakings which supplied gas and water: ironically the commercial concerns which originally conducted these services had been bought on his brother's proposal.

Despite the Committee's findings some suspicion lingered on in the public mind. In September 1905 a writ was served on the *Daily News* a leading London Liberal paper which had reported that Kynoch did not actually make cordite and instead sub-let their contracts. This theme was taken up by a Liberal Party candidate. The action against the *Daily News* was withdrawn when the paper published an apology. In June 1906 the case against the candidate came to court and damages obtained, one of the few which Chamberlain won.

As the retrenchment programme began in 1907 so did the company's greatest legal and commercial conflict. This was to continue for four years through the various courts, ending like Alfred Nobel's case, at the House of Lords.

The play began with a prelude in July 1906 when the War Office rejected two batches for "low velocity and excessive pressure". The company requested a re-proof which was duly carried out. The result confirmed the original analysis. In August the War Office asked the company to remove the rejected lots and asked them to "expedite manufacture as much as possible and give a definite date when deliveries may be expected". Kynoch, replying, stated that they were having difficulty with a number of batches and that the "abnormal heat has produced conditions hostile to cordite and we dare not push till cooler weather supervenes, by September we expect normal conditions and so overtake arrears".

Apparently the company made up for lost time during the autumn and winter. In the spring of 1907 the real trouble began when the War Office rejected a batch because it contained mercury. This metallic element, unique in that it normally exists as a dense heavy liquid, which has many industrial uses, was to have the star role throughout the drama in invisible quantities. The company in response stated that they had checked the lot in question. It had been supplied in July 1901:

> There was no mercury used by us and no substance other than those in the specification. If therefore the presence of mercury has been found it is not due to any act on our part. We take it for granted that when you say mercury has been found you mean the mercury line has been shown through the spectroscope. We remind you that the spectroscope is an entirely new test and its use was not known to us, or we believe to anybody, until a short time ago, and we further remind you that it is a test so remarkably delicate as to show the slightest shadow of a shade of a trace of the chemical in question.

> How this trace could appear we cannot say; but many things would account for it, for instance the breakage of a thermometer in any house would release enough mercury vapour to respond to this infinitely delicate test, and yet it would not be true to say that mercury was in the cordite, although it would be true to say that the mercury line had been discovered under the spectroscope.

> What we think, however, to be more probable is that some slight trace of mercury may have been introduced through the guncotton. As far as we can remember, we were using at that time equal quantities of Walsrode [a German factory] and Arklow guncotton. There was certainly no mercury in the Arklow guncotton but there may have been in the Walsrode. It must be understood however, that we have no evidence of this and we had no suspicion at that time that mercury was ever used by Walsrode.

We wish to emphasise the fact that the cordite itself is and was, made of the purest materials and in the best way then known to us, we are confident that today, under every examination to which it could possibly be subjected, and after six years of storing, it is absolutely as perfect as we have no doubt you found it in 1901.

Of course we are well aware that your attention has been drawn to a dispute which is proceeding between us and the Home Office in reference to the use by us in the manufacture of high explosives [blasting] of one thousandth of one percent of perchloride of mercury and we do not wish to conceal from you that we have adopted of late years the same process in cordite believing it to ensure the permanence of the purity of the ingredients and believing that before submitting such cordite we had driven off in the drying process the last trace of even this minute quantity (317).

The spectroscope had just been developed and was derived directly from Isaac Newton's discovery in 1672 that white light is made up of all the primary colours. The instrument, a simple looking arrangement of glass prisms in a tube like a toy telescope, shows that each element has brightly coloured lines at certain intervals. Mercury, in even the most minute quantities, is particularly susceptible to detection under the spectroscope. This was just too bad for Kynoch (364).

Thirty years later an unidentifiable individual then working at Witton gave an account of seeing as a junior employee at the Royal Laboratory, Woolwich, how the test was carried out:

A cab came to the main door of the laboratory and out came a very correctly dressed old gentleman, and an assistant carrying a wooden box. The gentleman in question was Professor Sir William Crookes, and he had brought with him his spectroscope, in the use of which he was of course pre-eminent and this when set up, and the specimens examined led to a quite dramatic scene when the presence of mercury was definitely established (298).

Dramatic indeed. The play was to run four years, culminating in a West End showing at the Royal Courts of Justice and a grand finale at the Palace of Westminster. The use of mercury was not merely unauthorised, it was quite emphatically prohibited in all stages of manufacture of each ingredient and every type of explosive. The main reason for this was that the presence of mercury in even the smallest proportions - and very fine quantities would be quoted throughout the case - had the effect of masking the heat test which was applied as a matter of routine of all explosives. This had been developed by Sir Frederick Abel as part of his work on guncotton, originally to determine whether the cotton had been washed completely free of acid and whether any unstable material had decomposed in the product. The test was for purity rather than effectiveness (350).

The correspondence between the company and the War Office continued. Kynoch claimed in May 1907 that the use of mercury improved the products and was driven off in the drying process and that by "the application of a piece of silver foil any mercury which is present would be held by the silver and the heat test obtained without in any way being influenced by the mercury". The dispute dragged on and on until an action, indeed a double act lasting three days was heard in the King's Bench Division of the High Court, London in November 1908. Kynoch sued the King, Edward VII was on the throne at the time, who responded with a counterclaim. The Crown was represented by Sir Alfred Cripps, then a Conservative MP and later a Labour Lord. By agreement the two suits were heard together. Kynoch claimed the sum of £4,000 as payment due under the contract while the Crown wanted £5,000 from the company. All the facts, suppositions, statements and spectroscopic evidence were worked over again. The judgement found in favour of the Crown and awarded costs against Kynoch.

The company went to the Court of Appeal which rejected the case in March 1909. The show moved from the Strand to Westminster. On 25 February 1911 the Law Lords held for the Crown with all costs against Kynoch (317).

The directors noted that after all the expenses had been met, "about £200 would remain in the Company's favour". There is no indication as to how this was so. The damages had been £5,000 and the expenses must have been as much again.

During this long running saga there was a sideshow. This arose from Chamberlain's annual address to the shareholders in 1909 in which he fulminated about the heat test, the Inspectors and Captain MB Lloyd, hinting rather strongly that the Captain had shown favouritism towards Curtis's & Harvey while he was an Inspector. In 1908 he resigned to become a director of Curtis's & Harvey, which company used mercury. The government continued to approve and use their cordite while rejecting that made by Kynoch. Lloyd and his company issued writs against Chamberlain. The case was heard over three days at the King's Bench, in June 1910. Curtis's & Harvey, represented by Sir Edward Carson, admitted using mercury. Chamberlain, in his defence, as usual a colourfully choleric performance, denied publication and claimed privilege and fair comment. The Court found that while he had privilege he had overstepped the mark and awarded damages of £200 to Lloyd and £100 to Curtis's & Harvey.

Two weeks later the shareholders at the annual meeting heard that "the directors accept the verdict and being satisfied that it was in the best interests of the company that the public should be made acquainted with a side of the case which it had not been possible to put before them in any other way recommend that the Chairman be relieved of all pecuniary responsibility".

The dispute with the Home Office was settled at an early stage. Herbert Gladstone announced the details to the House of Commons on 27 June 1907. Kynoch had been convicted in the Essex Petty Sessions of using mercury. They lost an appeal to the Quarter Sessions and were about to appeal to the High Court. They agreed to withdraw this and the Home Office undertook not to prosecute in connection with a disputed quantity of explosives in the Kynochtown magazines which the Inspectors had impounded and which would be disposed of by a joint committee of the Home and War Offices.

While this related only to the Kynochtown factory, John J Mooney of the Irish Party tabled a motion for the reduction of the Home Secretary's salary, a common parliamentary device at the time, which he withdrew on learning that the matter did not affect Arklow. Gladstone said that the Inspectors never showed any partiality and were always willing to advise Messrs Kynoch and other manufacturers on developing legitimate business. He had been twenty-seven years in the House and his views on Ireland were well known. His first legislative child twenty-five years before had been the Arklow Harbour Act which had provided a grant and a further large sum on loan. He hoped his friends opposite would realise that his connection with Arklow was not wholly a bad one.

Chamberlain did not rely on his direct dealings with the Home and War Offices. On 10 April 1907, immediately after the War Office had first rejected batches of cordite for containing mercury he wrote to John E Redmond, member for Waterford and leader of the Irish Parliamentary Party since the ending of the Parnell split seven years earlier. They had apparently discussed the matter already:

> *I now enclose Memo disproving the assertions that you*
> *told me the Inspectors had made to Mr Gladstone. Of course*

you must be prepared, if there is one of them in the room, for further false statements, but you will be quite safe in disbelieving them. In any event I think my Board and I have now done enough to show you-

FIRST that we have established a right to have this case tried by arbitration under Section 56. Only an arbitrator accustomed to sift evidence and not liable to be affected by the fact that one of the parties to the dispute is a Government Department is capable of doing justice between these Inspectors and us;

SECONDLY that I have shown you that if the prosecution, as we consider it, is not stopped my Board must close the Arklow factory.

The memo appears to have been drawn up as a draft barrister's brief for an action, Chamberlain's favourite activity and quoted extracts from sections 56, 73 and 74 of the Explosives Act which authorised the Inspectors to enter factories, take samples and prosecute manufacturers for malpractice and negligence. The courts could impose fines and matters in dispute could be referred to an agreed arbitrator.

Chamberlain went on to claim that the company's products were better and purer than any others. The Inspectors were very hostile towards Arklow and were constantly seeking informers to give evidence against the management. One former English army officer whom they had employed and dismissed had come back stating that he had been approached by the Inspectors. He had evidence in his private papers which he offered to the company. The company "declined even to consider such a monstrous and improper suggestion". Another former employee, a chemist, told the company that he had refused an invitation from the Inspectors to give information.

In 1902, before there was any question of mercury, the Inspectors had impounded materials worth £2,500 in the Arklow magazines. The local magistrates had "refused to lend themselves to the attempt". Also in 1902 Captain Lloyd had attempted to prevent the manufacture of Arkite, "as this was an explosive which gave a great deal of employment in Arklow we protested strongly, as a result he withdrew, stating that his *error* was due to a slip in the records of his chemical adviser". Finally, they "refused to sanction the manufacture of another explosive at Arklow though permitting it at Kynochtown".

The Inspectors had powers which they could "keep in abeyance when they are friendly to a factory and use them tyrannically when they are unfriendly". Chamberlain wanted an Irish officer appointed an Inspector for Arklow. Many Irishmen were quite as well qualified. The company exported more than half of Arklow's output to South Africa, competing with two local factories and various German firms; more than a quarter to Australia and South America and the balance to Britain. "We are being pressed to move our factory to South Africa and we should be welcomed there and assisted in every way". In the ten years ending in 1905 no lives had been lost in Arklow while there had been thirty-one in other factories and six in the government factories. Four to five hundred were employed in Arklow. "We have reluctantly come to the conclusion that in justice to our general business we must give into *force majeure* and close the Irish factory and carry on our enterprise elsewhere. Of ourselves we have no redress, we must have the help of our Irish friends". Redmond did visit the factory at least once, whether at this time or later is not clear (322-4).

Possibly Redmond made representations privately to the various ministers. He did not table a question in the House. On 3 June 1907 he did ask a supplementary to a question by the member for Stowmarket, Suffolk where the New Explosives Company had a factory, who asked the Home Secretary whether his attention had been drawn to a statement by the Chairman of Kynoch Limited accusing himself of "straining the law and being unjust and hostile". The Secretary's attention had been drawn. He denied. The matter was *sub judice.*

Redmond asked the Secretary whether it was known to the Inspectors that other manufacturers were using mercury and that explosives were being imported from South Africa and Germany and "in these circumstances why is one manufacturer being singled out for this treatment?". Gladstone denied that one manufacturer was being singled out, "I am not aware of any explosive being manufactured with this ingredient where we are not taking steps to deal with it." When Redmond pressed further the Secretary scuttled for safety by saying the case was before the courts. John J Mooney and Willie Redmond, John's brother, asked other supplementary questions which the Secretary sidestepped skilfully.

Chamberlain therefore got no satisfaction from John Redmond and the Irish Parliamentary Party at Westminister and invoked the assistance of Arthur Griffith who in 1905 had founded Sinn Féin, *(Ourselves Alone),* which was to sweep the Irish Parliamentary Party from the stage of history at the 1918 general election.

At this time Sinn Fein had scarcely been heard of. It was conservative in outlook on social issues to the extent that social matters were considered at all then and was in favour of a dual monarchy of Ireland and Britain on the existing model of Austria-Hungary and was far removed from the post 1916 party let alone the two factions claiming the title in the 1970's.

Griffith was for most of his life a journalist editing and publishing, largely on his own, various political periodicals and pamphlets. He wrote a special signed front page article in *Nationality*, 31 July 1915, the weekly paper he was running at the time (342).

MUNITIONS
BRITISH GOVERNMENT AND IRISH TRADE

Some of the orators and journalists who support the English Government in Ireland have discovered a grievance against that institution and, greatly daring, grumbled. The grievance is that firms in Ireland are not getting orders for munitions. The English Government, however, is going to look into the matter, and so all is well, and those who believe that the Government has ceased to swindle Ireland can again occupy their minds with remembering Belgium, if they do not read further.

In July 1907, the Managing Director of Kynoch's wrote to me stating that the Chairman of that Company had read something of what I had written on Irish affairs, particularly on industrial conditions in Ireland, and that he was anxious to discuss the matter of industrial development in Ireland. I met Mr Arthur Chamberlain, Chairman of Kynoch's, and Mr Cocking, the Manager, by arrangement at the Shelbourne Hotel in Dublin. We had three interviews, at each of which I was accompanied by a friend of mine, a Dublin man of business. It was obvious on the second interview that Mr Chamberlain's real object was to protect Kynoch's from loss over its Arklow factory. Eventually this was effected. The substance of Mr Chamberlain's statements will be of interest just now to those who believe in leopards changing their spots and other phenomena.

Mr Chamberlain opened by saying that he had read a speech of mine, issued as a pamphlet, on the Sinn Fein policy, with the industrial portion of which he was in complete accord. As Chairman of Kynoch's, he had caused that firm to have something that might be called a private Industrial Survey of

Ireland made. The result was to satisfy him as a business man that Ireland was one of the richest in the material of great industries, that her people had a great natural aptitude for commerce and manufacture, and that nothing but ignorance, lack of capital or repressive government stood in the way of making her a great industrial and commercial state. All this was trite but it was interesting to listen to it recited from the lips of the head of England's greatest industrial concern.

Mr Chamberlain went on to describe the coming of Kynoch's to Ireland, and the birth of which it was to be the germ. Kynoch's satisfied by their investigators and chemists of the teeming natural resources had planned a scheme of industrial development through subsidiary Irish companies. The South-East of Ireland, which Kynoch's had discovered to be a richer pottery district than the famous pottery country of England, was to be worked by an Irish company financed in the beginning by Kynoch, the matchless iron of Leitrim was again to be wrought by Irish hands, and so forth. A pleasant scheme, after describing which Mr Chamberlain requested my opinion. My opinion was that to be wholly beneficial to Ireland, the scheme should be worked altogether on Irish capital; that I realised it was impossible in the present circumstances of Ireland to induce Irish capitalists to venture on any large scheme of national industrial development; that therefore a scheme by which Kynoch's would initially supply the capital and organise the development through Irish companies would be acceptable under some restrictions; but I asked Mr Chamberlain, whether he, as a great English industrialist really believed that the English Government would encourage Kynoch's, or any other firm or syndicate which it could bring pressure upon, to develop Ireland's industrial arm.

Mr Chamberlain replied that he did not. That it was a definite part of English policy to prevent any serious industrial or commercial development in Ireland. That he himself was convinced that the policy was wrong, but that it was equally held and practiced by Tories and Liberals, and it would be practiced until Ireland had a form of Home Rule under which she controlled her own finances and had power to impose protective tariffs. No other form of Home Rule would be commercially useful to Ireland. Mr Chamberlain was very anxious that I should not believe he held the same views as his brother Joseph. He was and always had been a Liberal and

Home Ruler, and he contributed a large sum annually to the Liberal Party funds.

These facts, as I told him, I already knew. I then inquired, that understanding as he did the secret attitude of English Government towards any scheme to seriously develop Ireland industrially, whether Kynoch's would face the Government opposition and carry out its scheme - or attempt to do so.

To this Mr Chamberlain indirectly replied by detailing the history of the Kynoch branch in Arklow, and the efforts made by the Government of Mr Balfour and the Government of Sir Henry Campbell-Bannerman to force the firm to shut down the branch. Finally, to compel Kynoch's to leave Ireland, Government contracts were removed. Mr Chamberlain described a somewhat lively interview he had recently had with Mr Herbert Gladstone, now Lord Gladstone, in which that minister told him definitely that if the Arklow factory were continued, the Government would see that as little Government work as possible would be given to Kynoch's. On the other hand, the Government offered no objection to Kynoch's establishing themselves in "any part of the Empire except Ireland", and the fullest support was offered to the Kynoch branch in South Africa.

I inquired why Mr Chamberlain came to the Sinn Feiners instead of to the Parliamentary Party, who were the allies and supposed to be the masters of the English Liberal Government. Mr Chamberlain replied that he had gone to the Parliamentary Party.

That the leaders knew all that was taking place, but that they would do nothing except privately appeal to the Government. Mr Redmond, Mr Chamberlain said, was an amiable man, but he was putty in the hands of English ministers.

A further interview developed Mr Chamberlain's plan for the co-operation of Sinn Fein. I inquired from him whether in return he would guarantee that Kynoch's would proceed with their original plan for industrial development in Ireland. Whether, for instance, they would supply the means for initiating the great pottery industry of the South-East.

Mr Chamberlain hesitated, but he finally replied he could not give a guarantee. The Government could hit Kynoch's in so many ways elsewhere that they could not as business men risk going on with the scheme. If there was Home Rule in the country Kynoch's might risk it. I remarked that no measure of Home Rule which permitted Ireland to protect its industries would be passed by either Liberals or Tories. Mr Chamberlain assented, but added that the Irish had political strength although they did not know how to use it to coerce ministries. However, the co-operation of Sinn Fein was not to be considered unless Kynoch's were prepared to go on with the original scheme, and thus this aspect of the matter ended. To save the factory at Arklow, however, - the closing of which would have meant the ruin of the town - we put Mr Chamberlain in touch with certain Irish business men, who afterwards attended a small meeting in the Shelbourne Hotel, as a result of which an arrangement was made which enabled the factory to be carried on without exposing Kynoch's to further boycotting by the English Government. I trust the gentlemen who know that "this is Ireland's war", and who demand a share in the making of munitions, will be comforted.

Arthur Griffith was writing in the context of the First World War and the demands being made by numerous interests for the government to place orders for shells and other military supplies in Ireland (Chapter Four).

There is no further evidence as to what arrangements Griffith made and there is no indication on the Kynoch side that Chamberlain ever called in Sinn Fein. In September 1907 the Kynoch directors discussed setting up two new companies, one in Ireland and the other in South Africa. The following February they noted that the new company, Irish Manufacturers Limited, had "taken over the cordite factory at Arklow". It is not clear if the Chemical Works had also been transferred. The board also decided not to set up a separate company in South Africa. In July 1909 the Witton directors allotted £53,000 for a new guncotton plant at Arklow, "to comply with requirements of the Admiralty so that Irish Manufacturers might secure their orders".

Although Arklow was in theory under a separate company, in practice Witton still held control and changes in personnel continued in the usual way between the various factories. In October 1908 the managers at Arklow were promised bonuses if the factory made a profit of £14,000 in the current year. Unfortunately there is no record of whether or not this was achieved as there are no separate figures for Arklow until 1913.

The arrangement with the Admiralty did not last any length of time. The new company was soon put into liquidation without sufficient funds to meet all liabilities. In August 1909 the Witton directors were asked by the board of Irish Manufacturers to contribute to the company's losses. They refused. In January 1910 the Witton directors voted "a gratuity of £500 to Mr Walsh, director of the defunct company, Irish Manufacturers, in consideration of losses he has sustained, Company apparently under no liability to him". The liquidation of the company was completed in April 1911 (675).

At the end of the day, after all the cases, claims, counterclaims, writs, libels, slanders, alleged and actual and the manoeuvre about the supposedly separate company, Kynoch found themselves restored to the official list of contractors approved for the supply of cordite for the public service. This made no difference. They got no further orders until the First World War.

ARKLOW, CLOAKROOM CHECK, BRASS HEXAGON
SOURCE 328

AMALGAMATION, ANNIHILATION

In 1894 when negotiations were underway between Kynoch and Nobel's for the supply of cordite pulp, Thomas Johnston, general manager at Ardeer, was anxious to obtain this business while Edward Kraftmeier of Chilworth was in favour of buying off Chamberlain from going into the high explosive trade even if necessary to the extent of the full value of the original contract. Chamberlain for his part made it perfectly plain that he was prepared to go into any and all markets which offered prospects of high profits.

Kynoch was an independent company manufacturing ammunition, guns, accessories, fog signals and a range of metal items which they were constantly expanding. Nobel's were the British branch of the Anglo-German Nobel-Dynamite Trust and were bound by various agreements with the German and other Nobel companies and also Kraftmeier's Powder Group. In 1893 Kynoch moved into black powder which was not a threat to Nobel's and the next year into cordite which very definitely was.

Nobel's were determined to meet head on the danger from Witton as they saw it in Ardeer. Johnston, writing to Kraftmeier in May 1897, outlined the situation at length:

Kynochs intend competing very vigorously with us both in blasting explosives and cordite .. in all our home and foreign markets .. we have come to the conclusion that through possessing metal and cartridge works we should be able to strike at them especially in a department in which if they make any money at all it must be there (306).

Nobel's went ahead and bought an existing cartridge works in Birmingham which they set up as a subsidiary, the Birmingham Metal & Munitions Company. This bold advance against Kynoch on Chamberlain's doorstep was not the sole measure which Ardeer took. It was the only one publicly known. Despite the "discordite" case Nobel's were prepared to supply the government who for their part were willing to place orders with Ardeer. The government, as a matter of policy, constantly changed from one company to another giving a firm a large contract this year and none the next while another company got a medium order followed by a large one later and so on (362).

Nobel's got over this difficulty by exploiting loopholes in company law as it stood at the time, to acquire control of three companies in such secrecy that nobody in the government departments concerned knew. The only evidence was in highly secret records in their head office. Under this system the British Explosives Syndicate, Pitsea, Essex; the New Explosives Company, Stowmarket and Pembrey and the Cotton Powder Company, Faversham came under Ardeer auspices before the First World War (302).

Chamberlain's threat to go into foreign markets was no doubt partly bargaining bluff for the purposes of the negotiations in hand. Certainly he always had the possibility of external expansion in mind. In August 1899 the Kynoch directors considered a proposal to set up a factory in Japan with "exclusive rights and privileges". Later in the month they had the mortification of noting that the Japanese government had placed a contract, apparently as a trial, with Nobel's at a higher price than their own tender. In November Kynoch made an attempt to obtain orders in China. Early in 1900 the company secretary visited Japan. In June the directors decided against going ahead with the proposal for a factory in Japan. On the face of it the decision appears to have been taken in the boardroom at Lion Works. It was actually made in Tokyo because in 1905 Nobel's built a works in Japan.

This must have been galling to Chamberlain, who finding himself baulked in one continent, began to look at another. The situation in the southern part of Africa was very promising despite the recent conflict between British and Dutch interests. There was tremendous expansion in the extractive industries, diamond and other mines were being developed and also quarries for construction materials; roads and railways were opening the interior. These and other purposes called for large quantities of explosives.

Nobel's were already in South Africa. In 1895 the Nobel-Dynamite Trust and the Societe Centrale de Dynamite, the Latin Group of Nobel companies based in Paris, jointly set up a factory at Modderfontein near Johannesburg which came more fully under Ardeer control after the Boer War. In 1903 de Beers Consolidated Mines, one of the country's biggest businesses set up the Cape Explosives Works and in July 1906 Chamberlain began negotiations for the purchase of this factory. Within a month he told the board that de Beers had refused to sell. It is doubtful if he tried very hard. It would have been far more his form to set up a new factory.

In April 1908 the directors considered a report from Cocking that Nobel's had approached him with a proposal that both companies should come to a price fixing arrangement for the South African market "or else ...". The directors resolved "to take no notice of Nobel's threats as the company had signed an agreement with the Natal government not to make any such agreements with competing manufacturers". Earlier in the month the directors had approved the agreement which Chamberlain had signed with Natal which would soon be a province in the Union of South Africa.

Kynoch built a factory on a raw jungle site overlooking the Indian Ocean, at Umbogintwini near Durban. Several managers and chemists went from Arklow and over fifty general workers and so names from the Vale of Avoca such as D'arcy, Hughes, Kavanagh, Kelly, Kenny, Lee, O'Connor, O'Neill with many others became common. In time more went to 'Twini as it was known, settled and intermarried (372).

Witton, Worsboro', Arklow, Kynochtown; in the southern sky, 'Twini, the fifth great jewel in the Chamberlain crown glittered. The successful start of operations did not conceal the company's precarious financial state. Full production was reached in the summer of 1909. In September, Chamberlain had to give his personal guarantee for a loan of £100,000 to pay for necessary equipment at 'Twini. Even this was not sufficient and in December an issue of debentures for £250,000 was made.

These desperate measures give some indication of the company's difficulties. A concern in sound condition should be able to finance expansion by issuing ordinary shares which would be expected to give a high annual return in good times, or preferences which would yield a small and guaranteed sum always. Debentures rank ahead of these in a liquidation. A personal guarantee is virtually a disgrace and removes from the individual the protection of limited liability.

Chamberlain told the 1903 annual meeting proudly that the ordinary dividend was ten percent which had been "paid continuously for the previous thirteen or fourteen years". This was going back to his assumption of the chair and was his way of saying that the shareholders owed their good fortune to his wisdom. With equal pride he pointed out that there were no debentures. As usual he complained of large expenditures on the government factories. He must have seen the way the wind was blowing. From 1904 profits fell badly and from 1908 to 1912 no dividend was paid on the ordinary shares. In the following two years small amounts were paid and very large sums during the War. Five percent was paid throughout on the preference shares. During the lean years the management had a practice of telling the workers in each department that that particular part of the business was losing money (299).

With the ordinary shareholders holding their certificates like so many spent cartridges, the directors resorting to the previously despised debentures and the chairman himself exposing his personal assets, arrangements were made to place Arklow at a distance from the enterprise as a whole. A new company, Kynoch-Arklow Limited, was set up on a rather more thought out and substantial scale than the shadow which had been so hastily cobbled together and as swiftly liquidated. The decision was taken in January 1911, four weeks before the House of Lords judgement and ten weeks before the final winding up of Irish Manufacturers.

Chamberlain announced the arrangements at the annual meeting held in July, a month later than usual:

> During nearly the whole of last year the directors have been occupied with important negotiations for the sale of the Arklow factory and business. These negotiations were in progress up to a few days ago and it was the impossibility of concluding them earlier or of referring to them in the annual report until they were concluded, that has delayed for a few weeks the annual general meeting.

> The reasons inducing the directors to establish the Arklow high explosives and cordite factory on an independent basis and under a separate board of directors were - firstly, that the concern being the most important industrial enterprise on the long line of coast south of Dublin, and the prosperity of the neighbourhood admittedly dependent on its success, the present time was specially opportune for offering to Irishmen an interest in a purely Irish factory and representation on its board. Secondly, looking at the position from the point of view of the Kynoch Company's interests the company still possesses in South Africa another factory which is already the largest single department and is still increasing, and which offers more than sufficient scope for the enterprise and ability of all the company's officers who can be spared from other and equally attractive work.

This was Chamberlain at his vintage, brilliant best, bluffing on a grand scale. It was also virtually his swansong as he had only two further annual meetings at which he said little of importance. The capital of the new company was 100,000 one pound shares all held by the Witton company and an issue of £210,000 in $5^1/2\%$ mortgage debentures of which £165,000 was paid to the Witton company which also guaranteed and underwrote the issue. The value of the lands, 430 acres (176 hectares), and machinery was £159,000; stock in trade £7,000; debts due to the company £21,000 and goodwill £28,000. There were seven subscribers with a nominal share each, Arthur

Chamberlain Junior, Cocking and five Witton office employees.

Negotiations indeed. All this was an internal paper transaction except for a sum of £8,000 in respect of stamp duties and other legal costs. The chairman of the new company was MF Armstrong, a London gentleman. One of the Witton directors with Sir Stanley Harrington and Edmond Clifford Walsh, both described as merchants, were on the board (308-9, 315).

Harrington was a founder member of Harrington Brothers, paint manufacturers in Cork who later amalgamated with Goodlass Wall of Liverpool. He was a long standing director of several companies including the Munster and Leinster Bank which in 1913 opened a branch in Arklow. Walsh was a publican and a member of both Arklow Urban District Council and Wicklow County Council. They were purely ornamental, Harrington was a reasonably prominent businessman with a title to boot and Walsh added a little local veneer (370-1,714).

The solicitors for the company, the trustees of the debentures and their solicitors, the brokers and the auditors, all were London firms. The registered office was in the City. The bank account was in Birmingham where the Witton accounts were kept. The board of directors presumably sat in the registered office. It would have made no difference if they never met as all decisions were made in Witton. While neither of the Chamberlains, nor Cocking was a director at first, in practice they ran Arklow as a department of the business as before. Indeed Cocking, addressing the Kynoch Social Club's annual dinner at Arklow, according to the *Wicklow People*, 18 February 1911, stated that the company changes were for purely legal and management reasons and Witton would always have complete control of the factory.

Under an indenture of January 1912 Witton transferred to the new company all the premises at Arklow, various processes, patents and trade marks registered in Britain, Canada, Australia and New Zealand; various magazines mainly at coalmines and also agencies throughout Britain. Arklow were to have exclusive rights for mining explosives throughout the world except Africa south of the Equator. North of this both companies could compete. Witton agreed to take, for Kynochtown, as much as Arklow could supply of guncotton, nitrocotton and cordite pulp under a contract to be renewed every five years (308).

Chamberlain had no concern for the eastern part of Ireland, nor of Birmingham, Essex, Africa or anywhere else he might have operated and he would have swept aside the whole elaborate and expensive structure at any time it suited his purpose. He had already set up and dissolved Irish Manufacturers and Kynoch Estates, a short-lived property holding and development company. Alternatively, and by far the most probable purpose for which the Arklow company was registered, the factory could have been disposed of, suitably segregated as it was from the business as a whole.

From the time of the negotiations in 1894 relations between Kynoch and Nobel's had been distant and distinctly competitive especially after Ardeer had branched into the Birmingham ammunition industry. Both companies came under some pressure from the House of Commons Select committee on War Office Contracts, more especially Kynoch. Nobel's were the stronger. Besides having the advantage of their secret subsidiaries, they appear to have had the edge in management skills.

In June 1906 Coleman du Pont, Lammot's nephew, then grand sachem of the Delaware based explosives company called to the Nobel-Dynamite Trust office in London, very much the multi-millionaire monopoly manufacturer from the good ol' US of A. He came to renew the agreement between the two firms, telling Henry de Mosenthal, the Trust's technical secretary, that there had been 130 explosives companies in his country which he had reduced to ten and if he had his way there would be only one. He was, of course, hindered by the Sherman Act, the main legislation against trusts or monopolies. He wanted to know why prices were so low in Britain. De Mosenthal said it was because of Arthur Chamberlain who refused to join any convention. "He asked where the man lived, when a man talked like that he wanted to be bought up, he was decidedly breezy and it looks as if he came with the idea of buying up the Trust, the Societe Centrale, the Powder Group and in addition any and all small fry, he absolutely staggered me" de Mosenthal wrote to Johnston (307).

The agreement was renewed without du Pont getting even breezier and buying up everyone. Certainly he did not purchase Kynoch. It is not clear if he met Chamberlain. Coleman's tinder on Arthur's flint would surely have been highly explosive. Nobel's and Kynoch must have felt themselves under strain from du Pont and Kynoch had serious financial difficulties. Both seem to have come to the same conclusion at the same time. Strength lay, if not in unity, then at least in some form of accommodation. Accordingly in 1907 Trade Associations were formed for High Explosives and Safety Explosives. Both companies were founder members and Kynoch-Arklow also affiliated (311-12).

By this time therefore Kynoch and Nobel's were able to sit around a table in London and come to arrangements about contracts and markets. Despite Ardeer's threats in 1908, relations, while not friendly, were not as belligerent as before. The iceberg was melting ever so slowly. By the autumn of 1912 it had melted to the point where Arthur Chamberlain Junior, who had become deputy chairman in the previous April, made an approach to Nobel's with a view to a very major change in the ownership of Arklow. He discussed this with FJ Shand, General Manager at Ardeer and Harry McGowan his assistant who was also Chairman of the High Explosives Trade Association (310).

Shand reported to Sir Ralph Anstruther, Chairman of both Nobel's and the Trust, "yesterday Mr McGowan and I had a long interview when Mr Chamberlain put before us an offer of a much more reasonable character than any hitherto submitted". Shand had made a careful review of relations, going back to the draft agreement of 1894 and an analysis of the financial positions of both Kynoch companies. He had a copy of the indenture transferring Arklow, which was filed in the Companies Office and was therefore a public document available to anyone who wanted to copy it. He had also obtained, by some slightly irregular means, a set of figures for Arklow's output which turned out to correspond to those supplied by Chamberlain Junior.

Shand had a copy of the Arklow company's prospectus which stated profits in respect of the factory of £20,000 for 1908, £17,500 for 1909 and £13,000 for 1910 and also that cordite had not been made for several years. Currently the factory was making annually 1,800 tons of blasting explosives, 120 tons of guncotton and smaller quantities of other products with a net profit of £12,625. Chamberlain's proposal was that Nobel's should acquire fifty-one percent of the ordinary share capital. On this division of the profits Shand found that they would get a dividend of £6,439 representing a return of 12.625% which was clearly satisfactory.

This left the question of the debentures which was rather difficult. The position was that the public had taken up only a small amount leaving the Witton company, as underwriters, with the bulk of the issue which they were selling off in small lots through their brokers at ninety percent of face value. Chamberlain proposed that Nobel's should take up half the issue at ninety which Shand calculated would give a yield of $6^{1}/2\%$. He did not see the necessity for purchasing any of the debentures for the time being though it would give them a stronger say in running Arklow. Chamberlain did not press the point.

Shand thought that considerable extra profits could be made by ceasing collodion cotton and guncotton at Arklow in favour of Ardeer. Chamberlain was very anxious to come to an arrangement with Nobel's "though he would not admit that in selling us an interest in the Arklow business they were parting with what might be regarded as a poor asset. Indeed he claimed that this is the best year the Arklow company has ever had". They were short of cash and needed £20,000 for machinery to bring Arklow up to date and had come to an arrangement with the War Office and Admiralty for a contract at six pence ($2^1/2$p) per pound over the going rate. The Treasury had not approved these terms.

Shand thought that Arklow would eventually get the money elsewhere and also cordite contracts, "political considerations are likely to dictate that a cordite factory in Ireland will be supported by the War Office and Admiralty". Seeing many advantages, Shand offered to lend the money for the machinery. Chamberlain wanted to loan a proportion of the money from Witton in order to preserve their minority interest. They agreed that the Arklow company would not pay a dividend until after full depreciation, at Ardeer's discretion and also full payment of the debentures and all general and administrative charges. Shand "gathered that Mr Chamberlain Junior's views on depreciation practice are decidedly different from those of his father"(310).

It is very obvious that, if the arrangement went through and Nobel's obtained a majority interest in Arklow, they would have kept the acquisition a secret. Chamberlain wanted a private letter in which Nobel's undertook to run the company fairly on behalf of the shareholders. Obviously this was an insurance policy against any subsequent revelations. Shand agreed to give this letter. The transaction did not come to pass. It is not clear why. Most probably Chamberlain Senior did not approve. His character would have been to close down rather than become associated with any competitors especially the arch enemy in Ardeer.

By this time Arthur Junior was rising rapidly in the company. He had commenced as a very juvenile employee at Witton in 1899, becoming a director in 1905. From 1906 he had special responsibility for the paper mills in Dublin and became Chairman in October 1913 when the old dictator died aged 71. The new mandarin's first action, actually implemented before he took the chair, was to sell the paper mills, "thus putting an end to a constant if inconsiderable drain on profits, the company retains an important interest in the business which in the hands of experts in the paper business is expected to pay regular and satisfactory dividends", he told the shareholders.

Chamberlain, presumably from his experience, recognised that Kynoch did not have the necessary management expertise and sold the mills to a new company for £5,000 cash and one third of their shares which were held by Witton, not Arklow.

So, under the new chairman, Kynoch disposed of their only diversification in Ireland. They did make one minor investment. The *News-Letter*, 13 November 1915, reported that Kynoch, it is not clear which company, had bought an unspecified interest in the Whiterock Flint Quarry at Tinahely, a district west of Arklow. The quarry worked a vein of very pure quartz silica, not really flint in the strict geological sense. Silica is the main constituent in kieselguhr, the diatomaceous earth used in dynamite. The only major source of kieselguhr being exploited while Kynoch were operating in Ireland was at Toom Bridge in the Bann Valley, County Antrim. A report on this in 1899 noted that it was unsuitable for explosives. During the First World War the Dublin, Wicklow and Wexford Railway's Shillelagh branch drew considerable quantities of this material to Arklow (341, 369).

The War brought boom to Arklow on a scale never before seen or imagined, if on a small scale for the first year or so from the declarations of hostilities in August 1914. In November Chamberlain offered to supply 27 tons of cordite per week and in March 1915 the Witton directors noted with some surprise an order for 38 tons from the Admiralty, "the first for some time", even more surprisingly "without a rejection". In January 1916 the directors "resolved that the necessary advances be made to Kynoch-Arklow to keep them going". The amount involved was not stated.

The first balance sheet of Kynoch-Arklow, for the year from January 1912 to March 1913 showed a profit of £9,000; 1914 a loss of £7,000 which was set against the previous profit. The balance of £2,000 was carried forward and added to the profits of £10,000 in 1915; £40,000 in 1916; £36,000 in 1917; £30,000 in 1918 and a mere £750 in 1919 giving a total of £113,000 after payment of all expenses which came to £22,500 for the London office; £22,500 for directors' fees and commissions on profits; income tax £48,000; £86,000 was paid in debenture interest while just over half the issue was redeemed; depreciation was £37,000. The expenditures on wages and extensions to the factory were not given (315).

Many new process buildings were erected. There was not sufficient quay space on the factory side of the harbour for the huge cargoes being handled and an aerial ropeway, an electrically operated device for ferrying loads across from the other side, was installed. The number of employees increased from about four hundred to a figure close to five thousand at peak. Before long all available workers in and around Arklow had been recruited and arrangements were made with the Dublin, Wicklow and Wexford Railway for special trains to bring workers from as far north as Wicklow town, south from Enniscorthy and the inland line serving the districts of Carnew, Tinahely and Shillelagh. Workers living too remote from the railway stations were brought in charabancs, a five guinea name for a bus which was really a lorry with rough seating. Those who lived too far away for daily travel were accommodated in dormitories specially erected. A hospital was also built.

There was unparalleled prosperity in the town with more wage packets than ever before, indeed early in the War the practice of paying wages in packets rather than from the traditional tin cups was introduced. The total payroll at the height of the war was about £10,000 which accords with an average of £2.00 per week (373-8). Until the war the wages had not increased at all from 1895. The *Wicklow People,* 3 February 1912, noted that the average was fourteen shillings (70p) per week. On 25 January 1913, the paper, reporting a court case arising from an accident, recorded that the average including overtime was 14/6 (72^{1}/2p).

The vintners flourished more than anyone else. Excessive drinking was a serious problem during the War. In the most extreme case the government actually bought up the brewery and chain of public houses in Carlisle and operated the business for many years. As early as 28 November 1914, Major General LB Friend, Commanding the Forces in Ireland, issued a proclamation, which was published in the papers, under the Defence of the Realm Act. This law, commonly known as DORA, enabled the government to do practically anything and prevented the public from doing virtually everything.

The publicans were warned that "indiscriminate issuing of drink" to the factory workers, "thereby impairing the capacity of the company to fulfil important government contracts", would result in the closure of all the public houses in the town. This did not happen. No doubt EC Walsh was able to smooth over any difficulties between his fellow drinksellers and the local military establishment which was augmented considerably for the duration. Every time the shift changed a solid mass of humanity surged across Arklow Bridge to the bars. The owners and their staffs had to spend several hours drawing pints from the barrels which were not then equipped with dispensers.

During the War several workers were fined in the local court for not surrendering their matches and cigarettes at the entrance in exchange for cloakroom checks which were brass hexagons *(ILLUSTRATION 8)*. A number of strikes took place. The management tended to dismiss and replace general workers and negotiate with those who had essential skills. In July 1915 several hundred workers from the Wexford area went out and were discharged. In July 1916 a strike threatened by bricklayers engaged on building extensions was averted by an arbitrator from the Ministry of Munitions before it was due to commence. The artisans secured satisfactory increases and also bonuses. On 7 October 1917 at a meeting attended by several hundred, a branch of the Irish Transport and General Workers Union was formed. The Union was expanding rapidly at the time. A return of membership in January 1918 claimed 1,200. A more detailed census the following June showed 100 chemical workers; 100 in munitions, presumably explosives; sixty dockers, thirty rope runners all of whom presumably were working on Kynoch cargoes; six railway platelayers and thirty general labourers who were probably in the factory and a solitary grocery worker who no doubt was in the company's shop. The figures for chemicals and munitions members are remarkably round, indeed suspiciously so. In the 1970s none of the former employees had any recollections of the Union. Even by this time unions were not fully recognised in Witton. The one day general strike against conscription called by the Irish Trades Union Congress and Labour Party for 23 April 1918 was observed with band parades in the town according to the *News-Letter* (674).

Early in the morning of 21 September 1917 an explosion took place which killed 27 workers and injured six seriously and seven slightly. The official report was not published in the normal way. A typed copy was retained by the Inspectors and presumably copies were sent to the Home Secretary and the company. The investigation was carried out by Major A Cooper-Key, Chief Inspector. After exhaustively examining the factory and routine work practices he could find no reason even remotely likely to have caused the explosion which originated in one of the buildings 152,183 or 184. The force was carried by three trucks full of pulp which were standing on the tramline. Many more buildings were destroyed or damaged to varying degrees.

Cooper-Key rejected the theory that a German submarine had shelled the factory. Some time earlier a U-boat had sunk the Arklow lightship. The management told him of "several disquieting occurrences savouring of the Sinn Fein movement". Matches had been found in a bag of nitrocotton and flints in several boxes of pulp sent to Kynochtown. There were no flints on the roads in the factory nor in the district. Also there had been defiant notices on walls and anonymous threatening letters.

The Chief Inspector came to the conclusion that the explosion:

was due either to the careless act of a workman or to the wilful act of some person or persons unknown, and the evidence would seem to point to the second alternative as the more probable.

There is undoubtedly a distinct feeling of hostility on the part of the employees although I was assured that this applies more to the hands in the chemical works than those in the explosives area who are specially selected men. Grievances without tangible foundation are continually being aired and the officials state that in spite of every effort they cannot get in sympathy with the men. This is the more remarkable in as much as the town of Arklow owes its prosperity entirely to the company. Prior to the establishment of the works a decadent fishing industry was the sole support of the town whereas with thousands of pounds distributed every week in wages alone it is now one of the most prosperous spots in Ireland (319).

Cooper-Key had not an atom of evidence that the explosion was caused maliciously by Sinn Fein or anyone else and because of the wartime pressure for production he was "most reluctant to attach any blame to the management". He attended the inquest, held in the Social Hall the day after the explosion. The jury returned a verdict of accidental death stating that the accident would always remain "an unexplained and inexplicable mystery", adding a rider that the state should assist in making provision for the dependents of the deceased. Presumably this meant money in addition to payments under the Workmen's Compensation Act.   It does not appear that any such *ex gratia* sums were paid. Eight of the victims were interred in their respective home cemeteries and the remainder in a single mass grave in Arklow in a funeral attended by thousands. The *News-Letter*, 26 January 1918, reported the proceedings of the Quarter Sessions which under the Compensation Act made awards to the dependents, £80 was paid in one case; four got £100; eight from £225 to £300; the remainder were between £120 and £150.

The explosion was by far the worst in the entire history of war production in Ireland and held the record in industry as a whole until fifty died when the tanker *Betelguese* exploded at the Gulf Oil Terminal in Bantry Bay in January 1979. It was not, in the context of the First War, of even the least consequence when many thousands might be killed in a single day on the Western Front.

On 4 February 1918 the Witton directors considered a report, "a reduction of fifty percent to be made in the country's production of cordite" and two weeks later "the merger to date officially from 31 December 1916". These two separate developments were to come together and result in the complete close down of Arklow. The merger negotiations had been underway from around the end of 1915. In September of that year the Nobel-Dynamite Trust had been dissolved leaving Ardeer to pursue their expansion schemes without obstruction. The guiding genius was Harry McGowan, by then a director of Nobel's, who as Sir Harry became chairman and managing director on completion of the merger at the end of November 1918. Later as Lord McGowan he was at the helm of ICI for many years.

The new company formed for the merger was Explosives Trades Limited. In 1920 the name was changed to Nobel Industries and the head office transferred from Glasgow to London. The amalgamation was on a grand scale involving forty companies. Capitalised at eighteen million the old Nobel's had over half, Kynoch came a poor second at £1,600,000, Curtis's & Harvey ranked third at £900,000 while Kynoch-Arklow also ran at £212,000. A local board was set up to run Kynoch, Birmingham Metal & Munitions and various other interests. Chamberlain and Cocking were members of this and also of the Nobel main board. Neither could have been expected to get along very well with McGowan.

Before the new company the Merger Committee functioned for several months. The Witton minutes carried no formal resolution to set up Arklow, neither did the Committee, for the closedown. The decision was taken either on the first or eighth of February and became known in Arklow, through the papers, on Friday the fifteenth. A deputation comprised of the local clergy, James Dunphy had died in 1914, and a JP or two went to London immediately. A meeting was held at the Ministry of Munitions the next Monday, the deputation being introduced to the Minister, Sir Laming Worthington-Evans MP, by John E Redmond MP. Several other Irish Members were present and all the directors of Kynoch-Arklow, Armstrong, Chamberlain, Cocking, Harrington and Walsh.

The deputation expressed alarm at the threatened closure. The fishing industry had almost ceased to exist and the district had come to depend entirely on the factory. It was understood that a large reduction had to be made. The people of Arklow were content to take their fair share of the reduction. If such a calamity as the suppression of the industry was brought about it would be as discreditable to those responsible as it would be disastrous to Arklow.

The Minister was sympathetic. Ministers usually are.

He was aware of the serious results on the town. The Ministry had not singled out Arklow, similar factories were being closed in England, he gave an assurance that the factory would not be closed. The proportion of reduction would not be greater in Arklow than elsewhere.

The *News-Letter*, 23 February, reported this and numerous protests by public and voluntary bodies against the shut-down. In *Nationality* of the same date, Arthur Griffith reprinted his 1915 article supplemented with a stinging personal attack on Redmond. The main reason the government were reducing orders to the trade factories was that they had just brought into full production a huge cordite works in Gretna, Scotland.

William Field told the House of Commons, 28 February:

> *I am particularly interested. In conjunction with the late Austen Chamberlain [presumably he meant Arthur, Austen was still in the House] I had something to do with founding that factory. Sir Henry Campbell-Bannerman was the man who really established the cordite factory in Ireland. I trust the Ministry will only make a reduction to the smallest degree necessary in Arklow, because that factory has done better work than any other cordite factory in the United Kingdom.*

In April, Captain AJC Donelan, returned for East Wicklow in an uncontested 1911 by-election, who sat as a *Protestant Home Ruler* proposed that a shipyard should be opened for vessels of up to one thousand tons such as minesweepers and other Admiralty smallcraft. Probably he was prompted by the existence of John Tyrrell and Sons' boatyard. The suggestion was examined by Lord Pirrie, chairman of Harland and Wolff, who was Comptroller General of Merchant Shipping at the time, and the Commissioners of Public Works. The harbour as it stood was unsuitable because of the serious silting problem and also the walls needed strengthening. The cost would be at least £12,000 and the Commissioners doubted whether the Kynoch workforce of former agricultural workers would "readily adapt itself to shipbuilding". No more came of this (320).

In July the Witton directors noted still further reductions. The Ministry wanted Arklow to make 95 tons of cordite per week which indicates that the peak production must have been well over 100 tons as against the 200 tons per year when the factory began. The Arklow Harbour figures, which are incomplete, give for the years 1914-16 total exports of 158 tons of guncotton, 190 tons of cordite and 1,542 tons of unspecified explosives together with 2,464 tons of nitrate cake, 2,022 tons of nitrate soda and 1,296 tons of burnt ore (368).

Only about twelve hundred workers remained in the factory by Armistice Day, 11 November 1918, which was celebrated with a holiday and general jollification according to the *News-Letter* which over the next three years chronicled the long drawn out death pangs of the doomed industry and the various proposals for alternative employment.

A week after the end of the War five hundred workers were dismissed and a week later six hundred walked out the gate for the last time. Each was given an employer's reference of the usual type. In February 1919 the Kynoch Social Club held their last annual dinner in the Hall which was decorated with a large banner proclaiming "Eat, Drink and be Merry". At the same time it was reported that Cocking had visited the factory in connection with a replacement industry, a remote probability indeed (326).

On 7 July the Witton directors noted that "manufacture of cordite had ceased". This was just twenty-four years after the commencement. A month later they cancelled the mortgage debenture on the Arklow property to clear the title for sale. On 22 November the last, the very last, workers were dismissed along with the office clerks. A week later it was reported that the property had been sold to David Frame, principal of the Hammond Lane Metal Company who told the papers that he had extensive plans for the factory. He was almost as big a bluffer as old Chamberlain (313).

Over the following two years Frame systematically demolished the entire works. The machinery was scrapped including several electricity generators which had never been used. All boilers, vats, pipelines and other fittings were smashed into small fragments with two-handled hammers wielded by pairs of men, one of whom had to be left-handed. The timber was sold and shiploads of bricks sent away (374).

In June 1919 there was a rumour about a possible fertiliser factory and in February 1920 it was reported that a similar scheme was under consideration by the Irish Farmers' Union. This was founded in 1917, mainly to resist demands for improved wages and conditions by agricultural workers who were being widely organised by the Irish Transport and General Workers' Union at the time (344, 674).

The Farmers' Union held a conference at Galway in May and decided against the proposal, principally on grounds of cost. The sum mentioned was £250,000. The idea was obvious enough as the Chemical Works was fully equipped for sulphuric and nitric acids, both essential for this purpose. Other types of plant would have been required and even if the explosives buildings were not suitable these could easily have been removed. This happened at 'Twini which McGowan closed in favour of the Nobel factory at Modderfontein. On the proposal of the manager, WV Blewett, who had been at Arklow, the works was turned over to fertilisers, sprays and other products for agriculture. A joint company, African Explosives and Chemical Industries was formed with de Beers and the industry continues, staffed by the descendants of the original Arklow emigrants (372).

In Ireland the project was too far ahead for its time which is seen when the case of the purchase of International Meat Packers by Cork Co-Operative Marts in 1968 is considered. The society, when offered the opportunity of acquiring the two modern meat plants operated by the Company, raised three million in ten weeks, far and away the largest and fastest fundraising venture in the entire history of the Irish co-operative movement. Despite mounting an intensive modern advertising campaign the promoters had to take to the highways and byways explaining the proposal and even then it was not certain until a late date that the necessary amount would be raised within the time limit. If there was so much uncertainty in 1968 it is evident that such an undertaking would have been impossible fifty years earlier. Before the War Kynoch had experimented with fertilisers at Kynochtown which had a full scale research laboratory, that at Arklow was equipped only for routine testing and there was never any question of fertiliser production despite the fact that the Chemical Works was originally a fertiliser factory (345).

There was no possibility that McGowan or Frame would have sold the factory intact for any money. It was to be swept completely out of existence as Nobel Industries, applying new principles of rationalised production developed in the extraordinary wartime conditions, eliminated surplus capacity by scrapping many factories including all of Curtis's & Harvey, Kraftmeier's Chilworth and Kynochtown. Even in Witton many old and proud departments were closed. In July 1920 while Frame was still busily demolishing the premises a local committee was formed in the town which put forward proposals for retaining the laundry in the works, setting up a machine bakery, factories for fishing nets, soap and candles and so on. Nothing came of these and various other ideas.

In February 1923, as part of a complicated series of internal transactions, Nobel's paid Kynoch £189,000 for closing Arklow. Two weeks before this Chamberlain had resigned from the local and main boards. He turned his attention full-time to Tube Investments, a small company in the house of Chamberlain which had always been separate from Kynoch and by his death in 1941 when he was succeeded by his son, the third Arthur, had built this into a major rival to his former firm (366).

Alan T Cocking went from both boards in October 1920. He obtained a number of directorships including one in his original field, coalmining. Chemical engineer extraordinary and architect of Arklow, he died aged 70 in 1934 (329).

All that survived after Frame were a few concrete remnants and the great water tower which serves the caravan park occupying most of the ground with various public amenities on the remainder. The timber piling on the foreshore was removed by locals for firewood causing erosion and exposing a dangerous mass of ironwork. Kynoch Lodge is a private residence. The hospital continued for many years under the auspices of a voluntary committee as a tuberculosis sanatorium. Following the inauguration in 1948 of the system of large hospitals, the premises became the Arklow Bay Hotel (714).

After the closedown the acids suffusing the air ceased to turn the mens' beards yellow and the town was desolate. Many people emigrated. J M Goodall, the last manager, choose not to return to England and lived out his life in the town.

J W Parkes, a Birmingham chemist and expert on sulphuric acid, joined Goulding Fertilisers and was eventually joint managing director (357, 365).

In 1935 Arklow Pottery opened and in 1965 fertiliser production returned to the Vale of Avoca when the state sponsored Nitrigin Eireann Teoranta, Irish Nitrogen Limited, began production in a factory above the town. Like the previous plants NET use local pyrites for sulpheric acid and export the burnt residue to contintental smelters for extraction of the iron content as Kynoch apparently did. The factory has many by-products some of which are waste. A few years after the factory opened a submarine pipeline was built to dispose of one particular substance out at sea. Subsequently NET identifed a gap in the market for plasterboard which could be made from this material and set up a subsidiary, Arklow Gypsum, for manufacturing the product, *Argyps*. The site selected for the new plant was the area of the old Chemical works. In clearing the ground some extraordinary solid substructures and a series of tunnels defied all efforts by excavating equipment and finally had to be blown out of the way. So in the Autumn of 1973 a blast from the past echoed through the Vale of Avoca removing the very last vestige of the original factory on Ferrybank which inaugurated a century of chemical technology, first the Wicklow Copper Mine Company, then Kynoch and finally public enterprise.

Argyps was not a successful venture. In July 1980 the company in a submission to the Joint Oireachtas Committee on State Sponsored Bodies said that they intended to dispose of the undertaking hopefully to a company better placed to handle the product. The plant was closed the following September. In relation to the main factory the management claimed that they had lost large sums because the Department of Justice required them to reduce the nitrogen content of a particular fertiliser in order to eliminate its detonability thereby preventing possible use by terrorists. The loss had arisen because the application of limestone for diluting the nitrogen had caused pollution in the district, treatment of which had been costly (367, 717).

Nobel's and other companies formed Imperial Chemical Industries in 1926. Witton, re-named Kynoch Works, became the seat of ICI Metals Division. In 1977 ICI sold this business which they had earlier reconstituted as a subsidiary, Imperial Metal Industries, now simply IMI. Some years before this the Nobel Division, based at Ardeer, had been similarly reorganised as a subsidiary under the old style, Nobel's Explosives Company, presumably for the same purpose ultimately. This is an example of the process of disposal and renewal which continually goes on in the realms of industry and commerce (346).

In the first two years or so of the Irish Free State the Department of Defence manufactured cheddite, an explosive used mainly for civil purposes. This seems to have been a continuation of clandestine production during the War of Independence and to have been moved from secret premises to Defence Headquarters, Parkgate, Dublin on the changeover of administration. It appears to have been a semi-commercial undertaking on a small scale. Sales were low and not competitive against imported trade explosives and in October 1923 the Cabinet commissioned a report by an official of the Department of Local Government. The operation was discontinued some time afterwards (718, 729).

In Ireland during the 1960s several mines were opened, exploding the hallowed belief that the country had no mineral wealth and the quantities of explosives used in demolition, quarries and civil engineering increased to the point where a factory would be viable.

In May 1967 Irish Industrial Explosives Limited commenced production in a new works at Clonagh, Enfield, County Meath. Some 120 men are employed in the plant which consists of a number of isolated buildings surrounded by mounds in a comparitively unpopulated area. The company produce the full range of blasting explosives supplying the entire market in the country. Consignments for Northern Ireland are specially dyed as a precaution against use by terrorists. There are no exports. Imported accessories are marketed. Nobel's hold one third of the shares and a smaller proportion is held by the Societe Anonyme d'Explosifs et de Produits Chimiques, a French company. The balance in held by Irish interests, mainly Roadstone Limited, the large building materials firm (379-382).

Arklow was always a shaky part of the Kynoch empire and its existence was seriously threatened several times. The hopes raised in the last weeks of 1894 were realised within six months. A fifteen year old watching the construction would, before reaching forty, see grass growing on the ruins. No matter what the government did or did not do, even if they never manufactured at Waltham Abbey or never built at Gretna, Arklow would have been closed. It would have happened even if the plant was at Witton and if Nobel's never acquired Kynoch.

The foundation, operation and termination of Arklow provide illuminating instances of international capital operating in Ireland. In coming, Kynoch skilfully set up several Irish MPs against The Castle and Whitehall who were unable to object outright to the site. They cunningly played Nobel's against their German associates and exploited to the full Ardeer's peculiar relationship with the government. In the town they brought together for their particular purpose the Unionists and the Nationalists then bitterly divided into Parnellite and anti-Parnellite camps. This was a remarkable achievement. Had it suited their strategy they would have driven the divisions even deeper and indeed created a faction or at least its shadow in the form of the rumours of interest ostensibly opposed to the factory, so as to point even more convincingly to the alleged alternative sites. The manoeuvre of the meeting was in a class of its own.

While they were in Arklow Kynoch frequently threatened to leave. In the absence of trade unions they did not pay more than minimal wages and in general provided only the poorest of conditions. They never developed the numerous additional enterprises which they promised and never even supplied electricity to the town.

Arklow was merely a stake in their games with the government and with Nobel's to whom they offered the undertaking a number of times and to whom they succumbed eventually, lock, stock and barrel, in the extraordinary circumstances of the War and in the rationalisation which followed the factory was destroyed.

ARKLOW, VIEW, CHEMICAL WORKS
SOURCE 356

ARKLOW, VIEW, EXPLOSIVES FACTORY
SOURCE 300

CHAPTER THREE

INVENTORS

John P Holland

Sir Howard Grubb
and
Sir Charles Parsons

LVS Blacker

Louis Brennan

Several Irish inventors who are now quite forgotten were responsible for a number of weapons and devices of great importance in warfare.

While for the most part their research and development and the subsequent production took place outside the country, these individuals deserve to be included.

There are other inventors in the annals of Irish genius. These five were characterised by their common connections with warfare and by quite exceptionally high standards of theories and of skills to put their ideas into operation.

This Chapter looks at the careers of John P Holland who produced the first practical undersea craft; Sir Howard Grubb who invented the periscope and various other optical applicances for military use and his associate, Sir Charles Parsons, who developed the steam turbine; LVS Blacker who devised a veritable array of weapons, the *Hedgehog*, the *Petard*, the *Projector Infantry Anti-Tank* and the *Blacker Bombard*; and Louis Brennan who pioneered wire propulsion.

HOLLAND

The North Sea. The fifth of September, Nineteen fourteen.

The First World War is barely a month in business. A ten year old cruiser *Pathfinder* hoves into view. Beneath the choppy grey waters a new weapon lurks unknown to the Jolly Jack Tars above. The new vessel, a naval version of Jules Verne's fictional *Nautilus* of a few years earlier, is seeking a target.

Pathfinder suddenly shudders from stem to stern as the undersea man-of-war fires off a torpedo or two and goes down in the waves and down in history as the first ship to be sunk by a Holland submarine.

The U-21 has claimed the first victim in an entirely new phase of warfare. Seventeen days later the U-9 sinks three British cruisers, *Crecy, Aboukir* and *Hogue* in one hour and Germany gains the upper hand in the naval side of the War. Since then submarines have sunk shipping by the millions of tonnes.

A vessel which could travel underwater had been dreamed of for centuries and various attempts had been made to build such a craft. The first practical model was made by John Philip Holland who was born in Liscannor, County Clare around 1841. The name is common in some parts of Ireland. His father was in the Coastguard Service. He joined the Christian Brothers in 1859 and taught in their Cork and Dundalk schools. During this period he carried out design work on his idea for a boat to travel under the sea. Leaving the order he went to New York in 1873 where he became involved in Irish circles. After a short while he took up a teaching position with the Christian Brothers in Paterson, New Jersey, retaining his contacts in New York, nearby.

In the summer of 1876 Holland placed his idea before Jeremiah Collins, the celebrated Arctic explorer, who at the time was scientific and metereological correspondent of the *New York Herald* and founder of Clan na Gael, the successor body to the Fenian Brotherhood in the USA and Jeremiah O'Donovan Rossa a famous Fenian and also John Devoy who was for long the patriarch of the Irish Independence movement in North America.

An arrangement was made under which the Brotherhood would finance the submarine. It is not clear that Holland was ever a sworn Fenian. The construction of the *Holland 1* began in New York and was later transferred to Paterson where it was launched in May 1878. The second craft, named the *Fenian Ram*, was completed in 1881. Other models followed. Various differences developed between Holland and the Fenians and he sought other financial support.

In 1893 the John P Holland Torpedo Boat Company was incorporated in New York. Under special acts the United States Navy placed contracts for a submarine, the *Plunger* in 1893, for two craft in 1896 and two more in 1899. The business was absorbed in 1899 by the Electric Boat Company which later became part of the General Dynamics Corporation. Holland was squeezed out. He formally resigned his seat on the board a few days before his term expired in March 1904. The company had been valued at five million dollars at the time of the takeover. Holland was also defrauded of his patents.

In September 1904 Holland approached the Fairfield Shipbuilding and Engineering Company, Glasgow, with a proposal for a new design. He was in a hurry for a reply mentioning that he had an invitation to Japan to advise on submarine development. He was no longer young and felt that he might not live to come back. This approach to Fairfields apparently came to nothing and neither did a proposal he made to the Bethlehem Steel Company in the USA. He was awarded the Order of the Rising Sun by Japan.

In 1911 Holland resumed work on a project which he had pursued some years earlier. This was an amusement submarine to be operated at Coney Island, New York and other resorts during the summer season. He revived the idea with a view to use in Atlantic City, a popular watering-place in New Jersey. The craft would take passengers on half hour trips at a half dollar a head. An extension of this was to use submarines on various routes such as from the Great Lakes to the Gulf of Mexico and even on the transatlantic run.

Holland took out a large number of patents on submarines and components and on several devices unconnected with the craft. He also carried out some research on the strength of gunpowder of Waltham Abbey standard, presumably with a view to finding how guns would work on submarines.

John P Holland died on 12 August 1914, a few day after the outbreak of the First World War and just as the craft came into its own.

In 1900 Electric Boat issued a licence to Vickers, the biggest British armaments concern, for the construction of submarines to be used by the Royal Navy. The first was launched in the Vickers shipyard at Barrow-in-Furness in October 1901 and named the *Holland 1*, many more of the Navy's fleet were likewise called after the intrepid inventor.

In 1976 the National Maritime Museum, Greenwich, held an exhibition to mark the seventy-fifth anniversary of the Navy's introduction of the craft. Full recognition was given to John Philip himself and the fact that he originally developed the submarine to be used by the Fenians against Britain. This is more than he has ever received in his native land (383-97).

GRUBB AND PARSONS

One of the major problems which submarine crews had in the early days, before radio and other aids, was how to keep course without actually surfacing and going on deck to take bearings. There was also the question of how to observe ships without being seen.

Electric Boat and Vickers approached this jointly and commissioned Sir Howard Grubb who produced the periscope, a device which could be raised telescopically above the water and enabled navigators to find positions without taking the craft to the surface. Grubb perfected the invention in February 1902.

Grubb was born in Dublin in 1844 and studied engineering at Trinity College, leaving without a degree to join his father's optical business. The Grubbs were by far the biggest and most famous makers of telescopes in the whole world for many years. They supplied instruments to many famous observatories. For example when the 1888 Paris International Astronomical Congress arranged a world wide network of ten telescopes the Grubbs built seven. Some of these and of the many others they made are still functioning. Grubb took over the business on his father's retirement in 1868 and went on to pioneer many advances in optics and engineering systems. He also worked on methods of precise timing, a matter of much military as well as civilian significance.

In March 1901 Grubb told the Royal Dublin Society, of which he was a long standing vice-president, about a "New Collimating-Telescope Gun-Sight for Large and Small Ordnance". He claimed that this was a great advance on the existing sights. The *Kynoch Journal*, June 1902, described this and reported the following April that the War Office had carried out tests and that Vickers were about to commence mass production. It is not clear if the appliance was manufactured.

During the early part of the First World War Grubb made periscopes at his Dublin works. At some stage during the conflict he turned the factory over to manufacturing shells and transferred the production of periscopes, telescopes and other optical equipment to St Albans, near London.

The *Ministry of Munitions, Secret Weekly Report*, 2 June 1916, noted that Grubb had submitted a design for range-finders suitable for use at night. Also during the War he produced a sky searching device for finding enemy zeppelins and aeroplanes and a new type of gunsight for battleship turrets.

In 1925 Grubb retired and sold the business to Sir Charles

Parsons with whom he had been associated all his life. Parsons was the youngest son of the third Earl of Rosse who had in the 1840s built in the grounds of Birr Castle, County Offaly, the family seat, a telescope which was the biggest in the world until the 1920s. The remains of this still stand.

Parsons had a remarkable career. His greatest achievement was the development of the steam turbine, the culmination of two centuries of progress on steampower. This was first seen in June 1897 when Parsons, steering his *Turbinia*, cheekily cut in on the Royal Navy's salute for Queen Victoria's diamond jubilee at Spithead which was being reviewed by the Prince of Wales. None of the warships could approach *Turbinia's* thirty-five knots and the design was widely adopted for use in naval and merchant vessels. Parsons formed a new concern, Sir Howard Grubb Parsons and Company, building a factory at Newcastle-upon-Tyne where the firm still flourishes as part of a large engineering conglomerate. Liffeyside's loss is Tyneside's great gain.

Grubb was knighted in 1866 and Parsons in 1911. They received many other honours and distinctions before their deaths in 1931 (397-405).

BLACKER

Latham Valentine Stewart Blacker was a scion of the family of Blacker of Carrickblacker, Armagh and Lisnahanna, Tyrone who in his own generation could claim an ancestry stretching back a full thousand years to the Vikings. Born in 1887 he had, like several forebears, a distinguished career as soldier and explorer and was also an aviator and inventor of note. A Lieutenant Colonel in Queen Victoria's Own Corps of Guides, Indian Army, Frontier Force, he took part in many major operations in India and in the Western Front during the First World War. He led a force against the Bolsheviks in Central Asia in 1920 and received many high decorations. As an aviator he held aeroplane pilot's licence 121 and was associated with the early days of Royal Flying Corps and its successor the RAF. As an explorer he travelled widely in Asia and received recognition from learned societies in several countries. He commanded the expedition which flew over Mount Everest in 1933. There was historical full circle in this as an ancestor, also Colonel Valentine Blacker, held the post of Surveyor General of India. His subordinate and successor, George Everest, discovered the peak.

In the 1920s Blacker was in the Imperial General Staff. During the Second War he invented four weapons. The *Hedgehog* was extremely effective against submarines and accounted for fifty U-boats when it had been perfected in an extensive programme following Blacker's original idea of showering targets with mortar bombs. The *Petard* was fitted on the *Churchill* and other tanks. The *Blacker Bombard* was a mortar used against tanks. Blacker visualised this weapon being sent in waves of helicopters behind the enemy lines claiming that it "would win the war as surely as other novel weapons have won wars in the past". He was not the only inventor or soldier to draw the long bow. ICI produced 19,000 *Bombards* and 115,000 of the *Projector Infantry Anti-Tank* which appears to have been more effective than the *Bombard*. It fired cones of high explosive. Lord McGowan, in his chairman's address to the ICI annual meeting in May 1945, a few weeks after the War ended, said that six Victoria Crosses had been won by soldiers wielding this weapon. Blacker, who died in 1964, received £25,000 for his ideas which had begun when he bombarded his teacher's glasshouse in Bedford with a home-made black powder mortar (406-10).

BRENNAN

In the 1980s the world had at least two hundred different systems of guided missiles with a wide variety of guidance and control apparatus, radio, radar, sonar, television, infra red, gyroscope, spin stabilisation, inertial techniques and so on. About twenty are worked by wire.

The original system of wire propulsion and control was developed by Louis Brennan who was born in Castlebar, County Mayo in January 1852. At an early age his family emigrated to Australia and he became apprenticed to a watchmaker in Melbourne. It seems that he developed his idea for a wire propelled torpedo from watching a belt driven planing machine and observing that only one side of the belt was actually transmitting power. From this he concluded that belting could be attached to a pulley and used to transmit from a fixed to a mobile mechanism in a situation which did not call for a return.

Torpedoes were much in vogue at the time. Many models were being put forward and the Royal Navy set up their Torpedo School in 1881. In the same year Brennan persuaded the Admiralty that his idea was worthwhile to the tune of £110,000. They brought him to England and set up the National Torpedo Factory at Gillingham, Kent for the development and manufacture of Brennan torpedoes. The weapon was worked by a pair of wires which were unwound in opposition to each other at high speed from a winch on shore with a set of tracks to the water's edge. The torpedo had a range of about three thousand metres and could be manoeuvred about forty degrees from side to side. It was essentially for defending harbours and rivers and several stations were built around the coasts of Britain and Ireland. These seem to have been abandoned some years before the First World War.

Henry Campbell-Bannerman, Secretary for War, told the Commons on 3 May 1894 that Brennan's contract was about to expire. In addition to the original royalty various fees and expenses totalling £32,000 had been paid.

After this Brennan developed a monorail, a railway with one track. Around this time several other inventors were working on the same principle. An example in Ireland was the famous Lartigue line from Listowel to Ballybunion. Brennan had a full size working model in the grounds of his home in Gillingham which was the first to have a gyroscopic base. The system does not seem to have been developed on a commercial scale.

During the First World War Brennan was in the inventions department of the Ministry of Munitions assessing the numerous schemes, mostly of an impractical nature, which were submitted. One, which was preserved as a typical specimen, was an arrangement of rollers with various attachments which was intended to remove barbed wire entanglements. This was sent in by Harcourt Lees, a miller in Portarlington.

After the War Brennan went to the Royal Aircraft Establishment, Farnborough, Hampshire and worked on designing a helicopter until 1926 when the government decided to go ahead with the machine put forward by Juan de la Cierva of Argentina rather than the Brennan helicopter.

In February 1926, as his engagement at Farnborough was ending, Brennan wrote to Winston Churchill MP then Chancellor of the Exchequer stating:

> *I can claim to be the author of perhaps two of the most advanced mechanical inventions that exist, and I feel quite certain that I can perfect the helicopter if the Government have the same confidence in me that the War Department had in the days of my torpedo.*

> *I regard the helicopter as a stepping stone which will empower me to carry out another great scheme which will be of the utmost importance to the country, and I should be greatly honoured if you would allow me to come and submit it to you in the first instance.*

Churchill refused to receive Brennan and while there is no further indication as to what he had in mind, it is possible to speculate from the facts which are known. The torpedo had the disadvantages of limited range and application. The Washington Naval Treaty which followed the First World War placed restrictions on the number and size of the warships which Britain and the other signatory countries could have. Brennan had put a great deal of effort and public money into developing an aircraft which could remain stationary in the air. Churchill had been an army officer, journalist, author, First Lord of the Admiralty and Minister for Munitions. He had a flair for publicity and the unconventional and might be expected to support a new and unusual weapon which could promise to keep Britain in the forefront of the great powers. Perhaps Brennan had devised some aerial form of the torpedo which could be worked from a helicopter. There were several holes on the original weapon, the purpose of which remains unknown.

Brennan died in January 1932, a few days before his eightieth birthday. He had been knocked down by a car some weeks earlier in

Montreux, Switzerland where he was on holiday. Though he lived most of his life outside Ireland he did retain some contacts with the country. In 1892 he married Anna May Quinn of Castlebar and in 1922 was nominated a member of the proposed "National Academy for Ireland", a short lived attempt to replace the ancient Royal Irish Academy.

In Germany during the Second World War two different systems of weapons propelled and controlled by electrically operated wires were designed and used against tanks. These could be steered under the targets unseen by the crews inside and set off. The armour was usually weaker underneath. It does not seem that these systems were particularly effective. Also in Germany an aerial bomb or rocket worked by wire was partly developed.

The present guided missile systems worked by wire are *Swingfire* and *Hawkswing* by British Aerospace; *Bantam* by Bofors, Sweden; *Mosquito* by Contraves-Oerlikon, Switzerland; *AT-1* and *AT-3* by the Soviet Union; *KAM 3-D* and *KAM-9* by Kawasaki, Japan; *Dragon* by McDonnell Douglas and *TOW* by Hughes Aircraft Company, USA; *Entac* and *Harpon* by Aerospatiale, France; *Cobra* and *Mamba* by Messerschmitt-Bolkow-Blohm, Germany and *HOT* and *Milan* by Euromissile, a joint undertaking of Aerospatiale and Messerschmitt. All these are for use against tanks. Aerospatiale also produce the *SS11* and *SS12* which are surface to surface weapons used against both ground and sea targets and the *AS11* and *AS12* which are fired from helicopters. *Milan* was added to the armoury of the Irish Defence Forces in 1979 (780).

None of these manufacturers are prepared to admit deriving the idea from Louis Brennan or even ever hearing of him and claim to have developed the theory independently except Kawasaki who acknowledge that they got the plan from German designs after the Second War. It is probable that the others started from this point also and that the Germans got their inspiration from Brennan.

Louis Brennan, by a stroke of sheer genius, did originally discover and develop the principle of wire propulsion. He also had more than a touch of the Blarney. A royalty of £110,000 and expenses to match would have been substantial sums a century later despite the ravages of inflation. LVS Blacker's £25,000 compares badly (411-36).

CHAPTER FOUR

THE WORLD WARS

The first half of the twentieth century saw two major bellic holocausts, both fought on scales never before imagined. War became, to a great extent, a matter of industrial production and was no longer merely a question of having a bigger force than the enemy. A method of making a weapon or even a vital component was more valuable than an extra battalion. For instance, making a shell involved some thirty separate engineering operations, if these could be reduced by half the output would be automatically doubled.

During the First War a substantial measure of public control was placed on most aspects of industry in Britain from allocation of raw materials and machinery to raising of capital. The railways, then run by many separate companies, were brought under central management and various other measures were taken. During the Second War the British government had even greater powers and exercised controls over excessive profits which had caused great outrage in the previous conflict.

When Britain, France, Germany and the other countries made their declarations of war in August 1914, it was generally believed that it would last only a short time and would certainly be over by the end of the year. As the year passed into history and as the spring of 1915 was giving way to summer it was realised in Britain that the War would last longer and would be fought on a plane which would render the Boer War, the most recent experience, and indeed all accepted beliefs, tactics and strategies, as obsolete as the bow and arrow. Hostilities in Europe soon became bogged down on the Western Front, a ragged line of barbed wire entanglements and trenches interspersed with mountains of corpses stretching from the North Sea to the Alps.

Within a very short time the British forces had used up all the artillery shells in the arsenals. The existing arrangements for the manufacture and distribution of supplies could not even begin to cope with the demand though pressed to the limit and beyond. Every chain in the link was weak, mining and smelting, founding the metals, capacities for machining and filling shells and transportation between the various stages. There were many difficulties with personnel, too few skilled and semi-skilled workers were available, and in many factories large workforces were left with nothing to do when toolmakers and other key individuals went to the colours on call-up or voluntarily.

By May 1915 the inadequacies in the supply of shells and other munitions had reached the proportions of a public crisis. After bitter debate, dark hints of scandal and thunderous pronouncements from Lord Northcliffe in his numerous newspapers, the Ministry of Munitions was set up to produce and otherwise procure all possible supplies.

Large quantities were purchased in the USA and huge National Factories were set up throughout Britain. Some were run directly by the Ministry and others by local boards, the composition of which varied from place to place. By the end of the War some 125 such undertakings had been established in a variety of old and new premises (444).

The legislatures of the various countries regularly voted vast sums until the totals passed all comprehension. For example, in Britain the expenditure of the Ministry of Munitions alone, quite apart from the War Office and the Admiralty, increased from £50 million in the first quarter of 1916 to £170 million for the corresponding part of 1918 and the headquarters staff grew to seventeen thousand by the end of the War (442-3).

War Production was immensely profitable. Every firm and every town wanted a share of what was going. The demand was not confined to munitions. The armed forces needed huge amounts of foodstuffs and quantities, large and small, of practically every product. The chambers of commerce, industrial development associations, trades councils, local authorities and so on clamoured for contracts in their respective areas and in some towns formed local munitions committees, the better to press their claims on Dublin Castle and the Ministry of Munitions. The campaign was taken up in the House of Commons by William Field, John E Redmond and Laurence Ginnell in particular.

Five National Factories were set up in Ireland. The first was the Dublin National Shell Factory which was accommodated in an old margarine works belonging to the Great Southern and Western Railway, in Parkgate Street, directly across the Liffey from their headquarters in Kingsbridge, now Heuston, Station. Preparation of the premises began in November 1915 and production of eighteen pounder shells in March 1916, averaging 3,000 per week and totalling 491,148. At the outset it was decided to install equipment for 9.2 inch shells. There were several delays and production did not commence until April 1917. Originally expected to be 500 weekly, this target was never met and the total was only 4,895.

The Dublin National Fuse Factory was sanctioned by the Ministry in May 1916 and a wooden building with a concrete floor was erected in the yard of the works. Various types of brass and iron fuses were made, the total being 293,886 from March 1917 to the Armistice.

These factories were at first under the Director of Munitions with a manager, secretary and accountant reporting separately. In September 1917 separate boards of directors were set up, each with its own management. The Dublin plants provided training services for the others and also supplied cutters and other precision tools.

The Cork Munitions Committee was formed in 1915 by the two chambers of commerce, the two trades councils and the Cork Industrial Development Association to seek a factory and contracts for the city. On 22 April 1916 the Corporation agreed to lease a section of the public market run by their Tolls and Markets Committee at North Main Street and Cornmarket Street, the famous "Coal Quay". This had been found to be the most suitable of several premises inspected by representatives of the Ministry. Production began in February 1917 and totalled 30,041 of the 4.5 inch calibre. Some training for the Galway and Waterford factories was carried out (455-6).

In November 1916, responding to requests from the All-Ireland Committee and local interests, the Ministry set up the Waterford National Cartridge Factory in a station which the Great Southern had abandoned some years before on building a terminus nearer the city centre. A timber building, powerhouse, cooling tower and offices were erected. The plant was designed to produce 20,000 cases for eighteen pounders per week. Commencing in August 1917 the total was 247,637.

According to E J Riordan the equipment in this factory was particularly poor. When, after the War, most of the Ministry's records were destroyed, the machinery audit book for this plant was retained for permanent preservation as a typical specimen. This shows that Waterford was quite well equipped with machinery valued at over £70,000 (437, 439).

The *Ministry of Munitions Secret Weekly Report*, 8 July 1916, noted:

> *Representations have been received from Galway asking for the setting up of a National Shell Factory. No suitable machinery is however available locally, and in view of the fact that the policy of the Ministry is strictly to curtail the making of machines to produce the smaller shell as there are almost insuperable difficulties in organising in a remote place like Galway the manufacture of large shell, a reply has been sent to the effect that the most suitable class of work that the district could undertake would be work in connection with the Alimentation Branch of the War Office. This is represented at the office of the Ministry in Dublin and every facility will be afforded to Galway manufacturers.*

Alimentation indeed. The official who penned this screed must have been dreaming about a feast of Galway Bay oysters. At the end of the year the Ministry agreed to set up a factory for eighteen pounders. The premises selected was a former marble and granite works on University Road. Production began in February 1917 and totalled 30,713.

The manager, superintendent and manageress were English. There was one Canadian inspector and one Irish and a nurse for minor injuries. A few engineering students from the University College also worked in the plant. A three shift system was worked from 0600-1400-2200 in a six day week. Most of the seventy or so women employed were married to British soldiers. There were about forty men, mainly fitters and mechanics. When the news of the Armistice came through on the night of 11 November 1918 the workers switched off the machines, which the official history admitted were in very poor condition, and celebrated in the canteen with cups of tea. The machines were never turned on again and after a few weeks on clearing the plant the workers were discharged with a souvenir shell each (471).

The *Secret Weekly Report*, 7 December 1918, noted that the Ministry intended to sell the factories as going concerns. Some consideration was given to retaining the Dublin premises for use as army workshops. This was not done. It was used for many years by Cahill & Company, printers. David Frame expressed an interest in the Cork plant for a foundry. This did not come to pass and after some years as a garage it was acquired by the Lee Hosiery Company. The Galway works became Hunters' pram factory. The Waterford factory site was acquired by Waterford Ironfounders one of whose products in the late seventies was small-scale ornamental cast-iron cannon (479).

So the National Factories passed into history. At peak, jobs had been given to some two thousand workers, for many, no doubt, the first industrial employment. From the Ministry's point of view output must have been satisfactory. Even working with some second rate equipment there had been an acceptable cost of production. The *Secret Weekly Report*, 15 July 1916, carried an analysis of costs in Dublin and fourteen factories in Britain. Of these, eight produced at a lower cost than Dublin while six were higher. The total output of all types of shells was 526,797 and probably about the same in the private factories. The entire British production was 169 million.

There was apparently no particular antagonism towards the workers in the factories, even after the Easter Rising. On 18 May 1916 Laurence Ginnell asked Christopher Addison MP, Parliamentary Secretary in the Ministry, "whether Nationalists in munitions works in Ireland have been dismissed and Englishmen put in their places, to what extent this has been done and in view of the consequence whether it will be reconsidered?" The reply was "no such dismissals of Nationalists have taken place at the munitions works under the direct control of the Ministry, nor have the Ministry any knowledge of such dismissals elsewhere".

On 4 June 1915, just after the Ministry of Munitions was formed, a conference of engineering firms was held by the Belfast Chamber of Commerce to discuss the European War as the conflict was known. The chair was taken by SC Davidson, principal of Davidson and Company, Sirocco Works, the biggest tea machinery company in the world. Of the 29 firms invited all except four attended and after discussion a telegram was sent to David Lloyd George MP, Minister for Munitions: "the members of the engineering trade of Belfast and district are anxious to assist His Majesty's Government to the utmost extent of their power in the production of munitions of war and they are satisfied that Belfast can assist materially in this direction".

Further meetings were held in Belfast and London with the Ministry and arrangements were made for the formation of the Belfast and North of Ireland Employers' War Munitions Committee. This functioned for three years and kept very comprehensive minutes and accounts under Davidson's chairmanship. The president was Sir Crawford McCullagh, Lord Mayor of Belfast and a director of several companies. The secretary was Sir Alexander McDowell, a solicitor and Chairman of the Belfast Ropework Company. Both were government nominated members of the Irish Convention which sat in Dublin during 1917-18 with a view to finding a new form of administration for the country (448,470).

At a meeting with Christopher Addison MP, Parliamentary Secretary, the Committee stated that they considered the system of National Factories unsuitable for Belfast and that their various firms preferred to operate a joint scheme. They were willing to work with the trade unions. A meeting was held with a workers' committee in June and another in August after which apparently there were no more. The committee arranged a contract for 250,000 number five *mills* hand grenades. There was some discussion on the possibilities of producing eighteen pounders and some calibres of naval shells. None were made under the Committee's auspices.

The Committee set up a depot in a premises provided free by the Chairman. A manager and small office staff were engaged, a letterhead printed, a telegraphic address "Munitions, Belfast" arranged, a bank account opened and auditors appointed. Some sixty firms were involved in making and assembling the components of the grenades and boxes. The vast majority have long since disappeared. The most important were Bright's Patent Pulley Company; Chambers Motors, the only native Irish car company; Fairbairn Lawson Combe Barbour, the Falls Foundry and Workman Clark, shipbuilders. The concerns still in business were Davidsons; Robert Craig and Sons, engineers; James Mackie and Sons, the Albert Foundry, the largest textile machinery firm in the world; Robert Patterson and Sons, hardware; W Ross and Company, flaxspinners; Stanley Motor Works, auto engineers; White, Tomkins and Courage, millers; Broadway Damask Company; Braidwater Spinning Company; Island Spinning Company and the Old Bleach Linen Company.

Work commenced in July and the formal contract was signed in December. Difficulties arose with the Ministry over quality. At the beginning the Committee had arranged for "thirty-four gentlemen and thirty-three ladies who gave their services gratuitously, but as the job was lasting so much longer than originally anticipated, the Committee considered it desirable that their services should be suitably remunerated".

Their services were not satisfactory to the Ministry officials who rejected large numbers of grenades. In one instance 7,500 sent to the filling factory at Warmley, England, which had been accepted and stamped by an inspector from Woolwich were found to be defective. In another instance twelve particularly poor grenades were returned:

in a box which was not made in the North of Ireland, a very inferior article quite sufficient in itself to condemn anything it contained, we consider it very unfair that a special box of disgraceful construction with twelve defective grenades, specially picked out should have been sent to Woolwich as representing what we manufacture here.

The Committee claimed that only 3.9 percent had been rejected from their total output.

The contract price per grenade was five shillings (25p). The Committee produced the full 250,000. The last batch was delivered in July 1917. The surplus for distribution was £8,500 which was paid after the final meeting in May 1918 when the Chairman explained that "shortly after the contract was undertaken, the Honorary Secretary, Sir Alexander McDowell, was honoured by being appointed by the Government as Minister for Munitions for the North of Ireland and under these circumstances the operations of the Committee were confined to the contract". This was very much a courtesy title, an advance shadow of Stormont. According to the *Secret Weekly Report* and the *Levy Report*, he held the more realistic and less exalted title of Director of Munitions Supply (446).

Many of the companies carried out contracts directly for the Ministry. This must have been more satisfactory than the system under which some firms made components while others assembled and made the entire article, the various aspects being co-ordinated by the depot.

Harland and Wolff did not participate in the Committee. The *Secret Weekly Report*, 18 September 1915, noted that they were making machine tools for use by other firms in manufacturing shells.

Early in 1916 the All-Ireland Munitions and Government Supplies Committee was formed. The president was the Lord Mayor of Dublin, the vice-presidents were the Lord Mayor of Cork and the mayors of Londonderry, Sligo, Clonmel, Waterford, Limerick, Drogheda and Wexford, Sir James Long and John O'Neill, proprietor of the Lucania Cycle Works, Dublin who was also Chairman (449-50).

The membership was rather motley, being composed of 56 persons. Thirty-six firms were represented and there were four trade union delegates. The remainder were private individuals. The most important were Colonel Maurice Moore, a former British army officer who had been Inspector General firstly of the Irish Volunteers and later of the National Volunteers and Colonel Sir Nugent T Everard, a Navan tobacco grower, both were later Senators; Sir Stanley Harrington as a director of Harrington Brothers, paint manufacturers, Cork; the Dowager Countess of Desart, Kilkenny represented by her agent, and the High Sheriff of Waterford. Alec G Wilson, JP,MRIA, a son of Walter H Wilson one of the original partners in Harland and Wolff, who was later a Foreign Office official, was the only northern individual member (481-2).

The most important firms as far as actual munitions were concerned were the Dublin Dockyard; the Midland Great Western Railway; Sir Howard Grubb and Sons; Thomas Thompson and Sons, Carlow and Waterford; Philip Pierce and Company, Wexford and Robert Pulvertaft and Sons and the Lee Arrow Manufacturing Company, both in Cork. There were three woollen companies, three building contractors, four footwear firms and a variety of other businesses including two in the North, Williamson Brothers, bootmakers, Belfast and Gallagher and Company, linen manufacturers, Strabane (478).

The Federation of Engineering and Shipbuilding Trades, a British grouping and the two trades councils in Cork were affiliated.

The secretary was EJ Riordan, full time secretary of the Irish Industrial Development Association. He had previously been with the Cork Industrial Development Association, founded in 1903. Similar bodies were formed in other towns in the following years and in 1905 the first Irish Industrial Development Conference was held as a result of a suggestion to Riordan by Bertram Windle president of Queen's, now University College, Cork that there should be some method of identifying and guaranteeing Irish products as genuine. The conference adopted a resolution that the Irish National Trade Mark should be established. This was moved by Lord Dunraven and seconded by John P Boland who in Athens in 1896 won Ireland's first Olympic gold medal, for tennis, and was later elected MP for South Kerry. Such a trademark had become possible under recent legislation. The IIDA was authorised to administer the mark which they registered in many countries and was the only one of its kind in the world for ten years. It lapsed in 1969 on the dissolution of the IIDA. The *Guaranteed Irish* mark which is similar was inaugurated in 1975 (451, 452, 453, 474).

The All-Ireland Committee was in effect the IIDA. Their first event was the All-Ireland War Supplies Conference held in the Mansion House, Dublin on 21 February 1916. A statement was issued calling for National Factories, none had come into production by then; contracts for the private factories; equal opportunities with British firms in tendering; more discretion in placing large orders for the Ministry's local officials and the establishment of a testing and receiving depot. Riordan recorded an account of the Committee in his book *Modern Irish Trade and Industry* and in two articles (465-7).

In general Riordan complained that the Ministry's officials were hostile and unwilling to place contracts at all in the country. He was reluctant to acknowledge those orders which were given. For example, the *Irish Manufacturer's Directory* 1916, noted that "big contracts have been secured by Mr John O'Neill, the maker of the *Lucania*, for the supply of bicycles to the Post Office". Dealing with that department's orders in Ireland, Riordan ignored this although he must certainly have known (691).

The records of the Ministry, compiled by officials who could hardly have expected that their correspondence and reports would ever be available, show that they were willing and indeed anxious to place contracts with suppliers who were prepared to meet requirements by producing shells, fuses, components, boxes and so on to the standards laid down.

The case made by Riordan and the Committee was that Ireland, by contributing so many men to the fighting forces and so much money in taxation, more than was due as had been proved some years before the War, was thereby entitled, as of right, to a share of the business which was going. What Riordan really meant was that the commercial interests which he represented were entitled to a portion of the vast profits which were being made. He had no regard for the workers. The trade union presence on the Committee was purely nominal. Riordan, disregarding the elementary business principle that the customer is always right, thought that the Ministry should buy whatever the Irish companies produced, whether suitable or not.

Certainly in the early stages of the munitions crisis there was a lack of knowledge in London of the industrial capacity in Ireland which might be suitable for manufacturing shells and other supplies. This is understandable as the extent of Britain's own engineering resources was not fully known.

In April 1915 Arthur E Porte, a consulting engineer with offices in Dublin and Belfast wrote to the War Office offering his services, full-time if required. He stated that he was well known in the engineering trade and having spoken to some owners of workshops was satisfied that considerable quantities of munitions could be made in the country. A memo attached to this noted "the only big engineering firms in Ireland known to us are Harland and Wolff and Workman Clark and they are both shipbuilders in Belfast". A second memo observed that the machinery was specialised and it was doubtful if there was any in Ireland (438).

The Ministry did make every effort and set up boards of management for the country which was divided into two parts by a line running from Dundalk to Ballyshannon with offices in Belfast and Dublin. The *Secret Weekly Report*, 18 September 1915, recorded that the Ministry had changed plans and appointed Sir Alexander McDowell and Captain, later Major, Downie, respectively as Directors in place of the boards which accordingly resigned. This did not mean that the Ministry was any less interested in placing contracts with Irish firms prepared to meet requirements.

The *Report*, 2 October, noted that a "considerable number of orders have been placed, 4.5 inch shell in Dublin and Haulbowline and grenades, gaines, fuses, primers and various components". It is not clear what undertakings in Dublin were involved, nor whether the reference to Haulbowline meant that the Admiralty or War Office premises on the island in Cork Harbour had plant for munitions production or whether this was a casual way of referring to the shipyard at Rushbrooke, now operated by Verolme (page 209) or the Royal Victoria Dockyard in Passage West, also in the harbour. The same issue of the *Report* recounted that the "political party leaders, as well as the Government (Dublin Castle) have been of very material assistance in the task of organising the work, it is expected that several thousand workers will shortly be employed on munitions work in each area".

Two weeks later the *Report* noted that "Marked progress has been made in the works undertaken at Wexford, Haulbowline, Limerick and Cork. Orders for 250,000 ammunition boxes have been placed at Dublin, Cork, Limerick, Ballybrack and Kilkenny and other towns are asking for similar orders. In Dublin various precision instruments are being made by Booth Brothers and Ashenhurst, Williams and several other firms are showing great energy". Ashenhurst, Williams made shells and naval instruments (711).

The *Report*, 18 March 1916, noted the first meeting of the All-Ireland Committee and that sub-committees had been set up for Dublin, Belfast, Cork, Waterford, Wexford and Sligo. It also recorded that further contracts for ammunition boxes had been issued and arrangements for the supply of shell-making machinery to one firm in Waterford and two in Cork were underway.

Riordan complained in his book that in 1918 the Ministry refused to place orders for boxes in Ireland because they were under pressure from English firms which wanted timber, dried or undried from

Ireland. According to one commentator in July 1916, the Ministry had suspended orders to Irish box manufacturers until such time as they brought up to date their deliveries which had been "grossly behindhand" and that there would have been no difficulties if the companies had co-ordinated their efforts from the beginning instead of late and then unwillingly (461).

On 27 July 1916 the *Report* noted that contracts for 2,500 boxes per week had been placed with Brooks Thomas, Dublin and the Cork Timber and Iron Company. On 26 July 1917 Sir Laming Worthington Evans MP, Parliamentary Secretary, told the Commons that the Ministry were willing to place orders provided the Irish firms installed drying kilns.

The Ministry placed orders for shells with many firms including the railways and a number of other concerns. The Great Southern and Western Railway, the biggest, probably had the largest output. Their records show that production began in February 1917 and continued for a year totalling 996,972 fuse bodies, 555,368 fuse caps and 294,168 adaptors.   A contemporary account gives figures of 584,160 and 112,446 and 674,677 respectively. This also recorded the production of twelve machine tools for manufacturing high explosive shells and quantities of trench warfare equipment and noted that the Great Northern Railway produced six inch shells at their Dundalk workshops. The quantity is not clear. The London Midland and Scottish Railway, Northern Counties Committee made 1,400 shells of the 4.5 inch calibre in Belfast. The Midland Great Western made 4.5 inch shells and some trench warfare items (445, 454, 464).

Two existing firms set up special subsidiaries which were wound up after the War. The Dublin Dockyard established the Dublin Dockyard (Munitions of War) Limited. This company built a single floor factory with all machinery laid out in four rows, fully synchronised for starting and stopping. The plant was largely worked by girls as the Ministry did not allow the company to employ more than five percent men and boys. Twelve women underwent a course at Vickers, Barrow-in-Furness and trained the other two hundred who were employed. All soon were extremely skilled in working on the fine tolerances involved. Most had never worked in a factory before. A typical case was Florence Ross, previously apprenticed as a dressmaker at two shillings (10p) per week, in the factory she got an average of fifty shillings (£2.50) weekly.

The company provided a canteen which was run by the Irish Munition Workers Canteen Committee composed mainly of middle-aged ladies. The output was 3,000 shells per week on a two shift system. Three shift working which was found possible did not prove satisfactory (473,680-1).

The Cork Shell Company was a subsidiary of Robert Pulvertaft and Company, a local foundry. The Lee Arrow Manufacturing Company was formed in the first instance for munitions production, their equipment was designed to be turned over to civilian use after the War. The venture was apparently not successful as the local papers on 1 February 1918 carried the announcement of liquidation (460-1, 472, 675).

Various types of fuses and shells were manufactured by Ashenhurst, Williams, motor engineers, Dublin; Thomas Dockrell, Sons & Company, the well known hardware firm, Dublin; Thomas Thompson and Sons, engineers and founders, Hanover Works, Carlow and Neptune Works, Waterford; Philip Pierce and Company the famous Wexford agricultural machinery firm and JP Evans and Company, a wholesale and manufacturing hardware firm, Limerick (462, 476-7, 480, 711-13).

Besides the production in the National Factories and the various private undertakings, manufacture of munitions also took place in two seats of learning. The Belfast Municipal Technical Institute took part in the Belfast Committee's contract. In Dublin the Royal College of Science for Ireland which at the time was under the auspices of the Department of Agriculture and Technical Instruction and later became part of University College Dublin carried out various kinds of work under the direction of HH Jeffcott, Professor of Engineering who propounded the Jeffcott Motion, an important principle in dynamics (448,463).

From August 1914 to June 1915 the staff and students had classes in driving and repairing motor vehicles, building bridges and earthworks and signalling. These activities ended when a sub-contract was obtained from the GS&WR which had got a contract from the London Midland and Scottish Railway, Derby to manufacture fuse components for high explosive shells. The College had a wide range of machine tools. These were not suitable for mass production work without accessories which were not available at the time and so were made in the College and plans afterwards supplied to some commercial concerns. Several complete machine tools were designed and built.

The College produced several types of fuses. The Ministry changed orders usually just when the machine operators were becoming proficient on a particular pattern. At peak production the

College turned out seventeen thousand parts per week. These were quite tiny, machined to fine fractions of a millimetre. Most of the work was carried out by volunteers; civil servants, doctors, dentists and members of other professions such as the Law. From February to June 1916 barristers, solicitors and court officials organised in the Four Courts Munitions Association worked on weekends. Some girls were employed on both day and night shifts.

The College carried out toolwork for the Dublin National Shell Factory, the Dublin Dockyard, the Midland Great Western and several other firms. In the laboratories building materials were tested, calculations made and several hundred war optical instruments examined and some other operations of a secret nature were undertaken. The work continued until January 1919 when the College reverted fully to its normal role which had continued alongside all these activities.

One of the main complaints of the All-Ireland Committee was that there was no depot in Ireland for testing and receiving products required by the War Office. Such an establishment had existed until the 1850s. In March 1916 the Committee sent a deputation to the War Office and again in July. In correspondence which followed they threatened to hold a series of public protest meetings. Before these began the Ministry made an approach and the Committee sent another deputation to London and immediately afterwards the Minister, David Lloyd George, sent Sir Maurice Levy MP, a Liberal Party backbencher, to Ireland who duly submitted a report on the country's industrial and agricultural resources.

Levy visited Dublin, Belfast, Carlow, Kilkenny, Waterford, Tramore, Cork, Limerick and Galway. He met Sir Alexander McDowell and Captain Downie, the Directors of Munitions Supply and other officers and deputations from agricultural interests, various industries, local councils, trades councils, trade associations, chambers of commerce and various individual manufacturers.

As a result of these investigations on the ground and the consultations with the various groups he was satisfied there were many shortcomings in the arrangements for obtaining supplies. He received many justified complaints of inadequate information on contracts and specifications; undue expense and delay in going to and waiting in London; sending and receiving back samples and insufficient time for preparing and submitting tenders. The offices in Dublin and Belfast were too small and did not have the full range of patterns and particulars of articles required. It would be possible to obtain far greater supplies:

The majority of firms are conducted in a small way without the systematic organisation and experience of the business requirements of today. Therefore it is necessary that manufacturers should be rendered some assistance and encouragement. This, it is contended, can only be done by having men of experience, with the knowledge of War Office requirements in Ireland.

Some manufacturers appear genuinely anxious to do what they possibly can to assist Britain from purely patriotic motives and thus expressed themselves to do all in their power in the hope of benefitting Ireland by encouraging the development of her industries, but they expressed the view that Ireland ought to be given the same facilities as England, which they are denied at present and this they contend, cannot be done unless a depot is established.

I am of the opinion that supplies in much larger quantities can be obtained from Ireland if the people can be interested in the requirements of the Nation, and if the inborn sentiment that England only looks to Ireland when in need and the feeling of mistrust and lack of confidence in Woolwich and Pimlico [Westminster] can be dispelled from the minds of the Irish people, feelings which are strong in Dublin and the South.

Accordingly Levy recommended that a depot with an English businessman in charge should be set up in Dublin which was acceptable to Belfast interests. He made detailed suggestions for transport and distribution arrangements which would yield many advantages and economies. He also made proposals for increasing output of coal in the collieries of Antrim, Tyrone, Leitrim and of Kilkenny which could additionally produce sulphuric acid. As the cost of coal was high in some remote rural districts he thought that electricity should be generated from waterpower. These ideas apparently were not taken up.

Levy also studied agriculture closely and found that the farmers would not increase production without persuasion and inducement in the form of guaranteed prices. He recommended that the government should take control of the supply of maize, imported from North America and widely used for feeding pigs, and give a guaranteed price for pig-meat based on the cost of the maize. He also advised control of the potato crop and did not agree with the various compulsory tillage schemes which had been proposed.

Lloyd George received Levy's Report in November 1916. During the following summer the All-Ireland Committee held a number of public protest meetings to call for the depot. This was eventually established early in 1918 in a number of buildings in and around Westland Row, Dublin and was equipped to the satisfaction of Riordan and the All-Ireland Committee. It was closed in 1919 (446).

The trade union movement was involved in the munitions campaign to the extent that local branches of individual unions and trades councils supported the call for factories and contracts in their respective areas. The Irish Trades Union Congress also issued appeals. From the foundation conference in 1894 the national centre regularly asked the War Office to set up a testing and receiving depot; to give contracts for painting and repairing barracks to Irish firms and to implement the Fair Wages Resolution passed by the House of Commons on 13 February 1891 (459).

Workers in some factories were organised by the Irish Transport and General Workers Union; an internal census in June 1918 showed that there were 813 munitions workers in membership; Dublin One branch had 250 members and Dublin Three had 80; these were probably in the Dublin National Factories; Carlow Branch had 44, obviously in Thomas Thompson and Sons, Hanover Works; Waterford One had 160 men and 40 boys, presumably in the Waterford National Cartridge Factory and Thomas Thompson and Sons, Neptune Works; Limerick One had 197, these were presumably in JP Evans and Company; Maugherrow Branch in Sligo had two members listed as munitions workers, their employment is not clear. The daily papers of 24 and 25 January 1918 reported that the Ministry had agreed to pay the War Bonus of 12^{1}/2 per cent which had been sanctioned the previous November. The Union had served strike notice for payment (674).

Women and girls employed in munitions factories were organised by the National Federation of Women Workers, a British based union. After the War the members were transferred to the Irish Women Workers' Union. In April 1917 the NFWW obtained an increase from £1 to £1-4-0 (£1.20) for women employed on work customarily done by men. This was for a 48 hour week. Skilled men were probably organised by the Amalgamated Society of Engineers (457,475).

Women were employed extensively in engineering workshops and factories for the first time in the First War. Under various "dilution agreements" the proportion of unskilled to skilled workers was increased above the levels previously accepted by custom and practice. Under the Treasury Agreement for Acceleration of Output on Government Work, March 1915, women doing men's unskilled work were to be paid the men's 1ate. The Ministry and the employers contrived to avoid this throughout the War (468).

Two strikes took place in the National Factories. In Dublin during June 1918 thirty mechanics went out for three weeks and were fined £3 each by the local Munitions Tribunal. Soon afterwards four carpenters in Waterford downed tools and were fined £10 each. The official history recorded that these were the only instances during the War in which the Ministry prosecuted members of trade unions for illegal strikes (437).

The operational difference between the two Committees was that the Belfast Committee carried out a single contract and opposed National Factories. Some of the members undertook contracts for the Ministry or sub-contracts for other firms. The All-Ireland Committee concerned themselves mainly with lobbying for National Factories and contracts for member firms. Politically, most if not all, members of the Belfast Committee were Unionists. Some members of the All-Ireland Committee were no doubt Unionists. The majority were probably Home Rulers.

The Committees ig..ored each other. There was a measure of co-ordination between some of the members. Sir Crawford McCullagh, Lord Mayor of Belfast who was president of the Belfast Committee joined with the Lord Mayor of Dublin who was president of the All-Ireland Committee and the other mayors who were vice-presidents, in a committee which tried, unsuccessfully, to bring about a reduction in the price of domestic coal (447).

The Chairman of the All-Ireland Committee, John O'Neill was a member of the Committee on Industrial and Commercial Policy after the War which reported in 1918. He submitted a minority report clearly indicating that he did not envisage any separation of the two countries. He sought "the right to carry on our trade in the way most beneficial to our people" insisting that there should be various forms of assistance and subsidies for some of Ireland's trades and industries (469).

Essentially Riordan and the All-Ireland Committee stood for capital. They tolerated the trade union movement only so far as they could use it for their purpose as did the Belfast Committee.

Both Committees had bitter complaints about delays on the part of the Ministry. These could not be justified, especially in the early days when the department was being set up, itself a difficult enough task in civil service terms. It was moreover functioning in an entirely new situation in which existing systems had collapsed in the face of vast demands which furthermore changed from day to day.

Neither of the Committees nor any of the companies had any complaints about the level of payments. They were in a seller's market. War production was tremendously profitable. The more enterprising firms stepped in quickly and made substantial sums. An alert management will anticipate and act quickly when opportunities arise. Of course the work was temporary. It was possible to recover the cost of plant and machinery rapidly, at the overall risk of creating subsequent surplus capacity. Investment of risk capital involves this danger. A venture may fail or pay off to a greater or lesser extent. The cast-iron, gilt-edged investment cannot of its nature yield a high return.

*   *   *   *   *   *   *

ON WAR SERVICE, 1916 MUNITIONS WORKER'S BADGE
SOURCE 458

*In those terrible days we were a bastion to Great Britain
and her Allies. We have been a vast training ground for troops.
On our shores, our lakes and our mountains they practiced the
new arts of amphibious and mechanised warfare, preparing
themselves for the invasion of the Continent. From our ports
and bases aeroplanes went out to fight the battles of the
Atlantic. Out of our agricultural richness, food was sent to
England. Our factories produced all sorts of weapons of war
and our shipyards ships for the Navy.*

Thus spoke Sir Basil Brooke MP, Prime Minister of Northern
Ireland, at the opening of the Sixth Stormont Parliament on 24 July
1945. He went on to give statistics of the Ulster contribution to the
British war effort. Further figures were published later by DA Chart,
Deputy Keeper of Public Records. As their accounts of Harland and
Wolff's output (page 214) are so much at variance with each other
and the actual number of ships built, these production statistics must
be viewed with caution (483,489).

The scheme of National Factories in the First War was developed
into the more comprehensive system of Shadow Factories which were
built by the Government and operated by various companies for
management fees. Many were erected in the three years or so before
the outbreak of hostilities. Numerous companies expanded their
productive capacities. A great many branch factories, known as
disposal plants were opened. In Ulster various linen mills were used
for war production.

The emphasis in the Second War was on aeroplanes. The Ministry
of Aircraft Production was set up in the same way as the Ministry of
Munitions had been during the First War. While there was no
equivalent of that department, production of shells was vastly greater
in Ireland at some 75 million, turned out mainly it would appear by
James Mackie and Sons, the Albert Foundry; Davidson and Company,
the Sirocco Works and Fairbairn Lawson Combe Barbour, the Falls
Foundry.

Various factories produced a total of 180 million incendiary bullet
casings. Some 70 million were made by Charles Hurst Limited, a
Belfast motor engineering firm, in the sheds of two separate farms
near Bangor on the main Belfast road.

During the War a factory was built in Antrim, adjacent to the
town and Lough Neagh for the production of electric torpedoes. This
was managed for a time by Stone-Platt, well known boiler

manufacturers of Manchester, on behalf of the Admiralty who directly operated the Royal Navy Torpedo Depot which was part of the plant. A concrete testing station was erected a short distance offshore on Lough Neagh. Manufacture ceased at the end of the War and testing in 1947. The *Belfast Telegraph,* 21 December 1956, reported that the station was to be demolished. The factory premises continued in use, engaged mainly on maintenance of torpedoes, and underwent a number of administrative changes and was finally designated the Royal Navy Armaments Depot (Antrim) in 1974. The base, which employed some three hundred, was closed in 1978 following a decision taken under the Defence White Pape 1976 with its functions and some personnel being transferred to Plymouth (719-20).

The linen industry, mainstay of Ulster for generations, was of immense extra importance in wartime. In the First War the Ministry of Munitions bought up the entire flax crop in 1918 and '19 for use as aircraft fabric. In the Second, great quantities of finished articles were exported for dollars until the Lend-Lease agreement with the USA in 1941. From then on large tonnages of flax were imported from the growing areas in other provinces and overseas. Production totalled thirty million shirts representing ninety percent of all British forces requirements, including desert and bush types; overalls; kitbags; Mae Wests and other lifejackets; straps; ammunition belts; tarpaulins and a great many more items including the thread for sewing these together and for surgical use. The Belfast Ropework Co turned out 250,000 camouflage nets, innumerable types of lines and also steel boom defence nets. Littlewoods, the well known Liverpool football pools and mail order firm which manufactured parachutes extensively on Merseyside, set up a branch in 1942 in a disused mill at Carrickfergus. They made three million parachutes for human use and for dropping flares, mines and bombs and for other purposes including one of a rather bizarre nature, some fifty thousand miniatures replete with 'troopers' as decoys (444,489).

The Ministry of Aircraft Production, desperately seeking supplies of aluminium, opened a bauxite mine at Lyle Hill, Antrim. This yielded 300,000 tons processed at the plant which the British Aluminium Company had in Larne, nearby. Large quantities of scrap metals were gathered and many fine railings, including those around Stormont were taken down. There were salvage drives for many commodities in both Wars. Paper, fats for glycerine, and so on were collected and recycled.

The normal peace time products such as machines and components were used in huge quantities and the Ulster engineering, manufacturing and repairing firms were engaged at full capacity in making and servicing all types of equipment and vehicles. The firm of Hugh J Scott and Company made large numbers of electric motors, transformers and other appliances including rectifiers which enabled the USA forces to use their equipment on the British and European systems. The Hoffman Manufacturing Company, a British concern, set up a plant for making ball bearings in Portadown. Ordinary civilian goods were used in large amounts such as the tobacco products of Gallagher Limited which had the largest factory of its kind in the world at Belfast.

Most manufacturing operations were broken down into several small parts which could be carried on by less skilled workers and the dilution system of the First War was developed further. There was a vast welter of sub-contracts and cross-contracts and in most instances it is not clear which firm or factory produced a particular item. Official records are largely lacking and when available are generally uninformative. Many companies made unfamiliar products. Brooke quoted with pride a concern, which in peacetime had made farm gates, turned out intricate valves for submarines.

Some eighty thousand workers were involved in these wartime undertakings. Their morale was given serious attention. Sir Basil Brooke, Prime Minister 1943-63 was Minister for Commerce with the additional title of Production from January 1941 until February 1945 when he was succeeded by Sir Roland Nugent MP. At the beginning of the War the Northern Area Board of the Production Executive of the War Cabinet in London was set up to co-ordinate the efforts of all undertakings. This was changed in August 1941 to the Production Advisory Committee and in September 1942 to the Production Council. In practice there was no change as the same members continued to sit.

The Minister of Commerce and Production was in the chair. The members were the Parliamentary Secretary; the Permanent Secretary, Sir William D Scott who during the War was Regional Controller for the London Ministries of Supply, Production and the Board of Trade; the Deputy Regional Controller of the Admiralty; the Flag Officer in Charge (Northern Ireland); the Deputy Regional Controllers for Supply and Aircraft Production; the Regional Controllers for Factory and Storage Premises; the Director General of Machine Tool Control and the Permanent Secretary and Assistant Secretary of the Stormont Ministry of Labour. There were two representatives of the Engineering and Allied Employers (Northern Ireland) Association and two other employer members. There were three delegates from the Confederation of Engineering and Shipbuilding Trades and one each from the Amalgamated Engineering Union and the National Federation of Building Trade Operatives. The regional Controller of the Ministry of Information and other officials attended as necessary the meetings of the Council which were held monthly.

The Council's Executive Committee met each week and took such decisions as were actually made in Belfast. All of any consequence were made in London. The Production Council was largely an effort in public relations to put a gloss on the Ulster contribution to the War effort. While London decided on allocations of resources and levels of output there was a definite need for morale boosting exercises which no doubt could best be carried out locally.

One of the principal methods of maintaining the will to win was showing government films of which many were made during the War. These were quite distinct from ordinary commercial cinema films which continued to be made, many indeed on War themes.

Most of the factories were on shift working. This and other points posed problems in finding times suitable for showing the films. It was thought that Sundays would be the most convenient time for the greatest number of workers. The position was difficult and delicate, the showing of films being controlled by the Police Committee of Belfast Corporation under the Cinematograph Act 1909. It was necessary for the Production Council's secretary to apply to the Committee for permission and for Brooke to make a personal plea in support of the applications by the managements of the cinemas for the permits needed. The Council leaned over backwards by promising not to clash with church hours. The Burgesses of Belfast, that citadel of Calvinism, agreed. Not until May 1978 in the wake of vast political and social changes did they allow cinemas to open generally on Sundays. Special shows were also held in Belfast cinemas for entertaining service per onnel on Sundays (485).

The Production Council arranged talks by famous war heroes who addressed audiences in factories and other venues. Various meetings, lectures and exhibitions of posters and photos were held. Leading singers, musicians, comedians and other entertainers gave concerts. Promotions such as 'Spitfire Week', 'Warship Week' and so on were organised. Practical demonstrations were also held. In September 1943 a number of girls working in a shell factory went to sea and fired off some of their own products. Output improved immensely as a result. On another occasion workers in a factory making six pounder shells were enabled to do the same in the factory.

In the last year of the War and for several months after the cessation of hostilities the energies of the Council were taken up with the problem of removing a large air raid shelter at Queen's Quay Railway Station which had outlived its usefulness and become a traffic hazard. In 1943 there was a dispute about the price of the *Belfast Telegraph*, the local evening paper then 1¹/2d (¹/2p). There were numerous complaints, particularly by USA troops of street sellers charging what they liked. The management's case was that the public had often paid more than the normal price and that many of the USA soldiers had "spoiled the boys, tossing them not infrequently, sixpences for the paper".

The USA had a large naval base in Derry and major army and airforce bases in the Lough Neagh area. During the First War the USA had a naval airbase in Lough Foyle and bases in Cork Harbour (492-3).

Apart from the air raid shelter and the newspaper, several minor questions took up the time of the Council which served the useful bureaucratic purpose of another link in the chain of civil service reference, otherwise buck-passing, without infringing on any particular department's empire. The council was not formally wound up. It simply faded away (483-4,490).

Large numbers of Irishmen served in the British forces, Army, Navy, Air Force and Marines in both Wars. There was no conscription in the country during the First War nor in the North during the Second. Many thousands served in the medical, commissariat, transport and other services and in the Merchant Navy. Many more were employed in the construction of all types of installations and in all sectors of manufacturing and utility industries. There was indeed keen competition for Irish workers.

In the autumn of 1916 difficulties arose with Irish workers on the building of the government cordite factory in Gretna. The men were afraid that they would be liable for conscription following a court case in which it was held that an Irishman in Britain could be called up. The Ministry of Munitions took the view that this was not the case as far as the workers at Gretna were concerned stating that "their departure would put a stop to the progress of the factory which is urgently required". It took a special issue of *On War Service* badges and an assurance by the government in the House of Commons on 8 November 1916 to convince the men that they would not be conscripted. Rivalry between departments continued until February 1918 when the Ministers for Munitions, Labour and National Service agreed not to compete with each other for Irish workers (440-1).

In the Second War which was carried out on a far more intensive industrial level there was again a scramble for Irish workers. Various institutions, industries and individual firms had agents in Dublin for hiring including the Ministry of Labour; Standard Telephones and Cables; Guest, Keen and Nettlefold, the large steel company; Birmingham Corporation Transport and more, all poaching off each other. The best organised was probably a bureau styled *Light Metal Industry* sponsored jointly by the Wrought Light Alloys Association and the Light Metal Founders Association which was administered by a Birmingham firm of accountants (486).

Irish workers in Britain were liable to conscription with the option of returning home before call-up papers became operative. Occasionally individuals were enlisted without being informed of their rights and in some cases were released on representations being made by friends (487).

In December 1942 Colonel EJB Tagg of the Ministry of Aircraft Production visited Dublin and found that the procedures operated by *Light Metal Industry* were too slow and that "no Eire recruit can afford the cost of a travel permit, five shillings (25p), photo for the permits 3/-(15p) and medical examination 5/-(25p)". These sums were advanced to the workers some of whom failed to turn up resulting in the loss of the money. The War was costing several millions per day. Clearly the colonel was of an economical disposition. In September 1944 *Light Metal Industry* and the various other bureaux were closed down and replaced by a new central agency the United Kingdom Liaison Officer for Labour with diplomatic status and official channels to the Department of External Affairs and the Garda Siochana. The Officer made all the arrangements for the travel and employment of each individual from home to a specific job in Britain paying for the photo, medical examination and travel tickets by vouchers which prevented losses and paid three shillings pocket money.

The various departments and other interests involved did not like the new system and at a meeting in London shortly before its implementation each fought for their own particular personnel. The Ministry of Agriculture wanted farmworkers. The railways demanded railworkers and so on. During the War many Ulster factories employed workers from other provinces. Afterwards Stormont prevented this. Some thousands of Ulster workers went to Britain during the War and large numbers from all counties were employed on post war reconstruction schemes (486).

In March and April 1941 discussions took place between Sir Basil Brooke, Lord Beaverbrook, Minister for Aircraft Production and representatives of other departments on the possibility of obtaining power from the Electricity Supply Board. The Dominions Office found the idea impracticable on technical grounds and the War Office concluded that "the scheme has not sufficient military advantage for us to support it" (634).

Large quantities of foodstuffs were shipped to Britain from both parts. The British Government made a special allocation of tin, which was very scarce, to the Dairy Disposal Company, a southern state owned concern, to make cans for condensed milk. Fresh milk was not normally available to the fighting forces and large sections of the civilian population (490-1).

Some manufacturing took place in Dublin and elsewhere. Large numbers of striker pins, a wear part for machineguns, were made by Metal Products (Cork). Hammond Lane, Dublin produced anti-tank mine cases. Springs for grenades were made by Hilton Brothers, mattress manufacturers, Dublin and various other components by the Great Southern Railway, Inchicore, Samuel E Holmes Limited, engineers, Monasterevan and the Jewellery & Metal Manufacturing Company, Dublin. Some other parts were made by the Ordnance Research and Production Branch of the Army which was set up for the War. The Branch filled the grenades with yellow phosphorous made in an electric furnace at Defence Headquarters, Parkgate initially using rock phosphate from Florida and later from Clare. Potassium chlorate was also produced. Aluminium for smoke grenades was taken from aircraft which had crashed in the country. A foundry was set up in the Ordnance Workshops to refine the metal which was a difficult task because numerous grades were involved (722-6).

Both parts of the country experienced German bombings. On 26 August 1940 three persons were killed at Campile, Wexford in a daytime raid. On 2 January 1941 three were killed and two injured at Borris, Offaly and seven were injured in Terenure, Dublin. On the following night two were injured at the South Circular Road and finally on 31 May twenty-seven were killed and forty-five injured at the North Strand, Dublin. Bombs were also dropped, without causing fatalities, at several other places in Leinster (488,721).

These were apparently more by accident than intention. The Germans made several deliberate attacks in the North and particularly set out to blitz Belfast. In four major raids in April and May 1941 the Luftwaffe killed 889, injured thousands, wrecked 57,000 houses, severely damaged the Harland and Wolff shipyards, the prime target, numerous factories, public buildings and other property to an extent estimated at exceeding £20 million. The worst night was Easter Tuesday as chronicled by DA Chart:

Towards daybreak Eire fire brigades from Dundalk, Dun Laoghaire (the old Kingstown), Drogheda and Dublin brought their welcome help. They had rushed headlong through the night with their lights blazing and had everywhere been cheered as they passed through.

DUBLIN DOCKYARD SHELL FACTORY
SOURCE 681

CHAPTER FIVE

GUNS

The development of guns did not come for a considerable and rather unclear length of time after powder. Indeed guns did not become effective weapons for a long period. The inventive genius of humankind began to find and has never ceased searching for ever improved methods of making firearms. Guns were fitted on walls of towns and fortresses, on wheels and on ships, were built into crossbows and swords and made in numerous shapes and sizes from large weapons needing stands to tiny models for a man's watchchain and a woman's handbag. Artillery was first made in Ireland in the 1220s or earlier. This was well over a century before gunpowder came into use. At the time the term meant devices powered by springs or tightly wound up cords, catapults, springboards and other counterpoise systems. These weapons hurled large rocks, showers of stones, carcasses of animals which could create pestilential conditions in besieged strongholds, and any other missiles which were readily at hand. Volleys of metal darts, balls or bolts were also used, sometimes red hot and, depending on availability of materials and expertise, vessels of Greek Fire (page 2).

An inventory of stocks in the stores of the King's castles at Athlone, Limerick and Dublin about 1224 shows that mangonels, used for throwing rocks and so on, and from which the term gun may have been derived, were in common use by then. The Athlone armoury held two mangonels each fitted with 120 strings, several suits of armour and other equipment. Limerick was completely bereft of armaments, its contents being "worth scarcely eighteen [old] pence as broken dishes". Dublin Castle had two mangonels and a large supply of other weapons (509).

On returning to England in 1367 from his Irish adventure Lionel took his gun back to the Tower of London. In Dublin Castle at the time there must have been metal and wood artificers employed in making and repairing swords, lances, crossbows, armour, mangonels, and siege towers besides the various fixtures in the buildings. It seems perfectly probable that they would have at least experimented on making guns. Certainly guns were being made before King Richard II came. In May 1394, four months before his first visit, the King's Council in Ireland arranged for one Richard Sonner, a gunsmith of Dublin, to go to Carlow and make guns and other armaments for the defence of the town. No doubt guns were made afterwards from time to time in The Castle (510).

There does not seem to have been large scale production of any type of firearms sustained over a long period. William Cornell and Christopher, presumably his son, both described as armourers, owned property in the parish of St Werburgh in the liberties of Dublin from 1460 to 1500. Evidently they made items of armour and perhaps also guns (511-14).

In January 1642, Roger Boyle, Lord Broghill, writing from Lismore Castle, Waterford to his father, the Earl of Cork, reported: "I tried one of the ordnances made at the forge and it held with a two pound charge". At this time the Boyles had been making iron in the Blackwater valley for at least twenty-five years. In 1616 the Earl had drawn up an estimate of costs in making iron. It may well be that the Boyles made other guns. There is a distinct flavour of experimentation about this and certainly a two pound, approximately one kilo, charge was in the smallest league even then. Roger was appointed Master of the Ordnance in Ireland in 1648. His brother Robert propounded Boyle's law on gas, one of the fundamentals of physics (494,516-17).

In the early seventeenth century there were several proposals for the making of artillery. The first appears to have been in 1618. In 1624 it was suggested that the King should "grant a licence unto eleven gentlemen, to make iron ordnance to sell to the King, his friends and allies, the project will set many idle people at work, plant and maintain many English families and will add many men to the musters to answer all alarms". There was a similar scheme in 1632. It is not clear if any of these went ahead (520-22).

In 1626, Henry Wright and Richard Blacknall, who claimed twenty years experience, put forward a plan for making cannon from a large deposit of iron they had found in a Cork mountain, apparently in the eastern part of the county, which they leased from the Boyles. They were willing to pay £12,000 a year for the privilege, employ eight hundred Englishmen at eight [old] pence per day and make 1,200 tons of "good and clean ordnance" at £7 per ton, half the rate in England. They obtained a patent for thirty-one years to operate this arrangement. In 1632 Blacknall received a further patent to make brass and iron ordnance, shot and bar iron, for himself and his heirs (523-25).

On one occasion at least, foreign artificers were engaged to make guns in Ireland for the royal service. In this instance twenty men from the Walloon area of Belgium were hired in 1632 to make ordnance at the King's ironworks. The location of this is not clear. In 1610 the King had ordered the setting up of an ironworks. Probably several existed from time to time (504,519).

In 1643, during the Confederate Wars, the Irish side made some ship guns and a mortar which they used at the siege of Castle Coot, Roscommon. When guns were not available bluff might be tried. In 1641 the Irish used a leather gun in besieging Ballyaly Castle, Clare. Fifty years later during the war between King James II and William of Orange, Pierce Butler, Lord Galmoy, a Jacobite general, used two cannon made from tin and bound with buckram in an unsuccessful attempt to frighten the garrison of Crom Castle on Lough Erne into surrendering (527-9).

In February 1686 the opinion was expressed that muskets could be made at less cost in Ireland than in England. The author of this was Justin MacCarthy, Lord Mountcashell, a Jacobite who held numerous offices including that of Master General of the Ordnance in Ireland. The title had apparently been upgraded since Roger Boyle's day (518,676).

In October 1689 Richard Talbot, Lord Tyrconnell, King James's Lord Lieutenant, requisitioned a "quantity of steel to make firelocks". In February 1690 the Jacobites had some 150 men, including apparently all the smiths in Dublin, engaged in making guns. They were also making iron in Wicklow and Connacht (526,677).

In the last twenty years of the seventeenth century Ralph Bullen, Thomas Fitzpatrick, George Green, John Higgins, John Kennedy, Samuel Lyon, Samuel McDowell, Richard Spencer, William Trulock and John Wade were gunsmiths living in the parish of St Michan's adjacent to the present Four Courts. Possibly there were others living in different districts of Dublin (515).

In September 1705 the Irish Board of Ordnance wrote to the Lord High Treasurer pointing out that the demand for guns in England had been so great over the previous three years that none could be spared for Ireland and accordingly the Duke of Ormonde, the Lord Lieutenant, had proposed that guns should be made in the country. Tenders were received from six gunmakers, all apparently in Dublin. The order was for five thousand muskets, six hundred fuzees, six hundred carbines and six hundred cases of pistols. The contract went to John Van Bylaart, a gunmaker or agent, of Rotterdam under an

Order in Council made in April 1706. The arrangement was that ten thousand muskets were to be made, engraved "Ormonde", packed in deal chests holding fifty each, stored in a warehouse specially rented in Rotterdam and shipped to Dublin all for the price of £1-2-0 [£1.10] each.

The tenders submitted by the Irish makers were: Fitzpatrick, £1-3-0 (£1.15); Martin, £1-2-0 (£1.10); Symes, £1-1-9 (£1.09); Barrion, £1-1-1 (£1.05); Byrne, £1-1-6 (£1.07^1/2) and Maddock, £1-0-0 (£1.00).

Four of the offers were lower than Van Bylaart's, one was equal and only one was greater. These prices were for five thousand weapons. For double the quantity presumably the cost would have been lower still. Van Bylaart could not compete on price. It might be that he got the contract by quoting better quality and delivery. Possibly. This was in the reign of Queen Anne and although the daughter of King James, she had supported the Dutch William of Orange, married him and in due course succeeded him on the throne of England. This is far more likely to have been the reason why the contract which was during the War of the Spainish Succession, in which England and Holland were allied against Spain, went to Rotterdam instead of Dublin (495-6).

In June 1712 the Company of Goldsmiths of Dublin objected to the use of the symbol of the harp surmounted by a crown being used for stamping guns as an indication of proof, that is showing the weapons had been tested and found up to standard. The Goldsmiths, since before 1597, have had the right and the duty to examine and hallmark in the Assay Office all articles in gold, silver and (platinum) with the power to destroy summarily any items not of proper quality. Their stamp is recognised all over the world, as they proudly proclaim, the origin of what has come to be known as consumer protection. The Goldsmiths therefore objected to the mark being used on base metal. It is not clear what happened as a result of this nor whether the proofing was being carried out by the gunmakers or by an official establishment. There may have been an element of the "who does what" type of trade dispute in this. Around 1685 one F Maddock made in Dublin a twelve bore shotgun with richly engraved silver embellishments. This is now in the Tower of London. The goldsmiths may have resented the gunmakers infringing on their art (497,506,537).

Four Irish gunsmiths, at least, got orders during the Stuart Uprising in Scotland led by Bonnie Prince Charlie. In the middle of this conflict *Faulkner's Journal*, 10 December 1745 a Dublin paper, carried a joint notice signed by John Govers, Francis Lord, James

Powell and Michael Rainsford. They had a contract from the government and wanted to hire skilled gun workers.

A gun foundry existed in Dublin during the 1770s. The *Freeman's Journal*, 8 October 1778, published an attack on the "blundering supineness or treason of British ministers in five administrations since 1761" which had left the country with only seven thousand troops when at least twelve were required in peacetime. This was during the American War of Independence when a French invasion was widely expected. The paper went on to note that "a great number of brass mortars and howitzers have lately been cast and bored at our arsenal. They are of the new construction and very beautiful. These with the cannon landed from England about three weeks ago have furnished us with a train of ordnance sufficient for any emergency". It is not clear whether this factory was run by the Irish Board of Ordnance or was a private undertaking.

A few years later William Caldbeck, who had a gunpowder mill at Clondalkin (page 9) was operating a gun factory in the city. The *Freeman's Journal*, 25 October 1781, reported that Volunteer officers had collected "two very fine brass field pieces at Counsellor Caldbeck's foundry in Mark Lane which from the spirit of the times will probably supply most of the principal independent corps in the Kingdom. Too much credit cannot be given to Colonel Caldbeck for establishing at great expense this much wanted and most excellent foundry". Calbeck was an officer in the Lawyers' Corps of Volunteers and obviously had a good eye for business. The principal suppliers of small-arms to the Irish Board of Ordnance in the 1780s were Michael Hutchinson, James Rainsford and Thomas Trulock (505).

If the Board of Ordnance had a factory in Dublin during the 1770s it was certainly not in operation twenty years later when Richard Spear was the Board's agent for the provision of powder, guns, ammunition, and other stores. He made arrangements with the British Board's makers and the Clyde Company, a foundry firm in Scotland, for a supply of artillery and also bought cannon balls from the Arigna Foundry Company in Leitrim (673).

John Mallet, a brassfounder from Devon, settled in Dublin and set up the Victoria Foundry. In 1820 he made a number of three pounder guns for the Coastguard Service. His son Robert, a prominent engineer in the mid-nineteenth century, claimed these as "probably the very earliest British successful attempts in producing forged cannon in one piece, fired by a lock". This statement was in the course of an extremely long and detailed dissertation on the metallurgy, mechanics and mathematics of manufacturing artillery, delivered to the Royal Irish Academy in 1855. The paper certainly is the premier Irish contribution to the science. Mallet argued that any attempt at secrecy in gunmaking was futile and that an historical and technical library should be set up at Woolwich, seat of the British artillery service, available to all, pointing out that the openness practiced by the military establishments in France and the USA, where all advances were published, led to greater progress all round. During the Crimean War Mallet designed huge mortars for the British which were cast in London. Also during this conflict a gun was reputed to have been made from iron mined in Creevelea, Leitrim (531,534).

During the eighteenth and nineteenth centuries there was apparently some inventive talent among the Dublin gunsmiths. In May 1744 one Nathaniel Dunn showed the Royal Dublin Society a "small gun of his making, well executed which discharges two shots, one immediately after the other". In November 1786 John Gray exhibited to the RDS a gun which fired "two shots separately out of a plain single barrel with one trigger". In the meantime edged weapons had not gone completely out of use. In May 1758 Elizabeth Nix and her son George Kent were awarded a premium by the RDS for swords, bayonets and other items which they had made (501-3).

In 1839 John Rigby, a partner in the long established Dublin firm of W & J Rigby told the RDS of various technical improvements which his house had made in rifling of barrels and in the making of locks which he claimed brought about a great decline in the extent of duelling in Ireland and a proportionate increase in target practice shooting. In 1844 the RDS awarded The Large Silver Medal for W & J Rigby's Improved Mould for Casting Solid Balls. The *Catalogue of the Irish Industrial Exhibition 1853,* attributed to the Rigbys the credit for rediscovering in 1817 the Damascus process of making barrels in which alternate layers of iron and steel were treated with sulphuric acid to produce the fine finish believed to have been developed centuries earlier in the Middle East city and later lost (532-3,679).

Even with these interesting instances of ingenuity none of the Irish makers ever grew into large scale manufacturers. Robert McCormick, a gunmaker and acquaintance of William Drennan in Belfast, published a notice in the *Northern Star,* 19 December 1792, announcing that he had "constructed a firelock which he conceives to be an improvement on the arms now in use". He was willing to take orders for this weapon which he intended to have made in England under his own supervision. Apparently it was not possible to have the gun manufactured in Ireland in quantity (727-28).

This lack of productive capacity is borne out by Richard Spear in his efforts to procure small-arms for the Board of Ordnance. He knew the capabilities of each gunsmith and was aware that even all of them together could not possibly meet the demands of the 1790s and accordingly he bought in Birmingham supplies of barrels, locks, stocks and other components which he distributed among the various makers. Under this arrangement some one hundred thousand muskets and carbines and ten thousand pistols were produced. He also bought in Birmingham forty thousand stand of finished arms. The Birmingham Gun Trade regarded the Irish Board of Ordnance as a very good customer at the time (530,673).

The system of bringing in parts and contracting smiths to make up guns continued apparently throughout the Napoleonic Wars. A return of 1807 showed one firm and thirteen individuals engaged in this type of work for the Board of Ordnance: Lanyson and Patterson, John Alley, Ullen Birch, Nicholas Clark, William Cox, Michael Devereaux, Thomas Fowler, Thomas Harkey, R McCormack, T McDermott, Daniel Muley, John Rigby, Thomas Stewart, and James Willson, all of whom were in Dublin (498-9).

Clearly therefore, while the gunsmiths of Ireland were capable of assembling, and no doubt repairing, weapons they could hardly make all the individual parts, at any rate in quantity. The production of guns is a very complicated chain of separate operations. For example the Birmingham Gun Trade was, and still is to a certain extent, divided among a large number of specialist sub-contractors. Barrels alone, for instance, involve welders, borers, grinders, filers and breechers and there are several separate skills in each of the other components. While this is no doubt in part a reflection of the convenience of the industry in Birmingham, it does show that there were many distinct crafts involved, too many for the small demand in Ireland to support. There was an occasional specialist. Around 1812 a certain John Murphy carried on business as a barrel-maker in Dublin and perhaps there were others from time to time (539,690).

The market in Ireland must have been small. Even after the repeal of the Penal Laws which had placed restrictions on Catholics and Presbyterians owning guns and being involved in the arms trade, it is doubtful if sales increased very much. This means that the Protestant landed gentry must have been the main purchasers for a long period. Doubtless many of these would have bought guns from the leading West End of London firms and fashionable foreign makers.

Many Irish makers advertised in the newspapers and directories in the eighteenth and nineteenth centuries and many guns survive carrying names of makers in various towns. Such signatures do not absolutely authenticate weapons as having been made in Ireland as two examples show. The Cork Public Museum has a case of pistols stamped CRISPIN CORK. These carry the Birmingham Proof House mark and moreover the case has an ornate paper label bearing the imprint "Babington Sct". This is an abbreviation indicating that the plate was engraved by the printer. A W Babington was an engraver and printer in Birmingham in the 1830s when Joseph Crispin advertised in the Cork papers. Clearly, Crispin did not send to Birmingham merely to get a label printed (508,693).

The second example bears this out. The firm of T W Murray and Company, Cork, founded in 1828 and therefore among the oldest in Ireland, sold shotguns stamped MURRAY CORK, until the 1930's. All these were made in Birmingham, in the later years by the leading company of Webley and Scott (710).

This is the well known own label principle. Many shops today sell cans of beans and packets of biscuits carrying their own brands. This does not prove that the firms own canneries and bakeries. Rather they commission manufacturers to package goods to order. This was common practice with cartridges at least as far back as George Kynoch's day (295).

It is apparent therefore that most firms or individuals in Ireland who described themselves as gunmakers could no more make weapons than those today who hold themselves out as jewellers and watchmakers could actually make timepieces.

In 1967 Kevin James Patrick Vincent Kavanagh returned to Ireland with plans for a gun factory. Born in Wexford in 1918 he claimed to have spent many years in the British Secret Service. For a number of years after the Second World War he ran a works of sorts in Cheltenham which came under unfavourable notice from the Guardians of the Birmingham Proof House. In November 1967 he became a director and his brother Edward T Kavanagh became a director and secretary of a dormant company "Lamhthairgi Teoranta (Handwoven Products Limited)" which had been formed in 1950 to carry on a brushmaking business. The new owners changed the name to the Fenian Gun Company of Ireland Limited and increased the capital from £500 to £100,000 and in April 1968 to £180,000. They leased part of the old workhouse at Birr, County Offaly from Birr Projects Limited a local development group formed in 1965.

It was intended to manufacture an under and over, as distinct from side by side, double barreled shotgun which Kavanagh claimed to have invented and was going to be the greatest advance in armaments since the Kavanaghs began in the gun business which Kavanagh averred was in 1704. The design indeed won the Gold Medal and Plaque of Honour at the Brussels International Exhibition in March 1968. According to Kavanagh the Secret Service wanted him to set up in any part of Northern Ireland except Newry or Omagh. When he went to Birr he was obliged to accept two nominees of the Service on his staff. From 1965 Kavanagh had been reporting to the Service various movements of arms to Northern Ireland and at Brussels learned of a plot for an Unilateral Declaration of Independence by leading Unionist politicians. This was much heard of after October 1968 when the North exploded. It had been coined by Ian Smith, Prime Minister of Rhodesia, who had taken that step three years earlier. How much of all this was so and how much was Kavanagh's imagination is not clear.

In practice, while the factory functioned after a fashion until early 1970, hardly any guns were produced even though up to seventy were employed. The Firearms (Proofing) Act was passed in July 1968. This, while cast in general terms, was in practice specifically to facilitate the Birr factory. As there was no proofhouse in Ireland the products had to be sent to Birmingham or elsewhere for proofing without which guns could not be exported to most countries. Regulations under the Act were duly laid down and arrangements made for imported guns to be tested, for the Irish proof mark to be registered abroad and for the marks of other countries to be registered in the State. The Act enabled the Institute for Industrial Research and Standards to set up a proofhouse. This was done and the IIRS carried out some work for the Fenian Company. The mark of the Irish Gun Barrell Proof House was recognised by Birmingham, London and other establishments. Although no work has been done since the company closed and the Act is effectively a dead letter, the IIRS remains obliged to proof any weapon presented for the purpose (684).

The Industrial Development Authority approved and paid grants totalling £21,590. Another State agency, the Industrial Credit Company, paid £8,500 for a debenture and there were further borrowings from a bank. John Donnelly, a well known Dublin accountant, who was Chairman of the company became Receiver in February 1970 and later the Liquidator. The Registrar struck the company off in February 1978.

Kavanagh went to Mabe, near Penryn, Cornwall in May 1970 with a view to setting up a factory for his weapon claiming that he had large orders from the Winchester company in the USA and that the Birr business had been sabotaged. He also intended to manufacture another weapon the *Twistlock* and a cattle dehorning device. This came to the attention of Ian Paisley MP who visited him in December 1970. Earlier in the year Paisley had been elected to the Commons in both Stormont and Westminster. Founder and Moderator of the Free Presbyterian Church of Ulster, principal of the Puritan Printing Company and the *Protestant Telegraph*, chairman of the 'Ulster Constitution Defence Committee' and in general self-appointed saviour of Protestant Loyalism with indeed a considerable and increasing measure of popular support, he had for several years been swaggering across the stage of Ulster. In February 1971 Paisley began a campaign against the dastardly plot to slaughter loyal Unionists with the dehorning device. He kept this up for some time until he had extracted the maximum mileage and some other issue came along.

Kavanagh had difficulties with the Devon and Cornwall Constabulary from the time he arrived at his new home and after a long legal battle failed to get a gunmaker's licence. His application was turned down at Bodmin Crown Court in June 1974, the Judge remarking that there was a *Walter Mitty* ingredient in his character and to allow him a licence would jeopardise himself, his family, the public and the peace of Britain. Immediately after this he went through the motions of looking into the possibility of setting up a factory in Cork. This did not come to pass. He died in 1975 (540-52).

It is probable that some gunmakers made cartridges to orders of individual customers. The report of an explosion at the workshop of Trulock, Harriss and Richardson, Dawson Street, Dublin in March 1906 indicates that the firm made up cartridges. It is likely that any firm making cartridges obtained supplies of lead shot from Ballycorus Lead Mine on the Dublin-Wicklow border which was operated by the Mining Company of Ireland for many years until some time before the First World War. The mine works and long horizontal flue to a high tower on the adjacent hill form a striking feature on the local landscape. On 25 April 1916 David Lloyd George, Minister for Munitions, in reply to a question by William Field MP, stated that the premises had been inspected and found unsuitable for munitions production (536).

The annual report of the Inspectors of Explosives for 1900 recorded that Factory 197 had been licenced for the production of Henrite and safety cartridges at Galway. The report for 1902 noted that this factory had become 'extinct'. In 1909 Henrite Explosives Limited was formed for the manufacture of the explosive at Dartford, Kent and functioned for a few years. It is not clear if there was any connection with the Galway enterprise which apparently never went into operation (500,689).

Galway indeed had the only ammunition plant to last an appreciable period. In 1935 Irish Metal Industries Limited, formed the previous year, began making shotgun cartridges from the Eley-Kynoch range under licence from Kynoch, Birmingham and with Kynoch directors on the board. The factory was on Earls Island, Galway. The city was found to have slightly better transport facilities than Sligo which had also been considered. Production was discontinued during the Second World War and slumped seriously during the mid 'fifties when myxomatosis, the marvel of the age, largely eliminated the rabbit scourge.

In May 1975 the company announced that the manufacture was being terminated without loss of employment as the workers concerned were transferred to copper tube making and production of various ICI pharmaceuticals made under licence. The industry had become uneconomic. It was essentially an assembly operation, the cases, caps, filling and shot being imported and made up. For the previous few years there had been increasing competition from cartridges imported from the Soviet Union and Poland. The undertaking was typical of its time, an assembly business set up under the protectionist policy of the 1930s. The company never carried out serious marketing in the form of advertising and sponorship and, with the gradual dismantling of tariffs under the 1965 Anglo-Irish Free Trade Agreement and the 1972 Treaty of Accession to the European Economic Community, could no longer compete (538).

During the Second World War guns were manufactured on a large scale in Northern Ireland. Sir Basil Brooke told Stormont on 24 July 1945 that production had totalled over five hundred, apparently of heavy calibre; fourteen thousand barrels and other parts; forty-two thousand carbine machineguns and fifty thousand bayonets.

Harland and Wolff made barrels for 3.7 inch anti-aircraft guns and were one of only three manufacturers of heavy gun mountings for the Royal Navy.

This was certainly the largest output of guns, both small-arms and artillery, in any single period. It was also typical of the whole history of gunmaking in Ireland. Most instances were in wartime and formed emergency extensions to British production which ceased when hostilities ended (535).

In November 1933 the Department of Defence proposed the establishment of a plant which would produce the entire annual requirements of $4^1/_2$ million rounds of .303 rifle and 200,000 rounds of .45 revolver ammunition. The cost of construction was estimated at £200,000 with permanent employment for 107. The Department, while admitting that the cost of production would be 43% greater than the purchase of imported supplies, argued that it was necessary to have some home production capacity in case of emergency. The Department of Finance countered that the outlay was "incommensurate" with the employment, the cost of production as against importation was excessive and that it would be as difficult to obtain the necessary raw materials in wartime as finished products. However remotely located the factory would be within the range of continental bombers.

In July 1934 the Cabinet decided that the factory should be built, west of the Shannon and under the direct management of Defence. Some three hundred sites were examined and fifty noted which were reduced to seven, all in Clare. Four were surveyed in detail and in November a peninsula, Cullane, Kilkishen on Doon Lough was selected as the most suitable from the standpoints of water supply, drainage, access to powerlines and availability of accommodation. The government asked specialists to advise on the technical aspects. The most prominent was Joseph Reilly, Professor of Chemistry at University College Cork who had been chief chemist at a cordite plant during the First War and subsequently head of research at the Royal Arsenal, Woolwich. The others were his counterpart at University College Dublin, TJ Nolan and two civil engineers. Tenders were invited and several companies in Ireland, Britain, France, Germany and the USA submitted individual and joint proposals variously for all or part of the work of building and equipping the plant. The choice was narrowed to two, ICI and Gutehoffnungshutte, Oberhausen of Germany, a major international constructional engineering firm still in existence in the 1980s, which was quickly eliminated on grounds of remoteness and the nature of their corporate structure and methods while ICI were near and well known to the consultants. It was generally desirable to use British rather than European standards and systems. The ICI tender was £171,000 compared with £216,000 at the rate of exchange ruling for the mark in October 1935. Apparently Germany was not regarded as a potential belligerent at the time.

In January 1936 the subject was withdrawn from Cabinet consideration for the time being. A month later a committee representing the Departments of Defence, Industry and Commerce and External Affairs was set up to negotiate better terms with the two firms. This went on for two years. Eventually the companies were invited to submit fresh tenders on the basis of a specification prepared by Defence which laid down extensive detail including the proviso that turf was to be used for producing gas, steam and hot water. The plant would be operated for six months and maintained for a further six by the contractor. ICI submitted a tender on a somewhat different basis which would give them five percent profit on £270,000. They furthermore offered to train personnel in their own factories and undertook to make available for seven years all improvements and to give advice without charge except for travelling expenses. The German firm tendered £395,000 on an entirely different basis.

On 8 February 1939 both bids were submitted to the Cabinet by Defence. Again Finance opposed, pointing out that the differential between production and importation had risen to 70%. On 14 February the Cabinet decided to ask ICI to go ahead immediately. At this time there could hardly have been any doubt that Britain and Germany would be at war in the forseeable future. The next day a supplementary estimate for Defence was introduced in the Dail which made provision for the plant and an extensive programme of air raid precautions, construction of aerodromes, purchase of stores and equipment and other measures reflecting a greatly increased level of military and civil defence activity.

On 27 September ICI wrote informing Defence that owing to the outbreak of war they were unable to proceed, regretting that the decision had not been taken even six months earlier than it had and expressing "extreme willingness to tackle the job as soon as we are able". The factory was never built. The project would have been carried out under the auspices of the ammunition section of ICI Metals Division based at Kynoch Works, Birmingham. There was never any question of expanding the recently built shotgun ammunition plant in Galway. It is not clear whether or not the site was in Clare because the county was the constituency represented by the then head of government, Eamon de Valera (729-33).

MILITARY PISTOL BY RIGBY'S, DUBLIN, ABOUT 1810
SOURCE 507

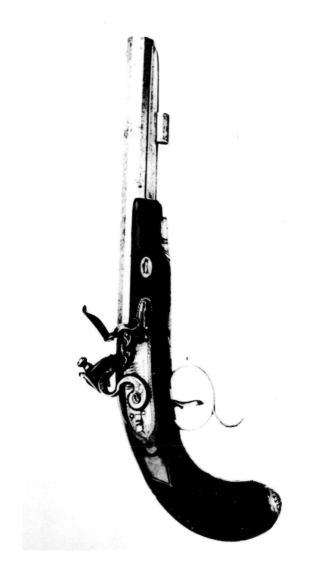

CHAPTER SIX

ARMOURED VEHICLES

The term "tank" was coined in Britain during the First World War as a code designating armoured vehicles moving on tracks which had been developed in response to the enormously effective German machine guns. The word very quickly found its way into everyday language. Many different types were developed. It soon became an attacking weapon and was fitted with flamethrowers, minesweepers and various calibres of guns. It was made amphibious and adapted for launching missiles, building bridges and various other purposes. Wheeled versions were also developed. A well known example in the First War and afterwards in Ireland was the Crossley tender. These were not by any means the first armoured vehicles in history.

In January 1245 King Henry III issued a mandate for the construction of four bretachiae, and the next month ordered four more. These were shipped to England later in the year. Bretashes, towers built of wood and fitted with wheels, were used in sieges for close attacks on walls. Machines of this type lasted a surprisingly long time, more than three hundred years after the introduction of gunpowder (553-5).

In November 1601 the English forces besieging Kinsale attempted to breach the wall with pickaxes under cover of such a vehicle which the defenders broke by throwing large rocks down on it (556).

The Irish who attacked Ballyaly Castle, County Clare, in February 1642, during the Confederate War, built what was known at the time as a *sow*, described as being thirty-five feet long and twelve broad, about twelve metres by four. It was built of two layers of thick oak planks, nailed and bound with iron, covered with two coats of cattlehides and sheepskins, "so that no musket bullet or steel arrows could pierce it, of which trial was often made". The equipage had four doors and four wooden wheels with iron hoops and was propelled by a system of levers (527).

In November 1689 Patrick Sarsfield, fighting for King James 11, used a *sow* in besieging Sligo. The defenders made a sally at night, killed the crew and burned the vehicle. This was probably the last used in Irish warfare (557).

In the First War the Great Southern and Western Railway built four armoured trains at Inchicore Workshops, Dublin. Each had a locomotive at front and rear and the wagons were fitted with machine guns and searchlights. Five wagons were reconstructed for use as tank transporters. During Easter Week 1916 the Great Southern adapted five lorries from Guinness's Brewery as armoured vehicles. Three were fitted with smokeboxes, actually large cylinders, from locomotives under repair which formed ready-made turrets while large steel plates were bolted on the others. In both cases slits for rifles were cut and false openings painted on as well as camouflage colouring. The cabs, engines and radiators were protected with steel sheeting. After the Rising the armour was removed and the lorries went back to conveying porter (464).

During the 1930s and '40s some fifty-nine armoured cars in five models on various *Ford, Dodge* and *Leyland* chassis were built in the Army Workshops at the Curragh of Kildare by the Great Southern Railway, Inchicore and by Thomas Thompson and Sons, Hanover Works, Carlow. These were of an adaptation or improvisation type rather than production models in the sense of an original design carried through to a systematic, large scale manufacturing operation. Some of the armour used had been fitted on Constabulary barracks during the War of Independence (558,729).

In the Second War some five hundred tanks were built by Harland and Wolff at Queen's Island, Belfast and also in a Shadow Factory at Carrickfergus. Testing was carried out at the Snowy Glen, nearby. The models were the *Churchill, Centaur* and *Matilda*. Late in 1943 the Carrickfergus plant was turned over to assembling USA army vehicles (483,489,559).

During the 1960s Short Brothers developed the *Shorland*, an armoured car on the *Land Rover* chassis. In 1979-80 the company introduced three new models, the *Mark 4* Armoured Patrol Car, the *SB 401* Armoured Personnel Carrier and the *SB 404* Anti-Hijack Vehicle which is specially designed for coping with aircraft seizures and other airport security functions. The cars can be fitted with turrets and various armaments, smoke grenade dischargers, searchlights and other equipment as required. By this time the range was in use by over thirty countries (734-5).

In July 1979 it was announced by the Industrial Development

Authority that a plant for the production of a range of jeeps would be set up in Ashbourne, Meath. There were two models for military use designated *Samo* and two civil, *Cournil*, with petrol or diesel engines. The design had a box section chassis and a body of two mm steel cut and bent. The project was a joint venture between L J Warnants & Company Limited, an Irish firm with the franchise for the importation of *Panhard* armoured cars from France for the Irish Army, and a subsidiary of Gevelot SA, a large French armaments firm, makers of the jeep. It was expected that the plant would employ fifty and produce four hundred vehicles a year with sole rights for all right hand drive countries in the world which include such major markets as Australia and India. The project was cancelled when the French subsidiary was liquidated (736-40).

More than seven hundred years after armoured vehicles were first made in Ireland, the world saw an entirely new model coming from the country with great expectations that its numerous novel features would make it superior to any in its class in the world.

The Timoney Armoured Personnel Carrier has 12.7 mm armour plate of an extra strong type made by Thyssen of Germany and three windows, the windscreen and one on each front corner, of laminated glass by Triplex of England. Both metal and glass can withstand 7.62 mm armour piercing ammunition at close range from such weapons as the Armalite rifle and other modern types. The gearbox is the Timoney two speed type with four forwards and one reverse. The engine is a Chrysler model. Top speed is 100 kmh with a maximum range of 960 km.

The turret can be fitted with twin 7.62 mm machineguns or a mortar or a 20 mm cannon or a missile launching system. The car has a periscope and seven slits, fitted with flaps, for the crew to shoot through. There are three doors, one at each side and one at the rear. The windscreen and observation hatch can be used as emergency exits. The car can carry eleven crew besides the driver.

The car can cope with all types of city and country conditions, particularly urban guerilla warfare, and can be transported by air. It is equally suitable for use as a troop transporter, mobile or static command post, as an ambulance, for scouting and patrolling and can be fitted with a bulldozer blade for demolishing barricades. It is amphibious and can be equipped with propellors. Air conditioning can be installed if required, the standard ventilation system is protected against petrol bombs or molotov cocktails.

The vehicle is designed by Seamus G Timoney who graduated in mechanical engineering at University College Dublin in 1949, obtained the PhD on diesel engines in 1961 and became Professor of Mechanical Engineering (Thermodynamics) at UCD in 1968. During the early 'fifties he was employed by Alvis Limited at Coventry on the design of the *FV 600* series of armoured cars including *Saracen* and *Saladin*. Later he worked for Teledyne Continental Motors on the engine for the *Continental* the USA's main battle tank, built by Chrysler (659).

He is a consultant to the British Ministry of Defence's Military Vehicle Engineering Establishment and the USA Department of Defence's Defence Advanced Research Projects Agency. He has designed a portable multi-fuel ignition-compression engine used for general purposes by the USA armed forces, an acoustic atomiser for the combustion of liquid fuel in boilers and has carried out extensive research on high specific output diesel engines, mainly in UCD and holds a number of patents in various countries.

Preliminary design work on the Timoney APC commenced in April 1972. Construction of the first prototype was carried out in a small premises in Dublin by Industrial Engineering Designers Limited and was completed in July 1973. The third was begun immediately afterwards and was completed in the following January. The second model was built by the Irish Sugar Company, a state concern, at their agricultural machinery works in Carlow between May and October of 1973. Trials were carried out by the Army from 1973 to '76 the first being tested to destruction while the others continue in service.

In January 1978 the government placed an order for five cars. These were built in a factory at Gibbstown, Navan, Meath owned by Gaeltarra Eireann the state agency responsible for industrial development in the Gaeltachts or native Irish speaking areas. Gibbstown is in the artificial Gaeltacht created in the 1930s by the resettlement of people from congested parts of the old Gaeltachts.

The factory is operated by Ad Tec Teoranta which was registered in July 1974 as Advanced Technology Limited. The name was changed when Gaeltarra took a 49% stake in October 1975. The majority shareholding is held by the Professor, his brother Eanna Timoney and their associates John Conveney and Des Kavanagh. All are engineers and directors the company. The Timoneys control Industrial Engineering Designers Limited founded in 1957 and Technology Investments Limited registered in May 1975 which holds the rights in the vehicle.

The factory is engaged in building trucks specially designed for forestry work, fitting firefighting and refuse crushing equipment to chassis for local councils, attaching other custom built accessories to vehicles and some other types of work. The factory also makes components for the European Space Agency, Messerschmitt of Germany and other aerospace concerns. The house of Timoney are agents for Heckler & Koch, large German manufacturers of machine-guns and other military hardware. Even given that the Gaeltachts are eligible for higher industrial development grants than other areas it would appear that the factory is not suitable for large scale production. Manufacture of this type, it is generally felt, can best be carried out in an intensive industrial infrastructure rather than a rural location several kilometres from a medium size town.

At the time the factory began only Short Brothers of Belfast had a functioning capacity of this type. The ending in 1985 of protection for motor assembly might make capacity available in the various Dublin plants if these have not been taken over entirely by the motor companies of Japan. By far the more likely course is that, in countries placing substantial orders, local companies will be licenced to produce the vehicle. In March 1977 the government of Belgium ordered eighty cars for their airforce and forty-three for police use. Arrangements were made for the vehicle, designated *BDX*, to be manufactured by Beherman Demoen, a major Belgian industrial group. At some £83,000 each this contract was worth £10 million.

Even with the obvious value of this business and the potential for employment it did not seem likely that the vehicle would be manufactured in Ireland on any serious scale. The State has invested considerable sums in the car through the Department of Defence and also Gaeltarra which has only one seat on a board of five.

The Dail Committee of Public Accounts examined the Department's involvement in a report issued in April 1979. In the period 1972-75 the sum of £180,000 had been paid to the company for which it received three vehicles worth £100,000 each on the market and all the plans which the Department's Accounting Officer considered reasonable for such a research and development project. One vehicle and part of another had been sent to the Belgian company which had claimed that the design had been developed "in collaboration with the Irish Army". The Irish company purported to reject this, stating that there were two entirely different designs.

There was no formal signed contract. The Chief State Solicitor advised that a "contractual relationship existed on the basis of the correspondence and part performance". The company had refused to sign an agreement drafted by the Department which apparently had stringent conditions, "the Department in insisting on its proposals to guard against possible exploitation would be endeavouring to impose too restrictive an obligation on the Company, one which might not stand up in law", the Solicitor observed.

The Committee found that there should have been a formal contract in which the Department would share in the patent and manufacturing rights and receive "a financial return on its investment in the event of the project proving successful". The committee concluded that while it was too late in this case it should be done in any future instances.

The commercial development of inventions is always delicate. Capital, while willing to accept subsidies resents the State being involved. A joint venture therefore has many potential points of conflict. While inventive genius, all too often unrecognised indeed maltreated in the past must receive every award due, the house of Timoney has an undue proportion of the bargain (560-7, 741).

TIMONEY ARMOURED PERSONNEL CARRIER
SOURCE 563

CHAPTER SEVEN

SHIPS

The Tower of London. Nineteen hundred and seventy-one. A day in late Autumn.

The hugh bascules of Tower Bridge rise to allow the passage of a grey painted cruiser to the dock which has been specially laid out for this survivor from the last great era of the Senior Service.

The telegraph from the bridge rings "finished with engines" and the mighty roar of the Parsons steam turbines fades out to finality after more than thirty years.

Over many centuries the ancient fortress has seen kings and queens, admirals and generals, politicians and plain people passing by. For long the centre of the British Empire, merchant ships have come and gone between the Pool of London and the furthest corners of the world, bringing in raw materials and exporting manufactured products. Ships of the Crown have carried the commands of monarchs and the forces to impose the regal writs on a hundred races.

Now one of these ships has come to stay as a floating museum. The vessel had been built in Ireland at the world's greatest shipyard.

The Tower of London. Seven hundred and fifty years earlier.

On 18 July 1222 King Henry 111 issues a mandate to the men of Dublin, Waterford, Drogheda and the other ports of Ireland to build galleys for the defence of the King's realm in Ireland.

In 1224 Henry 111 issued another mandate for the making of two hundred oars of ash to be sent to England together with two large shiploads of boards for galleys and longboats. In 1241 an order was issued for the King's galleys in Ireland to be sent, well manned, to Portsmouth. A quantity of boards was exported in 1250. No doubt many galleys were built in the meantime and for long afterwards as this form of craft continued in use for centuries. The Boyles exported timber in the seventeenth century (569-72,576).

It is clear that large quantities of timber were sent regularly to England for shipbuilding and other purposes over several centuries.

In 1599 the Privy Council of England, in correspondence with the Irish government, dealt with the construction of small boats on Lough Foyle. In 1609 the City of London Companies issued "Instructions for the Survey of the Derry (sic) Plantation" which included the timber resources of the region. In 1611 the London guilds or undertakers put forward an extensive schedule of proposals involving the export of timber to England and elsewhere and shipbuilding in which "the profit that may be made will be a great increase of strength to the King's Navy and very beneficial to the undertakers". A report by the surveyor general of customs in 1637 noted that ships of up to 100 tons were being built in the area by a private individual who was using timber which might be needed by the King. It is not clear if warships were built in the Plantation area. Probably pinnaces and other small craft were made from time to time, for local use at least (568,573-4).

In 1626 Henry Wright and Richard Blacknall, the artillery makers, noted that ship timber "is growing scarce in England and will do the same in Ireland." In 1698 the Irish Parliament passed an "Act for Preserving Timber Trees and Woods" which obliged owners of lands and ironworks to plant specified numbers of particular types of trees. On 8 November 1751 the Parliament voted a subsidy to one Robert Rainey, an iron founder of Castledawson, Derry for a method of smelting iron with turf instead of timber (523,577).

In the early seventeenth century the mighty East India Company had a flourishing shipyard at Dundanier or Downdaniel, on the Bandon River, a little way upstream from Kinsale, County Cork. This was in existence at least by 1610 when the Company found it necessary to obtain exchange control permission from Whitehall to remit funds to Ireland for finishing off one vessel.

By 1613 the Company had a dock, an ironworks, forges, stores, offices, dams on two streams, a bridge which should have been erected at public expense and three towns *Bantam, Hope* and *Thomas* for their three hundred English employees with a total payroll of £40 per week. There was a detachment of four light horse, six corslets and ten muskets from the Company's army quartered in Dundanier Castle.

The Company recounted all this in a petition to the English Privy Council complaining about Walter Coppinger and "other ill-disposed persons who have lately combined themselves to scatter the plantation and pervert those places to superstition and incivility" and had interfered in other ways. The Privy Council passed the petition to Dublin Castle observing that Irish timber was of excellent quality for shipbuilding and unless steps were soon taken, all the woods near the sea and navigable rivers would be lost. Plantings should be carried out, this had not been done in England.

It is not clear what satisfaction, if any, the Company got, how long they continued this elaborate enterprise nor how many ships, which were undoubtedly armed merchant vessels, they built. Certainly they took large quantities of timber to their shipyard at Deptford, on the Thames for years afterwards (578-82).

Over the following century some naval ships were built in Kinsale. In 1652 one Thomas Chudleigh constructed a flat bottomed boat to hold 120 soldiers which had the distinction of being taken over land by Oliver Cromwell's forces for use on Lough Leane, Killarney, to capture Ross Castle, the last action in the Confederate wars. A certain Richard Stacey got the credit for this craft. In 1667 Chudleigh built a boom for the defence of Kinsale. Whatever about the difference earlier, in May 1700 the firm of Studleigh and Stacey, King's Dockyard, launched *HMS Kinsale*, a frigate (583-4).

In 1632 Lord Strafford, Lord Lieutenant, built a fleet of ships for the purpose of dealing with the "rovers" who had been raiding the Irish coast in galleys. Strafford paid for this by levying the cost on shipowners and passengers (575).

In 1656 the *Harp*, a ketch, was built in Dublin, it is not clear whether by the Admiralty or a private yard (592).

It does not appear that any more naval work was done in the capital until the First World War when the Dublin Dockyard, now the Liffey Dockyard, constructed two battle practice targets and carried out repairs on a large number of war and merchant ships and also fitted out many gun platforms, submarine detectors, minelayers, depthchargers, bombthrowers and other devices. The company designed a vessel of 2,450 tons which the Ministry of Shipping designated as a Standard Ship (see pages 183, 242). Twelve were built in the yard and several by other companies, on the same plans (680-1).

Also during the First War the Ringsend Dockyard, Dublin, built a number of barges for the War Office which were used in the Western Front and Mesopotamia. In 1970 the Ross Company Limited, a Dutch controlled concern, built a yard on a green field site in New Ross, Wexford which specialises in the construction of barges of up to the largest ocean going tonnages. Many craft have been supplied to Nigeria, Sudan and other countries. While none have been for specifically military or naval purposes it is possible that some have been used for these or ancillary operations (746-7).

Although there were several shipbuilding firms in Cork through out the first half of the nineteenth century, it does not seem that any constructed naval vessels. One builder, Joseph Wheeler, moved from the city down the harbour to Rushbrooke, near Cobh on Great Island in the 1850s and set up a yard which was operated intermittently by various companies until 1929. In the thirteen years of closure which followed, the gate of the drydock was kept in repair by local volunteers. During the Second World War Irish Shipping Limited, set up by the government to bring in food and other essential supplies, used the yard to keep afloat their hastily purchased fleet of mainly obsolete vessels.

In 1959 a new company, Verolme Cork Dockyard Limited, was formed, forty-eight per cent owned by the government with the balance held by Verolme United Dockyards of Rotterdam which later became part of the Rhine-Schelde-Verolme Group. The Company rebuilt the premises and began a programme of bulk cargo carriers and other mercantile vessels. The yard also carried out ship repairing, general engineering and construction of modules and other equipment for the offshore oil and gas industry. Some twelve hundred are employed normally.

In December 1971 LONG ÉIREANNACH *Deirdre* of 974 tonnes, with one 40 mm Bofors gun, capable of over eighteen knots was launched. This was the first vessel ever built for the Irish Naval Service and the first of four all-weather ships originally designated as Fishery Protection Vessels and subsequently as Patrol Vessels. The second LE *Emer* launched in 1977 and the third and fourth *Aoife* and *Aisling* both in 1979 have the same Bofors and in addition two Oerlikon 20 mm guns and numerous technical improvements arising from practical experience. A second class of four ships, each equipped with a helicopter, is planned to follow in the 'eighties (585-7).

A sail training vessel named *Asgard 11* after the famous yacht involved in the 1914 Howth gunrunning was built in 1979-80 by John Tyrrell and Sons, the internationally renowned Arklow firm (714).

Smith and Pearson Limited, the long established structural steel firm of Dublin and Belfast which closed in 1979, set up a subsidiary, Warrenpoint Shipyard Company Limited, during the Second World War which operated in the old shipyard in Warrenpoint, County Down and built some twenty amphibious landing craft of the Mark 4 type and four of the Mark 8 type. At peak production some eight hundred were employed. The Warrenpoint Harbour Commissioners took over the premises after the closure in 1948. The firm also had a plant in Newry, nearby, in which they built parts of the floating Mulberry Harbour used in the D Day landings (590-1, 742).

In 1880, Frank Workman and George Clark, who had been apprentices with Harland and Wolff, resigned and set up on their own account with yards on the north side of the Lagan and also on Queen's Island. Apart from two dock caissons in 1888 they did no government work until 1904 when they built the *Squirrel*, a coastguard cruiser.

During the First World War the firm built seven patrol boats, *P 15, P 16, P 17, P 60, P 61, PC 69* and *PC 70;* sixteen boom defence vessels *BV 1 to BV 10 and BD 31 to BD 36;* four sloops, *Penstemon* and *Petunia* of the Arabis and *Syringa* and *Windflower* of the Auchusa class. The company also constructed four unnamed hospital ships, two unnamed steam launches, an oil tanker, *Appleleaf* and four ostensible merchant vessels, *Reventazon* a passenger and fruiter, *War Beetle, War Leopard* and *War Argus* described as cargo ships. These were for the Admiralty and no doubt were "Q" ships which carried concealed armaments.

The ownership of the company changed soon after the War and again in 1928. Early in 1935, shortly after the 535th order was delivered the business was acquired by National Shipbuilders Security Limited, an agency set up in the British shipbuilding industry to purchase and close down surplus capacity. This was a very controversial body during its existence and afterwards. The Shipbuilders and Repairers National Association, even in its swansong on dissolution in June 1977 when the industry was nationalised, hotly denied that the agency had ever closed a single yard.

Nobody in Belfast ever accepted this. Harry Diamond, the Republican Labour MP, said in Stormont on 24 July 1945 that while in 1941 German bombers had tried to destroy the Harland and Wolff shipyard and the Short and Harland aircraft factory, "some years earlier a band of British capitalists visited Belfast and with much less trouble and less futile effort than the Luftwaffe managed to remove completely the shipyard of Workman Clark". The Unionist newspapers had not objected.

Denis Rebbeck, director and later Chairman of Harland and Wolff and also a director of NSS, told the British Association meeting in Belfast in September 1952 that National Shipbuilders Security had indeed closed Workman Clark.

The north bank premises was dismantled and the yard on Queen's Island sold to Harland and Wolff. This included the engine works in which the company had built Parsons steam turbines under licence (588-9,605).

LE DEIRDRE AT SEA
SOURCE 585

An English shipyard manager, a German designer and a heap of mud piled up by an Irish engineer on which stood a small yard. Such were the original elements of what was, in any terms, for long the greatest shipyard in the whole of the world.

Although Belfast was incorporated as a borough in 1613 it remained a small town for over two hundred years. Most of the trade and commerce of the north-eastern part of the county was carried on by Carrickfergus on the north side of Belfast Lough and Bangor on the south. From the late eighteenth century several significant shipyards operated in Belfast. In 1839 the Belfast Ballast Board decided to make a bid for some of the business which the other towns had and engaged William Dargan, the eminent railway engineer, to improve the port. He deepened and widened the estuary of the Lagan accumulating large quantities of mud which he had to put somewhere. The result was known for some years as Dargan's Island until it was changed to Queen's Island in honour of Victoria's visit in 1849. For some years the artificial island which was not an island proper for very long, was laid out as a public park.

In 1847 the Ballast Board was reconstituted as the Belfast Harbour Commissioners and in 1853 built a small shipyard which they leased to Robert Hickson, principal of the Eliza Street Ironworks noting "the business has been commenced in a spirit which augurs well for its success and importance, the vessels contracted for being of a very large tonnage and the proprietor already finding it necessary to ask for additional space" (603).

Hickson had originally set up a foundry to supply plates to boiler manufacturers and shipbuilders. He did not find sufficient sales for his products and decided to build ships himself. Having no knowledge of the industry he engaged a shipyard manager who proved to be unsatisfactory. He advertised for another and in due course hired a twenty-three year old from Scarborough.

The future Sir Edward James Harland arrived in Laganside on a December day in 1854. Apprenticed at fifteen to Robert Stephenson and Sons, a heavy engineering firm in Newcastle-upon-Tyne, He progressed from the shopfloor to the drawing office. He left shortly after completing his indentures and, annual holidays being unknown in those days, took two months off to see the Great Exhibition of 1851. He then obtained a position with a Glasgow firm of marine engineers and shipbuilders and after two years became manager of a Newcastle shipyard.

Having spent three years in Belfast he "resolved to start

somewhere on my own account. I made enquiries at Garston, Birkenhead, and other places. When Mr Hickson heard of my intentions, he said he had no wish to carry on the concern after I left and made a satisfactory proposal for the sale to me of the Queen's Island Yard".

On 21 September 1858, paying £5,000 which he had borrowed, Harland became sole owner of the yard. In April 1861 he took Gustav Wilhelm Wolff into partnership and on the first day of 1862 they adopted the style of Harland and Wolff. Wolff had studied engineering in his native Hamburg and in Liverpool and had served on ships. Both were to become MPs for Belfast and Harland was also mayor for a year. In 1874 Walter H Wilson and William J Pirrie, later Lord Pirrie, became partners. The business was incorporated with limited liability in 1885, registered at Dublin. A subsidiary, the London and Glasgow Iron Shipbuilding and Engineering Company, was registered in London and was placed on the Admiralty list of approved contractors in 1885. In 1876 Wolff became Chairman and Harland a director of the Belfast Ropework Company founded on the basis of a small existing enterprise and within fifteen years was claimed to be the biggest factory of its kind in the world. The Ropeworks, always a separate enterprise, was closed in 1979 (594,600-605,743).

The firm prospered, building many famous ships including the entire fleets of the Bibby Line and the White Star Line, both out of Liverpool and pioneering many important techniques in naval architecture which made ships larger, faster and more economical. They specialised in passenger liners and cargo vessels and did not go in for warships to any extent. The design of naval craft was undergoing tremendous technical change in the second half of the nineteenth century. Stronger types of metals, bigger and better guns and other advances were being introduced. It cannot have been that the partners on Queen's Island were afraid of the challenges involved, rather they choose to stay with merchant ships.

The yard did build the occasional warship after the Harbour Commissioners constructed a new graving dock and connected the Island with the mainland. The first was *Lynx,* a gunboat of the composite type that is built partly of both wood and iron, launched on 24 April 1868; the second was *Hecla,* a depot ship in 1873; the third was *Algerine,* a composite gunboat in 1880; the fourth and fifth were the gunboats *Bramble* and *Lizard* both in 1886. The only other Royal Navy order before the First World War was *Enchantress,* an armed steam yacht in 1903 (592-3).

There was no family continuation from the four founding fathers.

Harland died without issue in 1895. Wolff was a bachelor and retired in 1908. Wilson's family did not become involved after his death in 1904. From then until he died in 1924, Pirrie, who had no family, was in command and was succeeded, after an interval, by Sir Frederick Rebbeck who came from Swindon to a Belfast engineering firm at the turn of the century.

Some years before the First World War the company became involved in an anonymous association of shipbuilding and armaments concerns which remained largely unknown outside the writings of two contemporary political activists. The pacifist, George H Perris told the International Peace Congress held at Leeds in June 1913 of an extraordinary web of interconnections between various firms. John Brown and Company with a shipyard in Glasgow and a steelworks in Sheffield held a "participating interest" in Harland and Wolff and controlled Thomas Firth, manufacturers of armour plate in Sheffield and the Coventry Ordnance Works (614).

The socialist, JT Walton Newbold, noted that Pirrie was a debenture trustee of each of these companies. Harland and Wolff had a large stake in Colvilles, a major Scottish steel company and after the War took control until the end of the 'twenties, when they sold the business for a sum which, while small in relation to asset value, enabled them to ride out the oncoming storm. The companies had cross-directorships for many years afterwards (615).

Several other concerns were involved in these loose and informal arrangements which did not constitute a group of companies in the accepted sense of the term. Rather there was an intricate network of cross-directorships, trusteeships and shareholdings which could be concealed easily as Nobel's did with their various secret subsidiaries (page 141). Ardeer indeed kept close observation on the ramifications of the businesses involved (598-9).

During the War Harland and Wolff built in Belfast the cruiser *Glorious,* the cruiser carrier *Vindictive,* the heavy monitors *Avercrombie Lord Clive, Havelock, Earl of Peterborough, Sir Thomas Picton* and *Terror* and five M Class coastal monitors *M29* to *M33.* The company also built several warships at their yard in Govan, Glasgow and as a result of the War obtained full ownership of the engineworks nearby in Finnieston which they had earlier established jointly with Burmeister and Wain of Denmark.

During the depressed, turbulent 'thirties the order book was often empty and the yard barely ticked over, with some public assistance, and acquired the remnants of Workman Clark. The shares, which had become quoted in an arrangement made towards the end of Pirrie's time, sank very low. As part of the effort to survive stationary engines, railway locomotives, electricity pylons, school furniture and other disparate products were made. Machinery and stocks of materials were sold with nails, screws, fittings, tools and other articles being peddled at any available outlets including country fairs. Minimal maintenance was carried out by a skeleton workforce.

During the Second War Harland and Wolff built a large number of ships. According to Sir Basil Brooke's speech to Stormont, 24 July 1945, there were 140 warships and 170 merchant vessels; by DA Chart's account 170 and 54 respectively. There are some discrepancies between the company's list and the Admiralty's. Many ships were sold or transferred after the war and in some cases there is no record of the precise arrangements. It would appear that the totals were 97 warships and 75 merchant vessels (489,592-3,748).

There were nine aircraft carriers, four cruisers, nine freighters, thirty-seven corvettes, twenty-six minesweepers, eleven tank landing craft and one depot ship *Adamant*.

The carriers were *Bulwark, Campania, Centaur, Eagle, Formidable, Magnificent, Unicorn, Warrior* and *Powerful* which, launched in 1945, was not completed until 1956 and then became *Bonaventure* for the Canadian Navy.

The cruisers were *Belfast, Black Prince, Penelope* and *Minotaur* which was renamed *Ontario* on going to Canada. Six of the twenty-six Bay Class frigates, *St Austell Bay, St Brides Bay, Tremadoc Bay, Whitesand Bay, Widemouth Bay* and *Wigtown Bay* and three of the thirty Loch Class, *Loch Craggie, Loch Gorm* and *Loch Killisport* were built.

Many corvettes were used during the War. Belfast built three of the ninety-six Castle Class , *Arnprior Castle, Sherborne Castle* and *Pevensey Castle* which was renamed *Pertoria* for the Canadian Navy. The greatest number of a single class constructed by Harland and Wolff was of the Flower Class corvette, thirty-four were completed and eight cancelled out of a total of 218, *Abelia, Alisma, Anchusa, Arabis, Armeria, Aster, Bergamot, Bryony, Buttercup, Calendula, Camillia, Chrysanthemum, Clarkia, Cowslip, Eglantine, Erica, Freesia, Fritillary, Genista, Gentian, Gloxinia, Heartsease, Heather, Hibiscus, Hyacinth, Kingcup, Mallow, Orchis, Peony, Periwinkle, Picotee, Pimpernel, Rhodendron* and *Vervain*.

This number was nearly equalled by the Algerine Class minesweeper of which twenty-six were built and two cancelled, the flagship *Algerine* was followed by *Acute, Alarm, Albacore, Cadmus, Chameleon, Cheerful, Espiegele, Fantome, Hare, Jewel, Liberty, Mutine, Onyx, Pickle, Pincher, Plucky, Ready, Recruit, Rifleman, Rinaldo, Rosario, Spanker, Squirrel, Rattler* and *Vestall.*

In the autumn of 1942 eleven tank landing craft were built for D Day. *Boxer, Bruiser* and *Thruster* of the Mark 1 and numbers *3006* to *3013* of the Mark 3 type.

Between 1953 and '58 the yard built fifteen of the Ton Class, mahogany hulled, coastal minesweepers, *Kildarton, Kirkliston, Kemerton, Laleston, Lanton, Letterston, Levetton, Lullington, Maddiston, Maxton, Nurton* and *Repton* and three others which were renamed *Port Elizabeth, Mosselbaii* and *Walvisbaii* for the South African Navy.

The other ships built after the War were *Torquay* and *Berwick* frigates in 1954 and '59, *Kent GM* a destroyer and *Fearless* an assault ship in 1961 and '63. The flagship of the Leander Class of frigates was launched in 1961 followed by *Waikito* for the New Zealand Navy in 1965.

Finally, *Charybdis* also of this Class, rolled down the ways on 28 February 1968.

By this time the company was in a very uncertain position which by the onset of the 'eighties had not been completely clarified. In 1960 just a century after Harland bought the yard from Hickson and brought in Wolff the business was at its peak. The island, the four premises in Glasgow, Govan Shipyard, Finnieston Engine Works, Clyde Foundry and Scotstoun Engineering Works and the liner repair yards in Liverpool, London and Southampton were busy. Profits were high. Altogether a very satisfactory situation. It was to change dramatically when the liner trade, always the backbone of the business, collapsed with terrifying suddenness. All the branches in Britain were closed and employment at the Island slumped from 23,200 in 1960, itself the peak peacetime figure, to 14,714 in 1961 down to 12,582 in '62, to 11,681 in '64. There was a slight improvement in '65 when 13,019 were on the payroll. This was only a temporary respite. Over the following ten years the figure went down to fluctuate between ten and nine thousand, tending to decline. Workman Clark alone, in its prime before the First War, had employed ten thousand or more (595,605).

When EJ Harland and GW Wolff went into business, shipbuilding was undergoing rapid change from art and craft work to major modern heavy industry involving large sums in capital investment in the form of fixed assets and working capital for construction costs. Ships were changing from wood and sail to metal and steam. By the standards of a century later, the criteria of cost accountants, corporate economists, computer analysists and so on, a shipyard would not have been contemplated in a location so far from convenient sources of the essential raw materials, iron, wood, coal, canvas and cordage.

Nonetheless the firm began and flourished for most of the time and during the 1950s as much as in any previous period. From the end of the Second War until the early 1960s shipbuilding was a seller's market. Abruptly, a rising tide of technological advance and the confluence of various circumstances threatened to engulf the industry in Britain and indeed several famous firms foundered. In 1960 a ship of 100,000 tons was considered very large, by '67 vessels of treble that size were being built, ships of five times were being planned and the vision of the million tonner was appearing on the naval architectural horizon. Japan was the leading country in all this, closely followed by Sweden.

The last Harold Macmillan Conservative Party government set up the Shipbuilding Credit Scheme in 1963 which made available substantial mortgages for new vessels. In March 1966 the Shipbuilding Inquiry Committee chaired by Anthony RM Geddes, appointed by the first Harold Wilson Labour Party government reported. It was found that the industry which employed 53,000 in twenty-seven major yards had only fifteen percent of the world market as against fifty percent after the War. Numerous British owners were placing orders abroad particularly in Japan. Despite heavy expenditure on modernisation many British yards did not become competitive. Advising against nationalisation, Geddes recommended that the various companies should be formed into groups noting that Belfast as the biggest was a sufficiently large unit in itself (617).

Whatever the ideal organisation might be and whatever the relative position of Belfast might be, Harland and Wolff were on the very brink of bankruptcy having just lost £2 million on *Canberra*, the last liner built in the yard. No ordinary dividend was paid after December 1964 and no preference from June 1966. On Friday 23 September 1966 just 108 years after Harland had taken the helm, statements by the directors and the Ministry of Commerce announced that unless £1^1/2 million was made available directly the company would have to go into liquidation, not merely receivership.

On 12 October, Brian Faulkner MP, Minister for Commerce, introduced the Shipbuilding Industry Loans Bill which was duly enacted on 3 November. The company had come to the end of their accommodation with the Northern Bank and the Midland Bank which would not provide any further facilities without government guarantees. He explained that £1^1/2 million had been paid over under existing powers and the purpose of the measure was to provide up to a further £2 million. The Bill was passed unanimously with many Members and Senators on all sides expressing grave anxiety about the competence of the management, the viability of the undertaking and the possibility, if any, of repayment of the loan which was to commence after three and a half years (616).

In the following four years the Harbour Commissioners constructed the giant building dock capable of handling a million tonner or several smaller ships at the same time, surmounted by the huge cranes commonly called "Samson and Goliath" or less reverently "Big Ian and Eileen" which dominate the Laganside skyline. This was largely financed by the Shipbuilding Industry Board set up on the recommendation of Geddes.

On 6 July 1971 Robin Baillie MP, Minister for Commerce, told Stormont that the government were taking up four million shares representing 47.5 percent of the company's capital together with the right to appoint directors (622).

The company staggered from one crisis to another. In the ten years from 1966 there were as many chairmen as in the previous century. Shortly after becoming financial controller in November 1966 Sir John Mallabar, a London accountant, took the chair from Denis Rebbeck, son of Sir Frederick. Both left the company in 1970. There were immense difficulties with the vitally necessary reorganisation of the company's structure, operating methods, the very yard itself and the P200 scheme designed to improve throughput of steel from 1973 (607).

On 26 March 1975 during the last Harold Wilson government, Stanley Orme MP, Minister for State, Northern Ireland announced that the company would be taken into full public ownership. In the meantime further funds would be made available by Order in Council, the method of legislation for Northern Ireland since the abolition of Stormont in 1972. Shortly before midnight on 8 May Orme tabled an interim Order which provided more money: "if the Order is not passed tonight the yard will immediately close".

On 1 August, moving the Order giving effect to the acquisition, Orme told the Commons that since 1966 the sum of £26 million had been spent solely to keep the yard open; £33 million for development and a further £22 million in grants of types available to other businesses. The share capital of £11 million had been lost five time over. A further £60 million was being made available to cover losses on the current order book up to March 1979. After that the company would either have to make profits on each order or else close down completely. Orme bluntly told the House "if the company cannot demonstrate long before 1979 its ability to take on new work without loss, it will be time for the Government to call a halt and to permit the rundown and even the closure of the business".

The government compulsorily bought the shares still privately held, paying 8p in the £ on the preference and 9p on the ordinary. The undertaking would continue as a limited liability company under the relevant Northern Ireland legislation. The share capital is vested in the Stormont Department of Commerce.

In reply to a question about the powers of Parliament over the company Orme explained:

> One of the differences between nationalised industries and 100 percent public ownership on this basis is that Ministers will answer questions about the company in the House, as opposed to what happens in the case of nationalised industries, which made a yearly report and are not answerable in the House. This is an important point for people who are interested in parliamentary accountability to take into account.

> Lastly, there is the question of the company's relationship with British Shipbuilders. The Government having taken the view that Harland and Wolff should be treated separately from the rest of the United Kingdom shipbuilding industry, and having stressed the desirability of the company being - and being seen to be - owned by and responsible to the people of Northern Ireland, it will be essential to ensure that there is effective liaison between Harland and Wolff and the board of British Shipbuilders when that body has been set up. I cannot say today what form these arrangements will take.

At this point Enoch Powell, Unionist MP for South Down since the October 1974 general election, wanted to know:

> In what sense is it owned by the people of Northern Ireland more than the people of Cornwall?

Orme replied:

> In the special circumstances of Northern Ireland the Government took a decision to exclude the company from the public ownership proposals. The Department of Commerce will have a function of monitoring and control in helping the

company. We believe that when, as we hope, a satisfactory form of devolved government is arrived at, the Northern Ireland people will have a vested interest in this shipyard. That is Government policy.

On 13 August 1975 after one hundred and twenty-two years under the houses of Hickson, Harland, Pirrie, Rebbeck and most recently in an indeterminate status of not being either private or public, the great shipyard on the Lagan came under public ownership (620-1).

In March 1975 Merlyn Rees MP, Northern Ireland Secretary and Orme issued a programme for Industrial Democracy with worker participation accompanied by warnings that the future of the yard depended on everyone employed in Queen's Island. The Programme provided for joint consultation between workers and management at all levels up to the board with five of the fifteen seats being reserved for worker directors. Fully five years later, the trade unions for reasons which remain unclear, had not made the arrangements necessary for the elections (618-19).

Besides building ships, the company manufacture marine engines for other yards and a wide range of engineering and electrical equipment and fibreglass products and provide repair services for all sizes of vessels including wooden craft (608-10).

In January 1978 the company announced the formation of a subsidiary, Hawk Products, to handle a range of motorcycle accessories and in June a second, Harland-MAN Engines to make various types of engines designed by Maschinenfabrik-Augsburg-Nuerenburg of Germany (596-7).

On 18 April 1979 the Department of Commerce renewed the undertaking given in 1974 to guarantee Harland and Wolff's liabilities as far as these could not be met by the company. The report for the year showed a loss of £21.4 million. Employment had fallen to 6,292 manual and 1,920 staff. Contract prices were tending to be even less remunerative. There were several other serious problems and the Chairman's statement held out no prospect of profitable orders for several years while hoping that in the meantime the nucleus of the company would survive in a situation in which there was a world wide surplus of both shipping and construction capacity (606).

The first Margaret Thatcher Tory Government, elected in May 1979, shortly before publication of the annual report, decided to meet the loss and also provided a further £22 million for the following year. Announcing this at the Island on 23 July, Giles Shaw MP, Parliamentary Under Secretary with responsibility for the

Department of Commerce, pointed out that there would have to be further redundancies. Losses could not go on forever. Some yards would have to close. Belfast had the most modern equipment and it was up to all in the yard to improve productivity, which had actually fallen in the previous year, if the business was to survive.

In the fifteen years after *Charybdis*, no warships were built. By then only three yards in Britain were capable of designing and building 'first of class' types and another three of 'follow on' ships. The Ministry of Defence, while foreseeing little likelihood of placing orders for warships with Harland and Wolff, did claim to recognise the company's capacity for 'commercial' type ships and refits, among other yards. This position was reiterated in the Commons on 22 November 1979. Presumably any such orders will be for oil tankers and other auxiliary craft. At the same time the company had not given up hope of further Admiralty orders and claimed to be capable of building warships for any customer (623-5, 744-5).

On 1 July 1980 Shaw announced in the Commons that the company had lost over £24 million in the current year. Apart from a further decline of eight hundred jobs "streamlining the workforce to seven thousand" and the customary call for increased productivity, the statement had a remarkable flavour of sweetness and light entirely different from the minatory messages so frequent in former years. The government would immediately set up an "Independent Review Team to investigate with urgency, alternative possibilities for utilising the facilities and skills within Queen's Island".

The next day the Thatcher government's proposals for a form of devolved government in Northern Ireland were published. Obviously the government feared the consequences if the demise of the yard took place during the negotiations on the proposals. In the event of the proposals failing to materialise, or of any agreed structures collapsing, the Team might well find no future for the yard and come to be seen as a crew of undertakers measuring the corpse for the coffin.

Shipyards must now have well planned production programmes. Possibly the company could fit into their schedule a particular type of vessel which they could persuade potential customers is essential for the times.

Even if no further warship is built on Queen's Island one prime example survives and indeed flourishes as a floating museum in the Pool of London. *HMS Belfast* was laid down in December 1936 as the first capital ship in Britain's rearmament programme begun at a dangerously late stage in the 'thirties. It was launched in March 1938 and commissioned into service in August 1939 barely a month before Hitler's Third Reich tanks invaded Poland setting off the Second War. Badly damaged in November the giant was out of action until 1942 and was mainly on convoy duties for the remainder of the War except for providing bombardment support on D Day. The ship spent the next twenty years mostly in the Far East with two visits to Laganside before going to Portsmouth as Reserve Headquarters in 1964.

After a four-year struggle against the scrapyard the vessel was handed over to the *HMS Belfast* Trust, formed specially for the purpose, mainly under the auspices of the Imperial War Museum and was refurbished and fitted out with numerous interesting displays and on 21 October 1971 sailed majestically into a permanent mooring opposite the Tower of London (612-13).

An observer looking from Tower Bridge or London Bridge might conclude from the dilapidated state of the wharves and warehouses which line this stretch of the Thames that *Belfast* symbolises the declining state of Britain generally. The upper reaches of ports everywhere are in similar condition.

The British empire which *Belfast* was built to serve has vanished like that of the Third Reich. This splendid ship stands as a supreme specimen of the skills of Laganside shipyard workers who since 1853 have sent more than seventeen hundred vessels down the slipways and across the seven seas.

HMS BELFAST, POOL OF LONDON
SOURCE 611

CHAPTER EIGHT

AEROSPACE

The first proposal for the manufacture of aircraft in Ireland came, not as might be expected, from a firm already in existence such as an engineering concern or a company specially set up to exploit whatever home and export markets which might be available. The, literally fledgling, aero industry was wide open to anyone with workable ideas and there was great scope for enterprise. The first would be aircraft constructor was neither an old nor a new firm.

Lilian E Bland of Carnmoney, Antrim was an intrepid individual, a freelance journalist and photographer at the height of the Suffragette era. In December 1909, when in her early thirties, she offered her services in *Flight* magazine, the technical weekly founded the previous year. In its first two years Lilian wrote regularly describing her own work and discussing most competently the numerous problems raised by other aviators of the day.

In the 10 September issue she reported her first flight some weeks previously wearing most unladylike mechanic's overalls in *Mayfly* which she built of elm, spruce and bamboo. The engine was made by A V Roe, founder of a famous British aero company and the fuel tank, very appropriately, was a whiskey bottle filled with her deaf aunt's ear trumpet. Lilian was the first woman to fly in Ireland and very nearly the first person. Harry Ferguson, the famous tractor designer also of Belfast, had flown on the last day of 1909. This was certainly not due to any lack of business acumen on her part as in April 1911 the Ford Motor Company appointed her a dealer in Belfast. Soon afterwards a reader of *Flight* in Vancouver, who was a cousin, came to Belfast and they got married. Lilian gave the fuselage of *Mayfly* to the new Dublin Flying Club as a glider, sold the engine and workshop equipment and departed for the westernmost wilds of Canada so ending her brief, exciting and pioneering career in aeronautics. Belfast airport ought to be named after Lilian (626).

Some manufacturing of components and complete craft took place during the First War. The Dublin *Evening Telegraph*, 23 January 1918, reported that negotiations were underway for an aircraft factory in the captial. John Redmond MP, who died a few weeks later, was involved. The *Dublin Evening Mail,* 31 January, noted that two companies, Ashenhurst Williams (page 182) and G A Bruton, Earlsfort Garage had come to an agreement with an English concern for the production of aircraft at the second firm's premises and expected to employ a large number of cabinetmakers, joiners, coachbuilders and others.

On the same day Alfred Byrne, a Dublin MP and later Lord Mayor, asked in the Commons whether the Air Ministry intended to have aircraft construction carried out in the Dublin railway workshops as had been requested by the local branch of the Society of Coachmakers. Sir Laming Worthington-Evans MP replied:

> *The Request has been carefully considered. For the present it is not possible to make use of the facilities referred to as arrangements have already been made which are more than sufficient to meet all our present demands for woodwork in connection with the manufacture of aircraft. I hope it may be possible later on to make use of Irish coachbuilding factories for work of this nature.*

Worthington-Evans also told William Field MP: "it is proposed to utilise Irish resources for certain forms of aircraft work, some orders have already been placed". On 5 February John Redmond was told: "instructions have been given for a certain amount of work to be carried out in Dublin and an officer is making the preliminary arrangements".

Several plants which produced munitions at this time also turned out aircraft components. In June 1918 the Dublin National Fuse Factory and the College of Science began production of metal components. Thomas Thompson and Sons made parts for the Bristol Aircraft Company at Hanover Works, Carlow and Neptune Works, Waterford. Thomas Dockrell, Sons and Company made wooden parts in Dublin. During 1915 the Dublin Dockyard made a proposal to the War Office for setting up an aircraft factory. The parties were unable to reach agreement on terms (437,463,680, 711-12).

The only largescale manufacturing and certainly the only production of complete aircraft in Ireland during the First World War was by Harland and Wolff under contracts from three British firms. The company built three hundred of the *DH6* type for de Havilland, three hundred each of the *504J* and *504K* for Avro and were to make three hundred of the *V1500* for Handley Page. The order was cancelled and only a few were completed. All the planes were built in

Queen's Island. Some were assembled in Aldergrove and some in Britain (627).

On 28 February 1918 John P Boland urged in the Commons the setting up of an aircraft industry in Ireland. Contrary to belief there were engineering capacities outside Ulster. Many Irish men and women were working in British factories and could be employed afterwards in Irish engineering industries. In the previous year he had worked five hours a day for five months, beside his public duties, in making metal parts for planes and was soon sufficiently skilled, without previous experience. Within a few years, if not before the end of the War, aeroplanes would be crossing the Atlantic. "Ireland is the natural landing and jumping off place".

In time the country did become important in transatlantic air traffic. Manufacturing of aircraft did not really develop outside Belfast and several enterprises quite literally did not get off the ground.

Potez, a well known French aircraft company, set up Potez Industries of Ireland Limited in 1960 and built two factories. One, in Galway, for which the Industrial Development Authority paid grants of £539,800 did go into production and turned out some thousands of heaters. The other, in Dublin, for which the IDA paid £444,850 and which was supposed to make aircraft, never did. The company was in receivership from 1968 to 1976. During this time the Dublin property was acquired by Roadstone Limited. In 1978 the company went into liquidation and the next year Aer Lingus set up a plant in the premises for the repair and maintenance of engines of their own and other airlines's planes. Potez was quite a controversial issue in the 'sixties and came to be regarded as the classic failure of the industrialisation drive begun with the establishment of the IDA in 1949, in general and with Sean F Lemass's period as Taoiseach, 1959-66, in particular (628-9,749).

In 1968 Cross and Jackson Limited of the Isle of Wight built a factory on the eastern shore of Cork Harbour for the production of hovercraft. The company had no IDA assistance. The plant never went into production and the firm subsequently went out of business in Britain (750-3).

In 1978 Garrett Ireland Limited was formed by the Garrett Corporation of Los Angeles, major manufacturers of aero engines and avionics control systems of military and civil aircraft and part of the Signal Group of Companies, a large conglomerate. The IDA provided a site in the Waterford Industrial Estate on which the company built a plant, essentially an aluminium foundry, costing £2.3

million. Production commenced in June 1979, initially on a range of automotive parts which it was intended would be expanded to include aerospace and marine diesel engine components with the workforce rising from seventeen to 136 within four years (630-1,754).

In July 1979 the IDA issued preliminary details of a proposal by an unnamed German concern for the production of gliders in a plant to be located on the site of the municipal airport then being planned for Waterford. In November it was announced that the promoters, Ernst Grob of Stuttgart, had abruptly withdrawn just before the signing of the agreement. A machine-tool factory had purportedly been part of the project (755-6).

Early in 1944 Miles Aircraft of Reading Aerodrome, England set up a plant in an old weaving shed in Banbridge, County Down and a small works at Long Kesh Aerodrome, Antrim which became notorious in the 1970s as a internment camp and was renamed the Maze Prison. The Banbridge plant made and partly assembled all the components of the wood and fabric Miles *Magister* the first monoplane trainer, with the final assembly and fitting of engines at Long Kesh. After testing the planes were flown off into service. Banbridge employed 250 and Long Kesh fifty, both men and women. In 1946 the Banbridge plant was closed and the company moved to Newtownards where they remained about two years before leaving Northern Ireland altogether. The firm carried out various design and development projects for the Ministry of Aircraft Production. In April 1945 a prototype wooden house was exhibited at the Belfast City Hall. It was apparently not produced in quantity despite being brought to the attention of the Production Council by the company and claimed as the answer to the local housing problem (483, 632-3).

In the 1960s attempts were made to build autogyros in Crumlin, Belfast. Rex McCandless, an engineer without formal qualifications, dabbled in designing motor cycles, racing cars and a four-wheel drive vehicle which, in conjuction with Harry Ferguson, he attempted to sell to the British Army who ultimately selected the *Land Rover* instead. The McCandless autogyro, for one person and powered by a *Volkswagen* engine was somewhere between a helicopter and an aeroplane. Eventually he sold the designs to Robert Ekin, also a Belfast engineer who carried on in another Crumlin premises until the early 'seventies, with little more success (757-9).

In 1966 the aero engines division of Rolls-Royce set up a plant in Dundonald on the outskirts of Belfast for production of various components. The factory employed some eight hundred before being closed early in 1976. A proposal for Short Brothers to take over the

SHORTS SD3-30
SOURCE 641

premises was not successfull. Some employees did get jobs with Shorts in Sydenham (655).

In February 1980 the Stormont Department of Commerce announced the setting up of LearFan Limited in which it holds 49% with the remainder owned by the LearAvia Corporation of Reno, Nevada, leading light aircraft manufacturers.

Arrangements were made for the company to take over the former RAF base at Aldergrove and spend £20 million on production of *LearFan.* This is a new turboprop plane for eight persons built largely of graphite reinforced plastic, a new material claimed to be superior to aluminium, with most of the components being of British manufacture. Employment is expected to reach 1,250 within five years. At the same time a proposal for the production of *Tiger, Cheetah,* and *Cougar* planes was being negotiated by the Department of Commerce with Gulfstream America and the Zwaam Group (760-2).

The country's only major, long lasting aerospace factory began production in Belfast shortly before the Second World War. The firm of Short Brothers were the first manufacturers of production aircraft in the world, that is machines commissioned, designed, made, sold and used in significant numbers.

Oswald and Eustace Short began making aerial balloons in Hove, Sussex in 1901 moving to London later. In 1908 Horace, the eldest brother, joined the firm. In the next year, soon after beginning their first heavier than air machine, they received an order for six planes from the Wright Brothers, Orville and Wilbur of the USA, who had pioneered heavier than air flight in 1903. John T C Moore - Brabazon, holder of the first British air pilot's licence, flying a Shorts plane in 1909 won the £1,000 prize offered by Lord Northcliffe through his *Daily Mail* for the first British plane to fly a circular mile.

In the following years Shorts built the first planes to take off from a ship and to carry a torpedo. The head office and main works were set up at Rochester, Kent with a branch at Bedford. Between the Wars the firm pioneered the world's first all metal plane and developed several seaplanes, the major type of the time.

As the Second War approached, a subsidiary, Short and Harland Limited, was set up jointly with Harland and Wolff. The old company became Short Brothers (Rochester and Bedford) Limited and held sixty percent of the Belfast business. Harland and Wolff had the balance. A Shadow Factory was set up at Sydenham adjacent to the shipyard and Belfast Harbour Airport.

Production commenced in the summer of 1937 and expanded

enormously two years later on the outbreak of hostilities. The necessary extensions were built at Sydenham both by the company and by the Ministry of Aircraft Production. Several premises in and around Belfast were taken over as dispersal factories: Aldergrove; Altona; Daff; Dawnay; Glen Printing Works; Hawlmark, Newtownards; King's Hall, Balmoral; Largymore; Lambeg; Long Kesh and also Maghaberry which is still in use. There were twenty separate storage premises around Belfast (483).

Harland and Wolff and many engineering firms produced components for Shorts. One firm made disposable paper petrol tanks. Sydenham turned out some 1,200 Short *Stirling* bombers, slightly more than half the total of this type; 133 of the 750 Short *Sunderland* flying boat and numbers of plane designs by other firms, the Rolls-Royce *Spitfire*, the Bristol *Bombay* transport and the Handley Page *Hereford* bomber.

On 30 January 1943 the Minister for Aircraft Production, Sir Stafford Cripps MP, wrote to Sir Basil Brooke MP, the Stormont Prime Minister, advising his intention of compulsorily acquiring the entire share capital and assets of Short Brothers under Defence Regulation 78. The management of the world's first aircraft manufacturing company had collapsed completely (632, 634).

Lord Teviot raised the matter in the House of Lords on 13 April:

This action on the part of the Minister has caused considerable alarm and concern in the business and financial world. I look upon it as establishing a very dangerous precedent not only from the commercial point of view, but from the political point of view.

Lord Listowel replied on behalf of the government:

The noble Lord said he did not take exception to the Government taking over the management and control of this firm, but what he did object to was that the Government should acquire the financial assets of the business. I hope, although I am not sure that I shall succeed, to be able to convince him that it would have been impossible for the Government to establish full and effective control of the firm without acquiring its financial assets. From the information I have received the state of affairs in this firm had been unsatisfactory for a very long time. Lord Brabazon, will, I am sure, bear me out on this point. Indeed, it was evident for a considerable period before the present Minister of Aircraft Production took office. Left to their own devices the management of Short Brothers had not

*succeeded in putting their house satisfactorily in order. The
Minister then tried to help the firm out of their difficulties.
Nevertheless things continued to drift along unsatisfactorily.*

*It was only at this juncture, after private enterprise had been
given every opportunity to prove itself worthy but when
nevertheless the state of production in the business continued
to be unsatisfactory, that the Minister availed himself as a last
resort of the compulsory powers under Defence Regulations. I
understand that up to this stage he had the approval of the
noble Lord. It was a difficult decision. Many Ministers would
have allowed things to drift. Evasion of difficulty is not
unknown in Government Departments. This expropriation of
the shareholders does not show any wanton interference with
private property.*

A former Minister for Aircraft Production, Lord Brabazon of
Tara, who had taken his title from the ancestral home in County
Meath spoke:

*My mind goes back to the very early days of flight when I
and Charlie Rolls [of Rolls Royce] gave the Short Brothers
their first order for a balloon. Later I gave them their first order
for an aeroplane which never did leave the ground. Then they
made another plane for me and it won the Daily Mail prize.
Those are heroic days of the past.*

*When I was at the Ministry, I tried to give Short Brothers
all the help I could by detaching personnel and so on. But
things got no better and it was obvious, considering the money
the government have put into the firm - nearly three times their
capital - that the government must take measures to improve
production. I see no reason to complain of what the Minister
of Aircraft Production has done in this matter. The blame rests
entirely on the directors of Short Brothers. To suggest that Sir
Stafford Cripps is trying to nationalise the industry by a trick is
a most unworthy suggestion for anybody to put forward. I do
not believe it for one moment. Frankly had I been in Sir Stafford
Cripps' place I would have done exactly the same sort of thing.*

So the entire share capital of Short Brothers (Rochester and
Bedford) Limited and the management, not always the same in
business, came to be vested in the Ministry of Aircraft Production.
This was only to be the case for the duration of the War. At least that
was the intention of various influential figures in the Ministry, which,
like Munitions earlier, was staffed to a great extent by individuals

recruited from commercial undertakings and other civilian fields. Most, if not all, of these believed that the state should not engage in business enterprises and certainly not when these could be carried on at profits.

On 21 September 1944 E N Plowden, Chief Executive of the Ministry, submitted to the Minister a memo on the future of the two companies:

Although I agree that matters concerned with the future of Shorts and Short Harland are important I think that it would be a mistake if we tried to settle their future in a hurry and without due thought.

At the present time one firm develops and modifies and the other builds aircraft, and I am very doubtful if it would be wise to amalgamate the two under compulsion. Moreover, we have not yet decided on who will take over Shorts, and whoever they may be, surely they should be given time to consider what is the best course to adopt.

The aerodrome in Northern Ireland is not good enough at present and I suggest Sir Basil Brooke should be asked whether he is prepared to improve it or provide a new one.

Common sense, I think, dictates that it would be just as well if we wound up Short Harland, though politically I don't suppose this is possible (635).

This is of course typical of a civil servant sitting in Whitehall and looking at a long list of Shadow Factories and dispersal workshops most of which would not be needed after the War and although apparently conscious of possible political repercussions was quite unaware of the importance of the factory in the industrial life of Laganside. While due allowance would be made for the closure of the various branches, in the local view Syndenham was of vast consequence. It was relatively more important than a similar factory in Birmingham or other comparable area in Britain. Chronic unemployment had prevailed in Ulster and indeed throughout Ireland in the 1930s and also in Britain. There was such a lower general level of industrialisation in Ireland that the Belfast factory was of far greater value than it would have been in a corresponding area of Britain. The relative importance of the factory was increased very much in the psychological sense by its association with Harland & Wolff the flagship of Belfast, Ulster and indeed Irish industry. The feeling in Belfast at the time would have been that the setting up of the factory was no more than compensating for the loss of the Workman Clark shipyard.

Following this ominous memo the Committee on the Future of Short Brothers (Rochester and Bedford) was set up. The Committee found that the firm had property of their own worth £190,000 and premises provided by the Ministry which had cost £1,350,000. The company's machinery was valued at £170,000 while the Ministry had supplied £630,000 worth. There were three relatively minor subsidaries in England. The accounts had not been balanced since 1941. There were purchasing committments of £30 million which would take two years to settle:

The Committee found the Belfast group of factories are much more up to date, compact, efficient and strategically better placed than those at Rochester. The advantage which Belfast possesses in the fixed assets prompted us to enquire to what extent the personnel of Short Brothers, on whom depends the continued existence of the Company as an effective design and production organisation, would be likely to accept a move to Belfast. We are assured by all whom we interviewed that any attempt to move the headquarters outside England or Wales would almost certainly result in the disruption of the design team, and the loss of senior members of the production organisation. There was less unanimity about the probable effects of an attempt to move to say, NW England, but we were informed that even in that event there was a considerable risk that the cohesion of the design and production teams would be weakened and their loyalty to the Company impaired.

The Committee gave lengthy consideration to the type of business which the company should carry on after the War. There were three major openings and one minor ancillary option. The company could continue as a normal aircraft design and manufacturing organisation; as a highly specialised design and development unit working on a limited number of projects; specialise in redesigning for mass production, selected military types which would be used in a future war. In addition to one of these the firm might take on other work such as building busbodies which they had done before the War. The Committee recommended the first option (636).

This left the question of the particular corporate constitution in which the enterprise would be conducted. There were four possibilities; continuation as a limited liability company in which all the shares would be held by the government; as a government or royal factory; as a public corporation or if it were decided not to continue the business under state control in one of these forms it could be sold

SEACAT
SOURCE 642

back to private ownership.

The Committee found numerous administrative and technical disadvantages with each of the three possible forms. In the case of a limited liability company there would be difficulties about Parliamentary accountability and the role of the Comptroller and Auditor General. If the business became a Government Establishment or Royal Factory "there would be a danger that the comparatively unattractive rates of pay would induce at least the younger and more adventurous members of the staff to seek new jobs, which would have a weakening effect on the organisation".

The third option involved setting up a public corporation on the model of the London Passenger Transport Board or the British Overseas Airways Corporation. These were private companies endowed with monopolies by Acts of Parliament, with portions of their capitals guaranteed. In addition BOAC had heavy subsidies without which it could not have existed. Both were later nationalised.

Under such a scheme the directors would be appointed by the Minister. The shares would be sold to any investors attracted. The government would have to guarantee both capital and interest "since it would be impossible to finance the undertaking on the basis of its own credit". The management would not be open to the criticisms of customers as were those of LT and BOAC which operated routine services far removed from the highly technical field of aircraft design. The other objections also applied.

Overall the Committee reported:

> *We suggest that whatever be the legal form of an organisation which is effectively owned by the Government, it will be impossible for it to be treated as if it were a truly independent competitor, because it could neither exercise vis-à-vis the Government, or indeed private customers, that energetic salesmanship, nor take such serious financial risks, whether by quoting cut prices or otherwise as would be necessary to compete effectively with the other firms in the industry in securing a fair share of such orders as are available. It will therefore have to be guaranteed a certain minimum of work to keep it in being.*

> *The consequent absence of the pressure of competition will quite naturally induce a complacent feeling of security which will inevitably sap the initiative of the design and production executives, with the result that its products will probably degenerate. Similar tendencies in a public utility are kept in*

check by the possibility of complaints from the public. In a business which depends for its value, as exclusively as does aircraft, upon constant progress; and when the services rendered are not capable of evaluation by the public in general or some large section of the public, some deterioration will be unpreventable. Even, however, if the organisation remained highly efficient, it would be impossible to avoid the suspicion that the Government was unduly favouring its own creature, except by such consistent harshness towards the organisation as would effectively discourage its personnel and hasten its decay.

The Committee rejected the retention of the business in any form and recommended selling it back to private enterprise along with the three minor subsidiaries advising that this would not be done immediately as:

There is still considerable uncertainty as to the future size and prosperity of the aircraft industry. Grave doubts exist as to the role of flying boats in the future of both military and civil aviation. It is to be expected that the price likely to be obtained for the company in the immediate future will fall far short of the £1^1/2 million paid by the Department for the shares.

There remains the difficult question of Short and Harlands. We regard it as impracticable to contemplate the continuance, into peace-time conditions, of the situation in which the Government is a majority shareholder only, 40% of the shares being in private hands, in a business which must derive most of its orders from the Government.

In any case the scope for the continued employment of Short and Harland in conjunction with Shorts is very small. It has no separate design organisation, and the contracts placed for the products of Shorts' design team are unlikely to exceed the capacity of Rochester. On the other hand the political consequences of closing down Short and Harland would be undesirable because of the serious effects on employment in Ulster; the Company's pay-roll at present numbers over 8,000.

We can see no alternative but to dispose of the Government's shares either to Harland and Wolff, in the expectation that they would introduce some other aircraft firm into the Company in place of Shorts, or directly to some such firm which would be prepared to work in harmony with Harland and Wolff.

*We accordingly recommend that Short Brothers' interest
in Short and Harland should be sold as soon as possible.*

The report was signed by Sam H Brown, Chairman, and sent to
Sir Stafford Cripps in January 1945 who replied with instructions. He
accepted the proposal that the company should continue as a normal
aircraft design and manufacturing organisation with headquarters for
the time being at Rochester which he regarded as a "most
uneconomical unit". He was completely opposed to selling the
company back to private interests. There were to be no major changes
until after the election due at the end of the War. In the meantime
the directors were to conduct the business and their relations with the
Ministry as any other firm, consulting only on such matters as major
expenditure and their own fees and observing the "fair wages clause"
and the policy of the "good employer". The small subsidiaries could
be disposed of. The Stormont government was to be consulted in
regard to the Belfast factory (636).

The Committee could hardly have expected otherwise from
Cripps who was one of the leading figures on the left of the Labour
Party, so far to the left indeed that he had been expelled for advocating
a *Popular Front*, a term much in vogue in the 'thirties, of all groups
opposed to the policy of appeasing Hitler being pursued by Neville
Chamberlain, Prime Minister at the time. Cripps went on to hold high
offices in the Wartime Coalition and the landslide Labour government
elected in July 1945. A prominent member of the Bar, he was no mere
theorist, having held management positions at Waltham Abbey Royal
Gunpowder Factory and in a Ministry of Munitions plant during the
First War (654).

Over the following year there was some discussion on the
possibility of organising aircraft design and manufacture on the basis
of an Imperial Aircraft Industry. Numerous proposals and alternatives
were mooted. Amid all this the future of Short Brothers (Rochester
and Bedford) was considered by a sub-committee of the Lord
President's Committee on the Distribution of Industry. The Ministry
of Supply, which had absorbed Aircraft Production, put forward a
proposal to transfer Short Brothers to Belfast completely. The
decision was made on 29 May 1946 and announced to the workers at
Rochester on 12 June by Arthur Woodburn MP, Parliamentary
Secretary, Supply who explained the advantages of Belfast, the
difficulties in Rochester and the need to make the best use of the
facilities. Several hundred employees and senior apprentices would
be offered employment and accommodation in Belfast while the
various buildings in Rochester would be made available to

replacement industries (637).

Despite protests from local interests in Rochester the transfer was carried out over the next eighteen months. The British company was wound up and that in Belfast became Short Brothers and Harland Limited. While the government continued to hold the majority of the shares, stakes were held in the 'fifties and 'sixties by the Bristol Aircraft Company and Rolls-Royce. Ironically one of the directors of the company was the Chairman of the Committee which had been so strongly opposed to the government retaining the business in any form, Sir Sam H Brown, a London solicitor who had held various positions in the Ministry and was under secretary from 1943. Returning to private practice after the War he was knighted in 1946 and was a strong Conservative. Apparently he found no difficulty in reconciling his opposition to public ownership of the business in general and Belfast in particular with sitting in the company's boardroom in Sydenham (694).

After the war, coinciding with the transfer to Belfast, flying boats went out of use almost completely which meant that the greater part of the company's technical expertise was immediately obsolete. The firm manufactured other company's designs such as English Electric's *Canberra*, Handley Page's *Victor* and Bristol's *Brittania*.

Short Brothers and Harland also designed a number of new planes, the history of which showed clearly that the government ownership did not guarantee large sales to the RAF. The first, in the early 'fifties was the SA4 called the *Sperrin* after the mountains in Derry and Tyrone, was intended to be Britain's first long-range jet bomber. The Ministry of Supply, normally parsimonious, paid for the production line before the prototype flew, a most unusual procedure which was not applied to the *Vickers 660*, the successful rival. Three models were built and used in various tests and experiments. This venture lost £3$\frac{1}{2}$ million and further large sums were spent in vain when the RAF did not order the *SCI* vertical take off and land plane which the company developed in the late 'fifties.

In 1961 the company got a contract from the British government to develop a new freighter plane for both military and civilian use, it was to be the first long-range freighter for the RAF.

Originally intended to be called *Britannic* the name was changed to *Belfast* when the contract went to Shorts.

The company had not sufficient resources to carry out all the research, development and production. London was not prepared to advance the full costs which left the company in the position of having

TIGERCAT
SOURCE 643

to apply to Stormont for assistance. This was provided in the Loans (Belfast/Air Freighter) Act introduced on 9 March 1961 by Captain Terence O'Neill MP, Minister for Finance.

The Minister explained that it was proposed to make up to £5 million available to Shorts for the plane. The company expected a large sale for both versions which was suitable for all types of cargo and were planning to build a minimum of thirty which was the break-even point. By then the craft would have paid for its development costs and further orders would bring in profits. To begin with there was a contract for ten from the RAF. The Bill was welcomed on all sides of both Commons and Senate and passed unanimously with many expressions of confidence in the future of the Ulster aerospace industry. The RAF did not order any more after the first ten and there were no contracts for the civil version. Further assistance to the company was provided under the Aid to Aircraft Industry Acts 1963 and '65 (650-2).

In April 1969 Stormont passed the Aircraft Industry (Loans) Act. Introducing this on 13 March, Roy Bradford MP, Minister for Commerce told the Commons:

> Shorts' past experience, particularly in the aircraft field, has not been free of difficulties. The cancellation of the _Hawker Siddeley 681_ and the failure to sell _Belfast_ freighters apart from the original order for ten, created serious problems. There is also the general problem that the scale of aircraft projects today makes it difficult for a relatively small firm to maintain a place in the industry.

> The firm has done a great deal to help itself. It has produced a most successful missile in the _Seacat;_ it has also developed the _Skyvan_ and is at present conducting a vigorous sales campaign. It would be unfair not to acknowledge the firm's achievements in the field of technology. Nevertheless the fact is that in spite of considerable financial assistance from public funds in the past, we are again called upon to offer a loan of up to £3 million failing which the company will face serious difficulties.

> The present problem however is not so much a shortage of orders as a shortage of working capital to develop a very substantial programme of work. The missile department is flourishing. Apart from that, Shorts are sharing with Fokker in the development and production of the _Fellowship;_ they are completing the _Belfast_ contract and building _Skyvans_ and in

addition have secured the important contract for podding Rolls-Royce engines for the new Lockheed aircraft.

This is a very considerable programme. The firm's past difficulties have prevented it from accumulating reserves and, as a result of detailed investigation, it is apparent that £6 million is required to enable the firm to carry on with this programme. Of this amount the United Kingdom Government have asked us to provide 50 per cent.

The Northern Ireland Government, I must say frankly, would have preferred not to be a participant in this loan so that responsibility would have been undivided. At the same time, we recognise the arguments on the other side. We participated in the Belfast loan to the extent of £2¹/2 million. Westminster has also provided a further £9 millon of which £1 million was an advance on the £6 million now found to be necessary. Its contribution therefore, has been substantial. Moreover, we cannot ignore the importance of the employment provided by the firm in the Belfast area (653).

Several Members and Senators on all sides echoed the obvious doubts in the Minister's tone and expressed grave fears as to the future of the firm. The measure was passed unanimously.

At the time of the Act there was a proposal that the Rohr Corporation of California would take a majority stake in the company. This did not come about. The company went to develop manufacture of components, such as wings, for other firms and also aerostructural work especially podding which is the fitting of casings and support systems to engines prior to installation on aircraft. This is done for various aerospace concerns in Britain, Europe and the USA.

Skyvan proved to be emninently successful from its introduction in 1963. This, with twin turboprop engines by the Garrett Corporation of Los Angeles, is the heaviest light aircraft of the short take-off and land type in the world and is built in both military and civil versions to take either twenty-two passengers or two tonnes of freight or any combination according to the requirements of individual owners. This version can carry an armoured car, a field-gun or a number of smaller items and can be used for transporting troops, paratrooping, surveying, evacuating, searching and rescuing and virtually any other function as it can travel at very low speeds and operate to and from rough fields in remote areas, jungles or places without modern facilities.

In order to meet new requirements of the USA the company

began modifications to *Skyvan* in 1972 which led to a new model, designated *SD3-30* after four years. A military version can be built and a third the *SD3-MR Seeker* is for use in the prevention of pollution and smuggling, security of oil and gas installations, fishery protection and other offshore operations. *Skyvan* and *SD3-30* have been sold to more than twenty-five countries in all continents. (*ILLUSTRATION 17*)

Until the 'sixties the company manufactured a number of non-aerospace products including domestic appliances such as carpet sweepers and *Metaluk* a combined clothes wringer, ironing board and table; various items of furniture; milk churns; some types of computers and forklift trucks (655-6).

The first weapon ever used was undoubtedly a stone followed by a stick. The next step must have been to break a stick into a convenient length, with for preference, a hefty knot at the business end. This, therefore, must have been the first weapon which involved any actual making. The Irish shillelagh, a stout, well seasoned blackthorn, celebrated in song and story, is a worthy member of the cudgel class of weapon. Both stones and sticks are still used in late twentieth century Ireland (649).

In 1959 the Ford Aerospace & Communications Corporation, a subsidiary of the Ford Motor Company, began production of the *Shillelagh*, a guided missile fired from tanks. The specification laid down for this system by the USA Department of Defence was that it should be "simple, reliable and lethal" just like the ancient weapon from the ancestral homeland of Henry Ford himself. The company, in their sales pitch to the Pentagon, bought several hundred souvenir shillelaghs from a Dublin firm for distribution among the top brass of that citadel. Ford claimed in 1971 that more of this had been manufactured than any other missle in the world (657).

In Ireland three missiles are made by Short Brothers. Development of *Seacat (ILLUSTRATION 18)* began in 1958 and was completed in 1962. The weapon has a two stage solid propellant motor by IMI, Imperial Metal Industries, the present Kynoch company and is guided at subsonic speed by radio with a radar or closed circuit television tracking system. The warhead is high explosive with contact and proximity fuses. Range is 3.5 km, length 1.48m, diameter 0.19 m and weight 6.3 kg. It can be fitted in small craft and is used against low flying planes and ship-to-ship surface skimming missiles.

Since 1970 Shorts have produced *Tigercat (ILLUSTRATION 19)* a land version of *Seacat*. This is intended for defending land stations, particularly airports, against low flying planes and is mounted on a trailer with a separate vehicle for the control equipment. At the Paris Air Show in 1979 it was announced that a mark two version was available. Subsequently a surface skimming varient was produced.

The warhead has a firepower equivalent to six 40 mm guns with a saving of 70% in crew members. It is in use by Argentina, Australia, Brazil, Britain, Chile, Holland, India, Iran, Jordan, Libya, Malaysia, Quatar, South Africa, Sweden, Thailand, Venezuela and Zimbabwe.

The company's third missile is *Blowpipe (ILLUSTRATION 20)* which was developed initially without British government support. It is small enough to be carried, fired and controlled from a shoulder unit. It is supersonic, has a high explosive warhead and an infrared actuated proximity fuse. It is 1.4 m long, 76 mm in diameter and can be fitted with the *IFF* identification system to prevent it hitting friendly targets when fired in error. It can be used against low flying planes, tanks and other ground targets. British Aerospace produce a version for fitting on submarines designated *SIAM*. A new guidance system was perfected in 1979 and the mark two version the following year. The system is in use by Britain, Canada, Oman and seven undisclosed countries, some of which are members of NATO.

Shorts manufacture advanced equipment for training operatives in the use of the missiles and also three target systems, the supersonic *Stiletto* adapted from the American Beech *AQM-37A* to British specifications, the *MATS-B* for both missiles and guns and a larger version of this designated *Skeet*.

For several years Shorts carried out research and development on *Sky Spy* an aerial surveillance system. Work was suspended in 1976 until such time as a joint venture could be arranged with another company. *Sky Shout*, an aerial loud hailing device audible from an altitude of 1,000 metres was perfected in 1980.

In June 1977 it was announced that the company's name was being changed from Short Brothers and Harland to Short Brothers. The following November a subsidiary, Short Brothers (USA) Incorporated, was formed with head office in Newport Beach, California, an important centre of the aerospace industry and a branch in Boston, the company having had offices in both cities for several years.

Shorts lost £2.4 million in 1975, £5.4 million in 1976, £4.6 million in 1977 and £6.7 million in 1978. On 7 December 1978 Don Concannon MP, Minister for State at the Northern Ireland Office, with responsibility for the Department of Commerce, announced in the

House of Commons that he had approved a five year plan, prepared by an international consultancy firm, which Shorts had submitted. A sum of £60 million would be made available up to 1982 for new equipment and working captial to be used in the programme. It was expected that employment would be increased by 300 to 6,500 and that the company would return to a profit making position by the end of the programme, the progress of which would be monitored regularly.

The company expected further substantial sales for *Skyvan, SD3-30, Seacat, Tigercat* and *Blowpipe*. In addition they anticipated more podding and other aerostructural work for Rolls-Royce, and the joint German-Dutch company Vereinigte - Flugtechnische - Werke - Fokker and also for Boeing, Lockheed and McDonnell Douglas, being the only European firm to carry out contracts for each of the "big-three" of USA aerospace.

In March 1979 the company set up Short Brothers (Australia) Limited to mount marketing and support programmes in the Pacific region with an office in Sydney. A small subsidiary had for many years previously been providing services at the Woomera and Jervis Bay aircraft and missile testing stations for the Australian forces.

In April 1979 a wholly owned subsidiary, Shorts Light Aircraft Company, was set up to manufacture trainers for military and civil use under an agreement with Piper Aircraft Corporation of the USA. Shorlac took over an old maintenance plant adjacent to Shorts' main premises which had been closed the previous year by the RAF. The project was cancelled after six months because of legal difficulties over the applicability of USA certification to planes assembled outside that country.

Seacat continues as the most widely used system in the world being in service with sixteen navies and outselling all others in its class. In the Falklands war in 1982 British use of the missile destroyed nine Argentinian planes confirmed and probably two others. *Blowpipe*, deployed against targets and under conditions for which it was not designed scored eight and two. At that time variants for fitting on armoured vehicles and helicopters were being developed. The publicity generated by the conflict brought considerably increased interest in the Belfast range of weapons.

In January 1983 Short Brothers announced that their airport would provide services for regional airlines and owners of private planes. The staff was increasing and the company had become the largest manufacturing employment in the province. New methods and materials were being introduced while some existing skills were no longer needed. The company had won twelve citations in the sixteen years of the Queen's Award to Industry scheme. Two were for technical innovation and the remainder for export achievement. By this time 150 *Skyvans* had been sold, about half being for military use. Production had commenced on a freight version of *3-30* and a larger passenger version the *360*.

Shorts have a policy of continually updating their products as distinct from changing models completely and expect that *Skyvan, Seacat, Tigercat* and *Blowpipe* will remain in service until the end of the century (638-48, 763-76).

BLOWPIPE
SOURCE 644

EPILOGUE

Over the period of eight hundred years covered, many different enterprises, with production methods ranging from the very elementary using the simplest tools and rawest of materials to the most advanced machinery and complicated of components, in widely varying conditions and circumstances, manufactured a most surprising diversity of war *matériel*.

There were very many undertakings both private and public. The private included independent craftworkers such as the gunsmiths, partnerships and companies of different sizes, quoted, unquoted and unincorporated. The public sector comprised work carried out directly by the forces, largescale enterprises by the Board of Ordnance and factories variously managed by and on behalf of the sponsoring ministries.

The numerous individual enterprises can be divided into ten separate forms constituting a complete classification; pre-industrial; defunct; dying; existing; emerging; improvisation; specific short-term; projected and abandoned and established without going into substantial if any production. The construction of bretashes and galleys, by the army and navy, took place before the development of any semblance of organised industry.

Robert Poynter made gunpowder solely on a contractual basis and Nicholas Grueber mainly so.

Ballincollig was as up to date as any black powder plant at the turn of the century. Although the product was well on the way to becoming virtually obsolete, the factory could certainly have survived some years had it not been acquired by a larger concern. Similar factories still exist in Europe. One such factory is THE FEDERAL GUNPOWDER WORKS, AUBONNE, SWITZERLAND, operated by the Swiss Army.

Arklow could well be in existance still if it had independence and competent management.

Irish Industrial Explosives plc manufacturers industrial explosives in County Meath.

Queen's Island is building ships for the merchant fleets of the world, and Short's design and manufacture aircraft and guided missiles.

Verolme was a flourishing concern for many years.

There are factories making armoured vehicles in Belfast and Meath.

Instances of improvisation are gunpowder at Limerick and *sows* at the sieges of Kinsale, Ballyaly Castle and Sligo and armoured cars in Easter Week and later. During the World Wars many firms made products outside their normal ranges, in some cases with special plants and subsidiaries. The National Factories and Shadow Factories were established only for the duration.

The Ernst Grob glider plant proposed for Waterford was cancelled just before the signing of the agreements and commencement of construction.

The Fenian Gun Company, Potez and Cross and Jackson while set up with premises and machinery did not get into production.

Throughout history millions have been killed and many more maimed while vast resources have been wasted, particularly in the twentieth century. Colossal quantities of metal have been formed into ships, aircraft, guns and innumerable ingenious weapons for destruction. Immense amounts of oil, timber, rubber, chemicals and other commodities have been squandered.

Barracks and other fortifications have been built expansively and houses, hospitals, schools, cultural centres and recreational amenities parsimoniously. Even still, incomprehensible resources of materials and of design and production capacities are expanded every day while large proportions of the world's population are on subsistence and even starvation levels.

The Second World War ended in 1945 with the first, and so far only, use of atomic weapons, the ultimate development from black powder six hundred years earlier. Since then many more elaborate and effective varieties have been made culminating in the neutron bomb which is apparently capable of destroying life while leaving buildings and other physical assets intact.

In 1961 Dwight D Eisenhower, a notable general of the Second War, in his valedictory address as President of the USA, warned of the advent of the "huge industrial and military machinery of defense". Since Eisenhower's time the *military-industrial complex* has grown to vastly greater dimensions (658).

After 1945 the USA and the Soviet Union emerged as the two great superpowers and divided the world between them, each with its own mutually respected block. They hold occasional alarms and excursions, Berlin, Korea, Cuba and countless lesser contrived crises and confrontations for the purpose of keeping tension on the boil and their respective client nations in line.

The old imperial powers of Europe, caught between the new

empires and finding themselves losing their colonies, which they had originally obtained by gunpowder, sought to solve both problems by coming together in a new block. The most important and least perceived characteristic of this agglomeration is that it is essentially an isolationist entity.

Ten days after *HMS Belfast* docked in the Pool of London on that autumn day in 1971 the Far Eastern Fleet of the Royal Navy, with which the ship had served, steamed out of Singapore and after a ceremonial sailpast began the last long voyage back to the cold island in the north and the White Ensign was run down after one hundred and fifty years East of Suez, having already been furled west of the great dividing meridian.

It was fitting. Three days before, the Mother-of-Parliaments, a few cables length upstream, had voted to throw its lot in with the new economic empire which it had spurned earlier and more recently courted and indeed importuned for admittance. The costs of maintaining the remnants of the British Empire, more recently and euphemistically the Commonwealth, had outstripped the return and the once proud pound had been devalued a number of times.

Ireland was soon to follow. In May 1972 the people voted overwhelmingly to join the economic empire, lured by profusely propagandised visions of unprecedented prosperity, a veritable Tír na nÓg. Such an appeal to greed is a flimsy foundation for any structure and while co-operation between nations is undeniably desirable it is difficult to see how any worthwhile edifice can be built downwards from above, especially when there is no real commitment on the part of the masses.

Even within its own terms the European Economic Community had made progress slowly at best, acrimoniously at all times and certainly without being seen as bestowing universal benefits in its various agricultural, industrial and social spheres.

At the onset of the 'eighties international tension appeared to be at the highest level for at least twenty years and was symptomised in Ireland by the formation of Nuclear Defences Limited. The company, an offshoot of an engineering firm in Straffan, Kildare offer to supply and erect various sizes of underground nuclear fallout shelters and since 1980 operate in the home and export markets. The establishment of this enterprise was a reflection of similar developments in Britain at the time (782-7).

The new economic empire, at least so far and in theory, has no military aspects. This does not disguise the fact that all members,

EPILOGUE

except Ireland are affiliated to the North Atlantic Treaty Organisation and also to the Western European Union - except Ireland, Greece and Denmark - a lesser known military institution (661).

In May 1978 the Political Affairs Committee of the Assembly of the European Economic Community produced a *Report on European Armaments Procurement Cooperation*. The procedure for the preparation of this document was initiated by the Liberal and Democratic Group which did not have any Irish members. It called for an "Action Programme" for the development and production of conventional armaments within the framework of the Common Industrial Policy. This would be carried out by the European Armaments Procurement Agency which the report recommended should be set up. It was recognised that the military and civil aspects of shipbuilding, aerospace, electronics and related industries could not be separated. A major factor was the necessity to reduce dependence on the USA for many weapons systems and types of equipment.

The report was considered by the Assembly on 13 June 1978 in a debate to which the Irish members did not contribute. The EEC Commission submitted to the Council of Ministers an *Action Programme for Aeronautical Research* in July 1977 and *Proposals for Concerted Action on Aircraft* in June 1978 (662-5).

In February 1979 provision was made under the first Defence (Amendment) Act of that year for certain new ranks in the upper echelons of the Defence Forces in order to bring these into harmonisation with those of other countries. In June the government announced a major reorganisation and expansion of the Army, Naval Service and Air Corps. This included the introduction of women's units for the first time. The Minister for Defence, Robert Molloy TD, explained the further measure giving effect to this in the Senate on 31 October, "subject to their exemption in normal circumstances from combatant status, women will be employed in a most comprehensive range of military duties". He did not accept the suggestion that women ought to be equally eligible for frontline duties which was made by Professor John A Murphy (Independent, National University Constituency) who quipped that there should be a marshal's baton in every woman soldier's handbag. The following December the Army demonstrated its latest weapon, the *Milan* anti-tank missile, wire propelled on the Brennan Principal (661, 669, 778-81)

Ireland has always been strictly and well nigh unanimously neutral and while popular opinion has never been tested on the subject it is beyond question that the vast majority would be totally against involvement in any alliance and certainly in any conflict. There can be no doubt that this would be equally the case in Northern Ireland.

The ridiculous situation persists into the 'eighties that when in 1963 the two superpowers signed the Partial Nuclear Test Ban Treaty Ireland became a signatory immediately even though the country could not even begin to think about manufacturing ordinary bombs, let alone atomic wapons, while at the same time successive governments of different complexions had failed to ratify the Universal Declaration of Human Rights promulgated by the United Nations fifteen years earlier and has still not done so after an equal lapse of time during which, for good measure, the country adhered to the subsequent analogous agreements, the Outer Space Treaty, the Non-Proliferation Treaty, the Sea Bed Treaty and the Biological Warfare Convention. Indeed this national hypocrisy was compounded in 1978 when the country marked the thirtieth anniversary of the Declaration by voting against the resolution, which was passed, at the special Disarmament Session of the UN, avowing that the use the nuclear weapons would be a violation of the Organisation's Charter. A speech by the Minister for Foreign Affairs, Michael O'Kennedy TD, on the anniversary failed to make clear the country's position (670,777).

While vast resources of materials and facilities which could be used in generating wealth for the world at large are still being dissipated in the arms race, it is becoming increasingly evident that the reserves of the planet, particularly of oil, are diminishing rapidly.

It is also apparent that industry, by and large, depends on public support of some kind. Even in the USA, seat of the capitalist system, large sectors of agriculture and industry are unable to carry on without assistance of various kinds from local and federal funds. It must also be the case that the many and mighty multi-national companies are major culprits in the waste of the world's resources with their policies of deliberately dispersed and duplicated production programmes, planned obsolescence and demands for subsidies, all conjoined with elaborate tax evasion schemes. The dictum expressed in 1953 by Charles Wilson, president of General Motors, "what's good for GM is good for America", now echoes hollowly from another age (672).

Internally businesses have changed greatly. Managements are now all powerful, moderated if at all and to a limited extent by trade union and consumer pressures. Share capital is of little consequence either as a source of finance or of power in an enterprise. Shareholders and boards of directors have, for most practical purposes, no voice in concerns of any size. This is also the case in co-operatives and other forms of mutual undertakings. There is now a tentative movement towards involvement on the part of the workforce in Ireland, beginning with some publicly owned concerns through the Worker Participation (State Enterprises) Act, 1977. Similar schemes are being experimented with in other countries.

It is certainly clear that the fundamental concept of the joint stock company laid down in the high noon of Victorian *Laissez-faire* in the Original Companies Act of 1856 and unaltered since then cannot for much longer continue to accommodate all the changes in business and society at large, even within the context of the capitalist system. There will therefore have to be new forms of enterprise for conducting industry and commerce.

Industrial civilisation is also being affected profoundly by automation. In 1953 Walter Reuther, president of the United Autoworkers in the USA, observed that machines which replace humans will not buy cars. These developments, which improve life immeasurably by eliminating many back-breaking and mind-bending tasks and by providing numerous amenities, are accelerating rapidly with advances in microprocessors and lasers. There is a growing realisation that the cost of industry in terms of pollution and other damage to the environment, may be excessive in the long run. The Industrial Development Authority claim to have a strict policy on potentially dangerous projects (671-2).

With the implementation of the Aircraft and Shipbuilding Industries Act 1977 the greater part of both were nationalised under two corporations, British Aerospace and British Shipbuilders. This was vital if either was to have any place in the world market. The government, at first under Harold Wilson and later James Callaghan, choose to exclude Harland and Wolff, already fully owned, and Short Brothers, the balance of whose privately held shares were acquired as a result of the legislation.

The reason for this, as outlined by Stanley Orme MP (page 235) was that the companies would, at some subsequent stage, come under a devolved government. The Stormont Parliament had been extinguished in 1972. The Assembly was elected the next year and its power sharing executive functioned for a few months in 1974. The Convention sat in 1975 and its Report with recommendations for the future governance of Northern Ireland was rejected by Westminster in 1976. Over the following years many suggestions were put forward from various quarters. In October 1982 a poll was held for a new Assembly with a four year term to which some functions might be devolved gradually. The electorate showed scarcely any interest and the elected, many of whom were abstentionist, little more. As the house continued to sit into 1983 amid calls for it abolition, there seemed to be no likelihood that any significant powers would be transferred during its first term and the prospects for a second appeared dim. At this juncture the shape of a devolved administration with any general acceptability which might emerge was as unknown as that of the next century's aircraft.

That Ireland, both parts, for the remainder of this century, let alone the following, will be profoundly different, cannot be doubted. From around 1960 old ideas, thinking, modes of living and indeed many hallowed precepts underwent vast changes. The institutions set up in 1795, Maynooth College and the Orange Order, were not immune to the whirlwinds blowing in all directions. Both came under external pressures and experienced severe internal strains so that at this writing it could not be predicted that either would see its bi-centenary in any recognisable form, if at all. By then religion may genuinely be a matter of private conscience not of public profession quintessential in each of the deadly dualities which have for so long vitiated life from the Lagan to the Lee.

Pending the establishment of a devolved government the entire equities of Harland and Wolff and of Short Brothers are vested in the Northern Ireland Department of Commerce which continues to exist being among the several responsibilities of one of the junior ministers at the Northern Ireland Office.

Under Section 48 of the Act the corporations are enjoined to "have regard to the need to consult, and wherever possible co-ordinate their activities" with the Belfast firms. In practice it would be impossible for any government to enforce this as a management, by inertia and otherwise, can always circumvent such a mandate however emphatically expressed. Certainly thus far, no formal channels have been set up between the headquarters of British Aerospace in London and British Shipbuilders in Newcastle-upon-Tyne with the respective companies and any communications are on the basis of old personal contacts.

The Aircraft and Shipbuilding Industries Order 1979 implemented new systems for the finance and control of both concerns with effect from April of that year. It is significant that this was made under the Northern Ireland Act 1974 not the nationalisation measure.

The practical, and presumably intended, effects of these arrangements are that the Ulster undertakings are not integrated with the British industries as a whole. There is a long standing and often repeated governmental assurance, on the well established bipartisan basis, that the Belfast firms will be "treated not less favourably" than those on the mainland.

This segregation would facilitate the closure of the businesses or disposal to any party willing to purchase. It is difficult for any British government to regard Harland and Wolff, even with such a central place in the Ulster economy, as other than a liability. A devolved government, of even the most atavistic hue, if such were even to function in the future, could not keep the yard afloat on the strength of its heritage alone (623, 655, 666-8, 715-16).

Shorts operate in an industry which is particularly prone to rapid changes in technology and of strategic and commercial considerations. Aerospace is very much a matter of the survival of the fittest. There is a precedent of sorts for the disposal of the business in that in 1969 there was a proposal for the sale of a majority interest to the Rohr Corporation of California. This was under a government of the Labour Party which is traditionally and fundamentally in favour state enterprise. This indeed is the party which moved Shorts to Belfast, the only example of such a transfer from Britain to Ireland. If that party could contemplate a sale of this kind it follows that the Conservative Party, who do not believe that the state should operate any profitable businesses, are all the more likely to do so. Indeed soon after the general election in 1979 the first Margaret Thatcher Conservative government decided to arrange a placing of a majority of British Aerospace shares on the market, effectively denationalising the concern. At the onset of the 'eighties other aircraft companies were planning to establish in Belfast. The development of a broadbased industry in the city would be of benefit to Shorts even if they lost personnel in the early stages.

The weapons built by Shorts are in the smallest range, at the far end of the scale from the great intercontinental ballistic missiles. There are about thirty others of the *Seacat* and *Tigercat* types including four by the Soviet Union and four similar to *Blowpipe* of which one is Soviet (660).

Harland and Wolff have not built a warship since 1968 and inclusion in the current calendar of war industries is really only honourable mention.

This leaves the Timoney APC. There are some thirty to forty others of the type in the world, about five being Soviet. In 1978 the house of Timoney built five for the Irish Army at the small Gibbstown works. Even if a full-scale factory could be justified this would be a duplication of existing capacity. When such a plant stands on Laganside there is no economic justification for setting up another on the Boyne or elsewhere south of that sundering stream (659).

It is now shown that Ireland has had a remarkable range of war industries.

From the early thirteenth century the air resounded to the thud of adze on choicest oak and ash being made into mangonels, siege towers and ships to be replaced in time by the rattle of rivet on iron and in turn the hiss and incandescent glare of welder on steel which is now giving way to computer controlled laser.

The pungent odours of saltpetre, sulphur and charcoal wafted for a century across the Lee Valley and were also known in Dublin.

For a generation the acrid fumes of sulphuric and nitric acids suffused the Vale of Avoca.

The searing heat of the gun foundry was felt occasionally and during the First World War the precision products of the lathe on many shopfloors were sent to the Front and even more so in the Second along with countless additional *oeuvres* of war *matériel* and many ships and aircraft.

That Ireland produced various explosives and weapons is not a matter for any particular pride except as regards the civil aspects. There was little or no native motivation in the enterprises as a whole. Almost every undertaking was a branch of British governmental or private interests reflecting the relationship between the two countries in the eight hundred years since the earliest traceable production.

It would be overly sanguine to expect that the demand for armaments will disappear in the foreseeable future as fighting has been going on since the most primitive ancestors first wielded stone and stick.

And so, with the armoured cars of Shorts and of Timoney thundering over land, the ships of Queen's Island and Great Island surging across the seas and the aircraft and missiles of Sydenham soaring through the skies, Ireland's War Industries face into the twenty-first century.

EXPLICATION OF SOURCES AND METHODS

Much of the documentation was in the major institutions of Britain because most of the undertakings were branches of British enterprises and as there is nothing published on Britain's war industries it was necessary to carry out extensive research in basic sources not directly related to Ireland. In practice this involved spending long periods in the various repositories as it is not possible to obtain material satisfactorily otherwise except in the cases of items of small size when it is feasible to buy entire copies, sight unseen.

It would certainly have been impossible to find the Tobins' slaving and other interests without going to Liverpool. The reason why Merseyside merchants paid a five figure sum for a mill outside Cork, derelict for twenty years, had been a complete mystery until then. The Liverpool Record Office would not allow photocopying of the Tobin Family history (Source 139) without permission. The copyright owner was Helen Mary Reid finding whom entailed following clues in the work, enquiries at the Middle Temple, the Strand Law Courts, the Old Bailey, an interview with the clerk to her former son-in-law, a high court judge, arrangements through his son and finally a visit to East Grinstead. Many other cases involved as many or more stages.

Likewise it would have been impossible to find most of the documents in the ICI archives, Kynoch Works and numerous other institutions without personal investigation.

An example of an item bought sight unseen is Source 150, an inaccurately cited reference to which was found in the course of background reading on the Liverpool slave trade. Enquiries to two libraries in Manchester indicated its location in Keele. It was obviously far easier to get the whole volume copied than to go and look as it existed in an isolated context.

In 1973 queries were published in several journals and newspapers seeking information. There was no response to those in the *Journal of the Cork Historical and Archaeological Society,* the *Dublin Historical Record,* the *Irish Sword, An Cosantóir,* the *Waterford News and Star* and the *Munster Express.* The *Wicklow People* elicited Sources 373, 374, 376 and 378. The *Connacht Sentinel* led to Source 471; Mary Lally had emigrated to Australia after the closure of the Galway National Shell Factory. A letter from her son stated that she was on her first trip home. A hasty visit to Galway before her imminent departure resulted in much useful data and the presentation of her souvenir shell.

275

Numerous documents were in private archives such as those of the various companies, professional and other organisations and certain British government departments. A great many of the 160 institutions have never been drawn upon in Irish or any history. More than half furnished only single items.

It was found that shortcuts or attempts were counter-productive. For example, Sir Thomas Brassey, a Ballincollig shareholder, was a first described as an "important" contractor. While this might well have passed muster it did not seem completely convincing and with a search his biography was traced, providing much useful information (page 56-57).

There was an examination of all the registers in the State Paper Office which run from 1790 to 1922 and a reading and indeed copying of many more documents than those cited. Large numbers of indexes, handlists and other guides in the public record offices in Dublin, Belfast and London were scrutinised. Vast volumes of calendars, parliamentary papers and other printed matter, especially in the National Library and British Library were read. There were searches in many other institutions which are not listed.

Some material was copied on the offchance of proving useful. For example, Source 417 which while interesting, did not seem particularly relevant except as a marginal possibility in the World Wars, fitted in very well with the Louis Brennan section. Conversely, much material which had seemed very valuable had to be eliminated because of inaccuracy, inapplicability or in the interests of optimality.

Parliamentary papers are also very difficult because there is no complete collection and no overall indexing system. It was fortunate indeed that the Tobin material in Source 243 turned up in the fourth or fifth of the ninety odd volumes on slavery in the Irish University Press reprints.

The Liverpool Record Office has an excellent indexing system which provided Sources 139-145 and 225-227.

The amounts of data extant are very variable. Huge masses of paper are available on the Board of Ordnances's involvements in Ballincollig and relations with the Tobins (Sources 98-102). There are many documents in the files of the Colonial Office and Foreign Office concerning the Tobins' African affairs of which three, Sources 179-181, are cited to give a flavour of this side of the story.

There is very little on record about the London investors who bought Ballincollig in 1889. The City newspapers of the time are singularly uninformative, even about prospectuses.

Over 1,000 folios were assembled on the "Six Thousand Barrels". Some are of little value such as Source 272, which while useful for corroboration, is included mainly for completeness.

This saga, documented so extensively, indeed excruciatingly, provides useful fresh coverage of the Fenian period and its aftermath. There is more than ample scope for a full length study of the relations between the Chief Secretary and Under Secretary in Dublin Castle, the Commander of the Forces and Judge Advocate General in the Royal hospital, Kilmainham and the Irish Constabulary; in Cork the military and naval establishments, the magistracy and local government; in London the Lord Lieutenant sitting in the Irish Office, Downing Street, the Treasury, the Law Officers and the various power centres in the War Office. There is much of interest in regard to the interplay of personalities, interpretation of duties and functions, statutory and administrative, *vis-à-vis* other departments, enforcement of the law and the varying approaches of the several individuals and institutions to a conflict with a private vested interest in an era when governmental intervention of any kind in commercial matters had scarely begun.

Only circumstantial evidence could be found on Ballincollig sales to both sides in the USA Civil War. The possibility of positive information coming to light on this matter is shown in the discovery in 1971, in the National Archives, of an important post-bellum document, a declaration of allegiance by Robert E Lee.

Chapter One has Sources 1 to 294 and also solely 692 and 703 to 706 which are under Multiple Reference. This is nearly half the total for one third of the contents. Furthermore these were far more dispersed than those for the other chapters. In addition practically all the manuscripts in One are actually hand written, few, if any, being copperplate. Source 202, dated 1890, is the earliest typed item found in the State Paper Office and indeed throughout this research.

The greater part of the Kynoch manuscript material is typed, the major exception being Source 318. When an exhaustive search in the London PRO for the government papers on the early cordite contracts proved fruitless a check in the Historical Manuscripts Commission's National Register of Archives gave the location of the minister's private papers in the British Library and thus the documents were found. It was necessary to copy these by hand, as in the case of Source 270, because the BL do not allow photocopying of manuscripts on grounds of age and possible damage. The PRO, in contrast, cheerfully photocopied Sources 1 to 4 which are a matter of six hundred years older.

The First World War is far better documented than the Second which has no equivalent of the *Secret Weekly Report* (Source 444). There are difficulties arising from the deliberate destruction of the bulk of Ministry of Munitions' records. Fortunately some documents preserved as typical specimens of their respective classes are of Irish interest (Sources 417, 438, 439).

While many sets of production records may not have survived after 1945, if indeed these were maintained in meaningful forms in the first place, there is reason to suspect that some may not have yet been transferred to or made available in the London PRO. There is an official history, see Source 535. Although all should be open by now, many files on Short Brothers, for example, remain closed until various dates later in the century. These would appear to deal mainly with questions relating to various premises in Belfast.

There are remarkable difficulties in ascertaining the number of ships built by Harland and Wolff (page 232). In general, Admiralty records are far more difficult than those of other departments. Indeed there was no administrative history of the Senior Service until the publication in 1979 of NAM Rodger's *The Admiralty* (Terence Dalton, London).

Many files in the State Paper Office are "not up" (Source 321). On the whole, it is unlikely that very much of real importance remains unavailable.

The only refusals to supply information were in Ireland. In England on the other hand, every facility was afforded including access to a number of private archives, from the most exalted, Windsor Castle, down. Material was made available in several governmental archives not normally open to the public. At the Propellants, Explosives and Rocket Motor Establishment, Sources 91-93, a chauffeured car was provided, this in the week after Derry's Bloody Sunday and the arson of the British Embassy in Dublin in January 1972 and moreover without any advance arrangement.

The difference in the volumes of materials created considerable difficulties in balance. It is not possible to amplify or condense data to fit the space and scope of any particular purpose. The policy has been to compress large masses rather than to expand small volumes. It would have been far easier to use both the materials cited and those excluded, to a far greater degree, extending from 600 to 1,000 pages, double and treble the final length, as in some drafts. Indubitably the greatest difficulty in historical composition is to steer an appropriate course between the *Scylla* of oversimplification and the *Charybdis* of excessive expatiation. The basic format is by product and undertaking. An enterprise which manufactured more than one product appears in each respective Chapter.

A steady process of reduction, by eliminating or paraphrasing quotations and by general consolidation of the text resulted in this length. When the work dealt solely or mainly with Ballincollig much technical and local information was included. Indeed the original orientation tended towards industrial archaeology. This was tightened when Arklow was reached. With the coverage extented to Inventors, the World Wars, Guns, Armoured Vehicles, Ships, Aircraft and Guided Missiles it became clearly impracticable to go into engineering, ballistics, metallurgy, mechanics, naval architecture, aerodynamics and so on. Therefore most of the remaining scientific and local coverage was removed. Even so, it was necessary to study extensively in the various technologies in order to acquire and convey some understanding, however generalised, of the relevant backgrounds.

Most of the information is on paper of some kind and skins in the cases of Sources 1 to 4. Use is also made of metal artifacts such as guns, Sources 506-508 and stencils, Source 213. The work carries a number of photographs carefully chosen from the large number of illustrative items collected. In two instances, Sources 323, 324 and Source 418, use is made of information on photos which are not reproduced.

Several maps and plans were copied of which three, Sources 97-99, are cited. There are many maps of Ballincollig in Source 101, the existence of which was not known in the PRO before the author's requisition, the first ever as in most cases, of the portfolios, in 1972. These were subsequently changed to a separate storage system. There is a map of Arklow in Source 315 which was in connection with the transfer of the property in 1912. It was thought that inclusion of these and of any of the numerous other maps, plans and drawings of machinery in various factories would not be justified in view of the fact that the work is not a technical treatise.

Some information was collected on clandestine production of armaments and explosives in several periods. It was felt on reflection that this could be more satisfactorily dealt with as part of a study of guerilla warfare.

War, it is averred, makes strange bedfellows. Certainly, after a long courtship, many different types of material consort comfortably: fourteenth century manuscripts with 1980 press releases; seventeenth century polemical tracts with twentieth century civil service memos; calendared letters with modern corporate correspondence; ancient regal mandates with modern ministerial orders; medieval alchemy with space age science; variant recollections of unsung workers with sonorous findings of great minds in the proceedings of learned societies and others equally diverse.

There are many surprising connections such as Ballincollig with Calabar and other exotic places in Africa and elsewhere. It could hardly have been expected that important information on Harland and Wolff would be found in such disparate documents as the secret records of Nobel's Explosives Company and left-wing pamphlets (Sources 598, 599, 614, 615).

The thesis brings out many sidelights on Irish history of which one gem is that it could be said that the gun was brought into Ulster Unionist politics by an Aberdonian adventurer (page 95). This was not known before despite the numerous tomes on that period. The Volunteer rally at Ballincollig which illustrates so well the fundamental flaws of Grattan's Parliament, had been long forgotten (page 14-15). There are many insights into the tenor of those times drawn from the *Westmoreland Correspondence*, the 620 series and other contemporary documents in the State Paper Office which have not been used to the fullest possible extent in Irish historical studies.

Metric equivalents are given as appropriate and these are used in the first instance where possible. When it is necessary to quote sums in shillings and pence decimal values are supplied.

SOURCE REFERENCE SYSTEM

All Sources are primary. Many are of types entirely new in Irish or any history and of the more usual, very few have been used before.

There are five categories under which all items are numbered consecutively from 1 to 787 comprising 335 Original manuscripts; 62 Calendared manuscripts; 151 Original Prints; 79 Parliamentary and 140 Information Supplied. Also there are five directories and fifteen newspapers. The individual number of each item and the disposition and aggregation of types are given in the Quantification of Sources (pages 359-362).

The first category consists almost entirely of handwritten materials of many different kinds with some typewritten and a few, found in archival holdings, printed for private use, generally with handwritten endorsements.

The second covers regular record publications for the most part with certain issues of learned journals and some items which do not fit readily into the third category,works given appreciable circulations.

The fourth is for debates, acts, reports and orders of the various legislatures.

The fifth includes both folk and living memories from individuals and also statements furnished officially by various bodies.

There are some borderline cases which are placed in what seems the most appropriate category.

Artifacts and unpublished photographs are treated as Original Manuscripts. Photographs published or distributed as publicity material are Original Prints. Selections of the photos taken, commissioned, purchased or otherwise obtained, including a great many not used, are donated to the National Library, the Irish and Local Studies Library, Belfast and the Cross River State Library, Calabar. Various artifacts, including some not listed, are donated to the National Museum and copies of certain recorded interviews to the Imperial War Museum, London.

Items are given under each Chapter, with those from the same repository together, chronologically as far as possible. The Sources for Chapter One, The Tobins and the Last Years are integrated and those for The Fenians, Six Thousand Barrels are separate. Most of those which relate to more than one Chapter are under Multiple Reference and any which are not are annotated as needful. Most of the newspapers are cited only once or twice and together with all the other items under Multiple Reference are cross-referenced to the text.

Certain periodicals and those learned journals with material other than calendared items are treated as Original Prints. Publications mentioned in passing are entered in the Index of Contents.

Reference numbers are given in brackets at the ends of paragraphs, omitting those which are reasonably obvious such as parliamentary debates where dates are sufficient, decisions of the Kynoch directors and any others quoted close together except where confusion might arise.

Folio, page or entry numbers and any other details available are supplied. In a number of instances such as Sources 101 and 308 which are heavy bound volumes and Sources 634-637, large files of loose papers, there are no such indications and sometimes not even dates. Locations are given for all unique and rare items and any other data of guidance to future researchers. All the institutions and individuals drawn upon are listed with the numbers of the relevant items in pages 363-367. Items without locations can be assumed to be in the national Library, British Library or other central, local or institutional repository as appropriate.

SOURCES, FOREGOING ITEMS

MS Dudley Westropp's "Irish Gunsmiths and Sword Cutlers" (*Irish Sword*, volume I, 1949, pages 181-187). Sources 497,501,502,503 and 696 are followed up from the article.

Professor AJ Otway-Ruthven's *A History of Medieval Ireland* (Ernest Benn, London, 1968, page 326) has a brief, unindexed allusion to Richard Sonner. Without this, Source 510 would not have come to attention.

Edmund Curtis's *A History of Medieval Ireland* (second edition, Methuen, London, 1938, page 345) and GA Hayes-McCoy's "The Early History of Guns in Ireland" (*Journal of the Galway Archaeological and Historical Society,* volume XVIII, 1938, pages 43-65) both aver that guns were first used in Ireland, and by the Irish, in the 1480s, on the basis of an entry in the *Annals of the Four Masters*.

JG Simms' *Jacobite Ireland* (Routledge & Kegan Paul, London, 1969, page 133) mentions gunmaking in 1690.

Leon O'Broin's *Fenian Fever* (Chatto & Windus, London, 1971).

SOURCES

Chapter One - Gunpowder Comes

ORIGINAL MANUSCRIPTS

PUBLIC RECORD OFFICE, LONDON

1   Henry de Snayth, accounts as keeper of the King's Privy
     Wardrobe, 1360-62   E/364/34

2   Ranulph de Hatton, accounts as Keeper of the King's Privy
     Wardrobe, 1382-96   E/101/394/2

3   John Lufwyk, accounts as Keeper of the King's Privy Wardrobe,
     1396-99   E/101/403/11

4   Appointment of Master of the Ordnance, 1414

     Patent Roll 2 part ii mem 22

ROYAL IRISH ACADEMY, DUBLIN

5   Entry 73 re lodgement of arms, Dublin Castle, pages 177-79:

     Irish Pipe Roll Extracts

     Manuscript 12D10

MUNIMENTS ROOM, CITY HALL, DUBLIN

The *Friday Book,* minutes of Dublin Corporation

6   Robert Poynter, February 1589, folio 24a

7   City Watch, 1597, folio 41a

8   Sale of powder, 1600, folio 59a

9   Salute to the Lord Lieutenant, 1603, folio 74a

10   Sheriffs of the Bullring, 1608, folio 92b
     (Copy, courtesy, P Smith)

LAMBETH PALACE LIBRARY, LONDON

11   Proclamation re gunpowder, Ireland, 1595
     Manuscript 612 F 39

INDIA OFFICE LIBRARY AND RECORDS, LONDON

12   Minutes, Court of Directors, East India Company

13   Letter Book of the Company
       (assistance Ian A Baxter and Anne Hill)
OFFICE OF PUBLIC WORKS, DUBLIN
14   Charter, Royal Hospital, Kilmainham
       (Courtesy, K Brewster)

KENT COUNTY RECORD OFFICE, MAIDSTONE
15   Evidence of Gruebers at Faversham, 1728:
       Faversham Borough Records Fa/JQR 21
       (Copy, courtesy, Arthur Percival MBE BA FSA, Faversham,
       author of Source 119)

ARCHIVES, ICI MILLBANK, LONDON
16   *A Souvenir of the Occasion of Presentation to Mr TR Curtis and
       Mr DJ Metcalfe on their Retirement from the Active Control of
       Curtis's & Harvey Limited, 1922*
       Compiled by H N Clapham, Secretary

PUBLIC RECORD OFFICE, BELFAST
The Papers of John Foster
17   Schedule of Gunpowder Imports and Exports, Ireland, Twenty
       Years ending 1779   D/562/8724
18   Schedule of Costs of Saltpetre   D/562/8725
19   Schedule of Costs of Production, Gunpowder, Duties, Bounties,
       England and Ireland   D562/8728
20   Letter from Whitehall to Dublin Castle re legislation for
       bounties on gunpowder   D562/8729B
21   Notice of Price Increases D562/8730 (printed).
       ILLUSTRATION 1

SCIENCE MUSEUM LIBRARY, LONDON
22   *Monumenta Pulveris Pyrii*
       *Reproductions of Ancient Pictures concerning Gunpowder with
       explanatory Notes*
       Privately circulated by Oscar Guttman, a leading explosives
       expert, London, 1906; 270 copies in English, German and

French; a large folio volume in wooden boards with engraved brass clasps; copy 221 bearing the bookplate of AT Cocking; director of Kynoch.

STATE PAPER OFFICE, DUBLIN

23,24   Caldbeck's Mills
620/38/149 June 1798
620/39/67 July 1798
Registered Papers

25   Letter from Henry Arabin to Dublin Castle
Official Papers 1803: 525/162/7

26   Memorial of Henry Arabin and Richard Chenevix to the Lord Lieutenant
Official Papers 1807: 228/4

27   Letter from Henry Arabin to Dublin Castle
Official Papers 1822: 539/6

CALENDARED MANUSCRIPTS

28   Pope Alexander 111 to King Henry II re Ireland; entry 38 of 1172
Calendar of Documents, Ireland

29   Construction of Dublin Castle; entry 226 of 1204

30   Reference to King's Mills; entry 2941 of 1248
Calendar of Documents, Ireland

31   State of Office of Ordnance, Ireland; entry 193 (6) of 1550
Calendar of Carew Manuscripts

32   Remuneration of Office of Ordnance; entry 363 of 1617
Calendar of State Papers, Ireland

33   Report by Sir Thomas Gresham; entry 1025 of 1560
Calendar of State Papers, Foreign

34, 35, 36   Reports re explosion, Dublin;
entries 21,22 and 26 of 1597
Calendar of State Papers, Ireland

37, 38, 39   Smuggling of weapons and gunpowder:
entry 116 of 1597
entry 201 (page 181) of 1599
entry 3 (page 296) of 1600
Calendar of State Papers, Ireland

ORIGINAL PRINTS

40 *Dublin Castle*

A Short Descriptive and Historical Guide for the use of Visitors
H G Leask; Stationery Office, Dublin, undated, c 1930s

41 "Notes on the French Congregation at Faversham, Kent and the Role played by the families of Grueber and Pigou in the Manufacture of Gunpowder"

May 1959, pages 139-40,

Proceedings of the Huguenot Society, London

PARLIAMENTARY

42, 43 Statutes of Kilkenny, XL Edward III, 1366;
II supply of armour to Irish forbidden
VI hurling forbidden, archery and lancing encouraged

Statutes and Ordinances, and Acts of the Parliament of Ireland. King John to Henry V. Edited by Henry F Berry; Stationery Office, Dublin, 1907

44, 45 Poynings' Parliament, 10 Henry VII, 1495
Chapter X, *An Act that the Subjects of this Kingdom shall have Bows and other Armour,* Rot Parl Cap 20

Chapter XII, *An Act that no great Ordinances be in No Fortresses but by the Licence of the Deputy.* Rot Parl Cap 23

The Statutes at Large, Parliaments in Ireland, 1310 to 1786. Published by authority, Dublin 1786

46 An Act for the Better Regulation of the Linen and Hempen Manufacturers
1763,3 George III, Chapter XXXIV

The Statutes at Large

INFORMATION SUPPLIED

47 Probable site of Grueber's mill, visited, courtesy, Finlay Colley

48, 49 Powder Mills in Ulster:

Sean C McMenamin, Public Record Office, Belfast

Alan McCutcheon, Director, Ulster Museum

50 Black Berthold:

O Haerdle, Stadtarchiv, Freiburg in Breisgau, translation, courtesy, Niall P O'Siochain, Munich

Chapter One - Leslie/Ordnance

ORIGINAL MANUSCRIPTS

STATE PAPER OFFICE, DUBLIN

The Westmoreland Correspondence

51   Plea to Parliament and the King for Relief, General Committee, (Catholic Committee), February 1791 number 12

52   *Declaration of the Volunteers and Citizens of the Town and District of Belfast,* July 1791 number 17

53   Necessity for Measures to counteract the Union of Catholics and Defenders, October 1791 number 22

54   Proposals for Relief of Roman Catholics, December 1791 number 27

55   Society of United Irishmen, Dublin, circular letter signed by James Napper Tandy, December 1791 number 31 (printed)

56   William Pitt to Westmoreland re Catholic Relief, January 1792 number 50

57   Arrangements for Catholic Convention, letter from meeting of Sub-Committee of Catholics of Ireland, May 1792 number 55 (printed)

58   Volunteer Cannon as far as have been ascertained by Returns, December 1792 number 83

59   Letter from Lawyers' Corps to Dublin Castle surrendering cannon undated, early 1793, number 201

STATE PAPER OFFICE, DUBLIN

Chief Secretary's Office, Registered Papers

60   Illegal gunpowder making reported near Belfast July 1796: 620/24/34

61   Prices of powder and saltpetre in Belfast September 1796: 620/25/131

62   Efforts to find gunpowder manufactory in County Derry (512) November 1796: 620/26/72

63   Report from Letterkenny re powdermaking in Derry May 1797: 620/30/119

64   Smuggling of powder, Dublin to North in tallow casks May 1796: 620/23/36

65   Smuggling of powder from America to Belfast in flaxseed casks May 1796: 620/23/129

66   Smuggling of powder, Belfast and Larne
      January 1797: 620/28/75
67   Smuggling of powder from Scotland
      January 1797: 620/28/91
68   Smuggling of powder in parcels of old clothes, Ballymena
      April 1799 :620/56/6

STATE PAPER OFFICE, DUBLIN

69   Report of activities of Defenders and United Irishmen; 15,000
      troops expected from France; arms to be landed at Cushendall.
      May 1796 Registered Papers 620/23/101
70   *Thoughts on the Defence of Ireland*
      August 1796 Official Papers 1796: 23/9
71, 72 System of signal towers:
      Construction; Official Papers 1804:174/18
      Abandonment; Official Papers 1809:183/61
73   Legal opinion re ownership of horsedung:
      Official Papers 1803:15/1
74, 75, 76   Correspondence re loans to Cork merchants:
      Official Papers
      1793: 40/5
      1796:40/35
      1797:40/37

STATE PAPER OFFICE, DUBLIN

77   *Papers containing Suggestions relative to the Sale of Gunpowder:*
      (1)   Letter, March 1801, with proposals for system of control;
      (2)   Letter, May 1801, reply to above;
      (3)   Further correspondence;
      (4)   Letter from Leslie, Travers and Company, Royal Irish
             Gunpowder Mills, near Cork, enclosing:
      (5)   *An account of the Quantity of Gunpowder sold by Leslie,
             Travers and Company, August 1800 to August 1801
             inclusive; distinguishing the Quantities sold in each month
             and the Quantities sold to Government from the
             Quantities sold to Individuals and the names of
             Individuals to whom sold.*
      Registered Papers 620/49/126

STATE PAPER OFFICE, DUBLIN

78   *Correspondence re Orders for Powder:*

    (1)   Letter from Dublin Castle to the Earl of Donoughmore, July 1801

    (2)   Letter from the Earl of Donoughmore to Castle, September 1801

    (3)   Letter from Leslie, Travers and Company to the Respective Officers of the Board of Ordnance at Dublin, October 1801

    Official Papers 1801:105/9

79   (1)   The Memorial of Leslie, Travers and Company, Proprietors of the Royal Irish Gunpowder Mills, near Cork, to the Lord Lieutenant re erection of magazine; undated c September 1801

    (2)   Letter from the Office of Ordnance, reply to above, October 1801

    Official Papers 517:105/10

NATIONAL LIBRARY, DUBLIN

80   Order for powder, April 1804; pages 62,63,64: Manuscript 175

    Ordnance Letter Book, Ireland

STATE PAPER OFFICE, DUBLIN

81, 82, 83   Documents re Leslies' Bank
Registered Papers
1824:10860   1826:13308   1826:14/517

PUBLIC RECORD OFFICE, DUBLIN

84   Entry re Charles Henry Leslie, 1824:
Index to Prerogative Wills, 1811-58

CORK PUBLIC MUSEUM; INSTITUTE OF BANKERS, LONDON

85   Notes for various denominations, signed and issued by:
Sir Thomas Roberts, Baronet and Company, Cork Bank
Roberts, Leslie and Leslie, Cork Bank
Charles Henry Leslie and John Leslie, Cork Bank (CONT'D)

Several specimens in the collections of: Cork Public Musuem
Institute of Bankers London

UNIVERSITY COLLEGE, CORK

86   Deeds and correspondence re ownership of Travers land at
      Ballincollig and Inniscarra:
      Beamish & Crawford Papers U122

      A collection of Beamish family papers found in the Lee
      Maltings, UCC, a premises formerly belonging to Beamish &
      Crawford, Brewers, Cork
      (Reference, Courtesy, Margaret McCarthy, archivist)

RDS LIBRARY, DUBLIN
Minutes, Royal Dublin Society (printed):

87   Saltpetre by John Stordy, December 1787, page 57;

88   Manure by John Mantel, March 1788, page 87;

89, 90 Saltpetre by John Mantel;
      February 1783, pages 57-58
      March 1794, page 75

PROPELLANTS, EXPLOSIVES AND ROCKET MOTOR
ESTABLISHMENT, WALTHAM ABBEY, ESSEX

91   Reference to expansion of Waltham Abbey Mills, page 33:

      *A Short History of the Royal Gunpowder Factory at Waltham
      Abbey*
      W H Simmons; typescript circulated privately;

      Controllerate of Royal Ordnance Factories, London, 1963

92   Survey and Report on Condition of Mill Buildings, Ballincollig,
      1828

93   *Centenary Memoir of the Royal Gunpowder Factory, Waltham
      Abbey, compiled from Original Sources*
      W Winters; published privately by the author, Waltham Abbey,
      1887 (Copies, courtesy, Malcolm McLaren, Head of Library
      Services)

CORK COUNTY LIBRARY

94   Entry re Wilks, page 249:

      List of the Freemen of Cork

STATE PAPER OFFICE, DUBLIN

95   Appointment of Wilks as magistrate:
      Official Papers 1808:261/20

PUBLIC RECORD OFFICE, LONDON

96   *Military Itinerary of the South of Ireland, 1796*
      Major General Charles Vallencey, Chief Military Engineer,
      Ireland
      WO 30 (63)

97   Map, Bantry Bay, fortifications etal, French fleet, 1796-97
      MPH 158:3803

98   Plans of the Royal Gunpowder Mills, Ballincollig drawn 1806
      by Charles Wilks, Superintendent
      MPH 844:3794

99   Plans, Ballincollig barracks, 1807
      MPH 185:3795

100   Service of George Napier, Superintendent, Royal Laboratory,
      Woolwich Board of Ordnance Establishment book, 1782-83,
      WO 54/216

PUBLIC RECORD OFFICE, LONDON

101   Three large bound volumes containing 1,250 folios of letters,
      memoranda, maps and plans, now separately filed; the deeds
      of transfer between Charles Henry Leslie and the Board of
      Ordnance and between the Board and Horsfall, Tobin, the
      entire correspondence on this transaction together with many
      documents from the 1820s to the 1850s
      WO44:102,103,104
      (microfilm in Cork County Library)

102   A small bound volume containing details of the tenures of the
      Board of Ordnance properties in Cork and Ballincollig.
      WO 55:2285

CALENDARED MANUSCRIPTS

Review of Volunteers, Ballincollig, September 1782:

103   Address to Charlemont;

104   Reply;

Volume 2, pages 338-42:

The Life and Times of the Right Honourable Henry Grattan MP; by his son, Henry Grattan, Esq., MP

Henry Colburn, London, 1839-46, six volumes

＊   ＊   ＊   ＊   ＊

105   Admission of Charles Henry Leslie as freeman of Cork;
       November 1784, page 995; (See Source 106)

106   Resolution in favour of Union;
       January 1799, page 1131;

The Council Book of the Corporation of Cork
edited and published by Richard Caulfield, Cork, 1876

＊   ＊   ＊   ＊   ＊

References to the Gunpowder Act:

107   Letter 327, 25 February 1793 (printed as "1792", correction
       sent to Public Record Office, Belfast and acknowledged as not
       previously known; correspondence PRG 9, 1974).

108   Letter 392, 28 February 1793

109   Letter 394, 4 March 1793

110   Letter 395, 6 March 1793

The Drennan Letters, 1776-1819

Edited by DA Chart, Deputy Keeper of Public Records;

Stationery Office, Belfast, 1931

Lords Commissioners of Saltpetre and Gunpowder;

111   Reference to proclamation re preservation of saltpetre, 1624
       entry 30, last paragraph

112   New proclamation, 1634, entry 79 page 579, second
       paragraph

Calendar of State Papers, Domestic

ORIGINAL PRINTS

NATIONAL LIBRARY, DUBLIN

113   Reference to Charles Leslie MD, pages 3-5:

The Present State of the Charitable Infirmary for the Year 1750

Corke: Printed by G Harrison, 1750

Pamphlets 1-53, 1750-1: 6550

CORK CITY LIBRARY

114   Reference to the Leslies as agents for the Hely Hutchinsons, page 98:

The Leading Speeches delivered at the City of Cork Election reported by Michael Matthews; Cork printed, 1812

   *   *   *   *   *

115   "Observations on Gunpowder"

The Honourable George Napier

Volume II, Science, 1787-88, pages 97-117:

Transactions of the Royal Irish Academy

116   Reference to charcoal distillation, pages 149-50:

Anecdotes of the Life of Richard Watson, Bishop of Llandaff Written by Himself at different Intervals and revised in 1814

Published by his Son, R Watson, Prebendary of Llandaff and Wells, London, 1818

NATIONAL LIBRARY, DUBLIN

117   *Observations on the Height of Carriage Wheels, on the Comparative Advantages of using One or Two Horses with One Carriage, and on Repairing Roads*

Charles Wilks, Superintendent of His Majesty's Gunpowder Manufactory at Ballincollig in the County of Cork;

Odell & Laurent, printers, Cork, 1814

P4 Cork, 1814

   *   *   *   *   *

118   *The Northern Banking Company Limited, 1824-1924*

Edwin D Hill;

McCaw, Stevenson & Orr, The Linenhall Press, Belfast, 1925

119   *The Faversham Gunpowder Industry and its Development*

second edition, revised, 1969, typescript, ISBN 900532 II 4

Arthur Percival; the Faversham Society, Faversham, Kent

PARLIAMENTARY

120   The Indemnification Act, 1793,33 George III, Chapter III, Dublin

121   The Gunpowder Act, 1793,33 George III, Chapter II, Dublin

122   The Gunpowder Act, 1794,34 George III, Chapter XVI, Dublin

123   The Gunpowder Act, 1795,35 George III, Chapter XXIV, Dublin

124   The Gunpowder Act, 1796,36 George III, Chapter XLII, Dublin

125   The Gunpowder Act, 1798,38 George III, Chapter XVI, Dublin

126   The Gunpowder Act, 1799,39 George III, Chapter IV, Dublin

127   The Gunpowder Act, 1807,47 George III, Chapter VIII, Westminster

128   The Gunpowder Act, 1814,54 George III, Chapter CXI, Westminster

129   The Relief of Bankers in Ireland Act, 1824,5 George IV, Chapter LXIII

130   *An Abstract of the Deed of Conveyance or Lease of the Lands of Ballincollig, in the County of Cork, in Ireland*
      May 1810 (242) XII, 403

131   *Expenditure of Sums granted by Parliament for an Artillery Depot and Powder Manufactory at Ballincollig and Store Magazine at Rocky Island; distinguishing the grants of the Several Years and also the Expenditure of the Sum of £11,545 paid for the like purpose during the Year 1809, and not provided for by Parliament*
      May 1810 (241) XII, 401

      Estimates of the Charge of the Office of Ordnance for Ireland; an Account of the Civil and Military Expenses of the Ordnance in that part of the United Kingdom:

132   For the Year 1811; March 1811, 8IA, page 16

133   For the year 1812; February 1812, 8IA, page 16

134   For the year 1813; May 1813, 220A, page 16

135   *Ordnance, Return of all the Houses, Apartments or Cottages belonging to the Ordnance*
      1822,625A, page 24

136   *Copy of a Memorial of the Gunpowder Merchants to the Lords of the Treasury, November 1818 and the Observations of the*

Board of Ordnance on the said Memorial
1819 (167) XVII, 223
INFORMATION SUPPLIED

137   Estimate of waterpower at Inniscarra Weirs:
      James Greene, hydrometrics engineer, ESB, Inniscarra Station

138   Purchase of Leslie's Wilton property, 1888, by Society of
      Missions to Africa
      P Jennings SMA, Wilton, Cork

Chapter One - The Tobins/Last Years
ORIGINAL MANUSCRIPTS
LIVERPOOL RECORD OFFICE

139   *The Annals of the Tobin Family of Liverpool and the Isle of Man*
      EQ 484
      Produced 1940 in twenty typescript copies, 95 pages, by RC
      Reid; based on a collection of documents, letters and other
      papers; while mainly anecdotes and reminiscences gives some
      useful details of the family's origins; not entirely accurate,
      several corrections sent to Liverpool Record Office, 1978

140   Lease of Powder House, Hanover Street, Liverpool, 1744,
      920 MD 342

141   *Correspondence and Report Respecting the Gunpowder*
      Magazines, 1836
      H 623, 4811 Gun
      Printed for limited circulation, apparently by Liverpool
      Corporaton

142   Liverpool Corporation, Special Committee, Gunpowder
      Magazines, minutes 1850: 352 MIN/GUN

143   Entry re the Tobin Family, pages 676-80:
      H 920 ORC (printed)
      Liverpool's Legion of Honour
      Edited and circulated privately by B Guinness Orchard,
      Birkenhead, 1893

144   List of the Mayors of Liverpool

145   Specimen *Sir Thomas and Lady Tobin, Ballincollig*
      Collection of Visiting Cards
      (assistance, Neville Carrick, Naomi Evetts and Janet Smith)

MERSEYSIDE COUNTY COUNCIL ARCHIVES,
LIVERPOOL

146   Membership, Liverpool Corporation, Dock Committee

147   Membership, Mersey Docks and Harbour Board

148   Receipted invoice on Ballincollig Company's headed paper for
       sale of powder to Birkenhead Dock Committee

       (assistance, J Gordon Read, Archivist)

EXETER COLLEGE, OXFORD

149   James Aspinall Tobin's academic career
       (assistance, J R Maddicott, Archivist)

UNIVERSITY OF KEELE

150   Entries re Irish transactions:
       Letter Book, 1748-49, William Davenport and Company,
       Liverpool African Merchants
       (assistance, Ian H C Fraser, Archivist)

NATIONAL LIBRARY, DUBLIN

151   Lectures on Egypt and America, Sir Thomas Tobin portfolio
       of looseleaf quarto paper

       Recollections of his travels
       Manuscripts 4110 (microfilm in Cork County Library)

GENEALOGICAL OFFICE, DUBLIN

152   Grant of Arms, Sir Thomas Tobin, 1855
       Manuscript 108, pages 89-90

153   Pedigree, Sir Thomas Tobin, 1855
       Manuscript 178, pages 195-97

CORK AND COUNTY CLUB

154   Minutes, Cork County Club
       (courtesy, WF Franklin, secretary)

VICTORIA HOSPITAL, CORK

155   Records, Board of Management
       (courtesy, JA O'Hara, secretary)

CORK ARCHIVES COUNCIL

156   Minutes, Cork Literary and Scientific Society
157   Membership, Board of Guardians for the Union of Cork

DET KONGELIGE NORDISKE OLDSKRIFTSELSKAB, COPENHAGEN

158   Membership, Sir Thomas Tobin
      Royal Society of Northern Antiquaries
      (assistance, T Ugensur)

SOCIETY OF ANTIQUARIES OF LONDON

159   Membership, Sir Thomas Tobin
      (assistance, FH Thompson)

ROYAL IRISH ACADEMY, DUBLIN

160   Membership, Sir Thomas Tobin
161   Purchase of gold caterpillar, minutes, 1881

SUPERINTENDENT REGISTRAR'S OFFICE, SOUTHERN HEALTH BOARD, CORK

162   Death Certificate, Sir Thomas Tobin

PROBATE DEPARTMENT, HIGH COURT, LONDON

163   Last will and testament, Sir Thomas Tobin

ROYAL NATIONAL LIFEBOAT INSTITUTION, LONDON

164   Service record, Lieutenant Arthur Lionel Tobin,
      Twenty-third Regiment, Royal Welsh Fusiliers,
      WO 76/221
165   Details of lifeboat *Arthur Lionel*
      (assistance, NF Stripp)

STATE PAPER OFFICE, DUBLIN

166   Thomas Tobin, Junior, to Dublin Castle re storage of
      gunpowder at Phoenix Park, Dublin
      Registered Papers 1836:2363

167   Correspondence and memorials re gunpowder, Cork, 1837
      Registered Papers 1837:84

168   Arrangements for Constabulary escorts on consignments for
      the Mining Company of Ireland
      Registered Papers 1845: Z 120 50

169   James Aspinall Tobin to Dublin Castle re magazines and
      railways
      Registered Papers 1846: 164684

PUBLIC RECORD OFFICE, BELFAST

170   Records, Londonderry and Coleraine Railway UTA I

171   Records, Londonderry and Enniskillen Railway UTA 13

ELEUTHERIAN MILLS HISTORICAL LIBRARY,
WILMINGTON, DELAWARE, USA

172   Record of purchase of Saltpetre,Liverpool, 1861

173   Description of Ballincollig, 1858
      Journal of a Trip to Europe, Lammot du Pont
      (Further details in "An American Powdermaker in Europe:
      Lammot du Pont's Journal, 1858"
      Norman B Wilkinson; volume 47, 1974-76, pages 85-96
      Transactions of the Newcomen Society, London)
      Longwood Manuscripts
      (assistance , Norman B Wilkinson, Director of Research)

NAVY AND OLD ARMY BRANCH, NATIONAL ARCHIVES,
WASHINGTON DC, USA

174   Indication of purchase of powder imported from Europe by
      du Pont:
      Records of the Chief of Ordnance pertaining to a List of
      Suppliers of Gunpowder, Record Group 156

HARBOUR OFFICE, CORK
Records of Cork Harbour Commissioners, 1814-1904

175   Minutes

176   Bylaws

177   *Abstracts of Receipts and Expenditures, Produce of Exports*
       1861-1904; 1862 and 1865 missing, printed for internal use

       (Courtesy, AC Feehely secretary; assistance, Denis Hurley,
       purchasing officer)

CORK ARCHIVES COUNCIL

178   Arrangements for construction of waterworks, Ballincollig,
       1892

       Records, Board of Guardians for the Union of Cork

PUBLIC RECORD OFFICE, LONDON

179   Reports on the palm oil trade, Calabar, 1828
       Colonial Office 82/1

180   Report by Sir Richard Burton re Establishment of British firms
       in West Africa
       April 1864

       Foreign Office FO 84

181   Protest by Liverpool Merchants against subsidy for the
       Company of African Merchants
       May 1864
       Foreign Office FO 84

PUBLIC RECORD OFFICE, LONDON
Memoranda of Association, Statutory Returns (weeded by PRO):

182   The Ballincollig Royal Gunpowder Mills Company Limited
       BT31: 552/2242

183   The Gunpowder Company Limited/The Ballincollig Royal
       Gunpowder Mills Company Limited
       BT 31: 4143/26728

184   The British and Irish Gunpowder Manufacturing Company
       Limited
       BT 31: 4068/26013

185   The Company of African Merchants Limited
       BT 31: 519C/798

186   The British and Continental African Company Limited
       BT 31: 7323/1860

187   The Liverpool Magazines Company Limited
        BT 31: 21247/31022

PUBLIC RECORD OFFICE, LONDON

188   Examination of James Aspinall Tobin, pages 13-19, 29-30:
        *Report of the Admiralty Committee of Inquiry into the Powder
        Hulks on the River Mersey*
        HO 45:9548/59447
        (This is printed in the usual blue book format of the time; it
        does not bear a command or other number and apparently was
        not published; the British Library and the Liverpool Record
        Office do not hold copies)

189   Correspondence of the Home Office with Liverpool Magazines
        Company, Manchester Ship Canal Company and other parties,
        1889-92
        HO 45:9548/59447

190   Operation in Ireland of the Explosives Act, 1875
        Several reports to the Home Secretary, 1877-91 by the Chief
        Inspector, Colonel Sir Vivian D Majendie
        HO 45: 9508/15848

UAC HEAD OFFICE, LONDON

191   The African Association Limited

        Company Index to Minutes of Management (and other)
        Committees

192   *The History of the United Africa Company to 1938*

        Typescript privately circulated by the company, 1938

        (courtesy, A Harrision and E D Kaye, public relations,

        UAC International, formerly the United Africa Company)

ARCHIVES, ICI MILLBANK, LONDON

193   Home Office Licences for manufacturing and storing
        gunpowder 1876-1909

194   Agreement, Messrs Curtis and Curtis's & Harvey Limited
        December 1898, certified true copy (typescript)

195   Minutes, Curtis's & Harvey Limited, 1898-1918

196   Memorandum and articles of association, Curtis's & Harvey
       November 1898
       (the BT 31 file, eg Sources 182-87, is not extant)
197   Tenancy agreements, houses in the Mills, various dates, 1903
       and later
198   Schedule of title deeds and documents, Ballincollig properties

REGISTRY OF DEEDS, DUBLIN

Memorials, Transfers of Ballincollig Properties:

199   Curtis's & Harvey to ICI (Explosives) 1943.29.106
200   ICI (Explosives) to ICI (Export) 1946.51.217
201   ICI to Minister for Defence 1949.35.106

STATE PAPER OFFICE, DUBLIN

202   Correspondence re orders for Martini-Henry rifle powder
       Registered Papers 1890: 20679 (typescript)
203   Papers re the final closure

    (1)   Memorial of Workmen, undated, received in Chief
            Secretary's Office, 14 August 1903

    (2)   Formal acknowledgement, 15 August

    (3)   Internal Castle memo

    (4)   Police report

    (5)   Police Report

    (6)   Correspondence with Department of Agriculture and
            Technical Instruction for Ireland

    (7)   Reply to Sir Horace Plunkett, Vice-President DATII,
            from Arthur Chamberlain, Chairman, Kynoch Limited,
            Birmingham, 11 September 1903 (Plunkett's letter not
            extant)

    (8)   Cutting, report of closure; *Cork Examiner*, 2 July 1903
Registered Papers 1903:19343

CORK ARCHIVES COUNCIL

204   Receipts, sales of minor items, rents, various dates;
       several specimens in author's possession; lodged 1971

205 Records, Cork Operative Coopers' Society
   Abandoned on dissolution in 1967; found by author in 1975 and
   arrangements made for lodgement

CHAMBER OFFICE, CORK
206 Records, Cork Chamber of Commerce

ORDNANCE SURVEY OFFICE, DUBLIN
207, 208, 209 Ordnance Survey Namebooks, 1841, 1900, 1934
   (courtesy Eamon de hÓir, placenames officer)

* * * * *

210 View, part of Eastern Area, May 1977 *ILLUSTRATION 3*

211 View, part of Western Area, May 1977 *ILLUSTRATION 4*

212 Author at incorporating wheel, October 1975
   ILLUSTRATION 6
   Commissioned by author, taken by Donal Sheehan, Cork
   Copies lodged in National Library, Dublin, 1980

213 Set of copper stencils for marking destinations on barrels;
   found in Mills, February 1979, by Donal Musgrave, Inniscarra
   and kindly presented to author

ORIGINAL PRINTS

214 Description of the palace of Duke Ephraim, King of Old
   Calabar, pages 324-25:
   Journal of an Expedition to Explore the Course and Termination
   of the Niger
   Richard Lander, John Lander; John Murray, London, 1832

215 Prices of muskets for the African Trade, Birmingham made;
   pages 419-21:
   The Resources, Products and Industrial History of the
   Birmingham and Midland Hardware District: A Series of Reports
   collected by the Local Industries Committee of the British
   Association at Birmingham, 1865
   Edited by Samuel Timmins; Robert Hardwicke, London, 1866

* * * * *

CORK PUBLIC MUSEUM
216 *Visit of Her Most Gracious Majesty, Queen Victoria, to the City*
   of Cork, August 3rd, 1849
   Souvenir booklet; George Purcell & Co, Cork, 1849
   Butter Market Collection

*   *   *   *   *

217   References to Sir Thomas Tobin, pages 428-29, 462-63;
      (See Source 218)

218   Reference to Athenaeum, pages 423-24:
      The Industrial Movement in Ireland as Represented by the
      National Exhibition of 1852
      John Francis Maguire; John O'Brien, Cork;
      Simpkin, Marshall and Co, London; J McGlashan, Dublin, 1853

*   *   *   *   *

NATIONAL LIBRARY, DUBLIN

219   Annual Reports, Mining Company of Ireland, 1824-64
      IR 552m2 and IR 622m3
      (Reference, courtesy, JRW Dick)

UNIVERSITY OF ALABAMA

220   "In Memory of Prof John W Mallet"
      January 1913, pages 1-47:
      University of Virginia Alumni Bulletin, Charlottesville
      (Copy, courtesy, Viola C Ayer, Reference Librarian) Gorgas
      Library

UNIVERSITY OF VIRGINIA

221   "Work of the Ordnance Bureau of the War Department of the
      Confederate States, 1861-5"
      JW Mallet, ex Lieut Col of Artillery and Superintendent of
      Confederate States Ordnance Laboratories
      VOLUME XXXVII, 1909, Pages 1-20
      Southern Historical Society Papers, Richmond, Virginia
      (Assistance, Keng Blackwell)
      Alderman Library, Charlottesville

EMORY UNIVERSITY, ATLANTA, GEORGIA

222   *The Supplies for the Confederate Army*
      How They were Obtained in Europe and How Paid For
      Personal Reminiscences and unpublished History
      Press of TR Marvin & Son, Boston, 1904
      (Assistance, Virginia JH Cain)
      The Robert Woodruff Library for Advanced Studies

*   *   *   *   *

223   *Life and Labours of Mr Brassey*
       Arthur Helps; Bell & Daldy, London, 1872

*   *   *   *   *

CORK CITY LIBRARY

224   Reference to Mills, page 7:
       Report of Pollutions on the River Lee
       Charles P Cotton CE; Public Health Committee, Cork
       Corporation, 1879

LIVERPOOL RECORD OFFICE

Series of Articles on the firms in the African Association;
Liverpool Review, weekly journal, October-December, 1887:

225   General account of the African Trade, 29 October;

226   Charles Horsfall and Sons; the Mersey Steel and Iron
       Company; 19 November

227   Tobin and Sons; the Company of African Merchants;
       The British and Contintenal African Company;
       10 December
       (no reference to Ballincollig)

BRITISH LIBRARY, COLINDALE, LONDON

228   Regular advertisement, 1894-95, in the *Sporting Goods Review*
       monthly trade journal, London

*   *   *   *   *

229   Advertisement, pages 88-89:
       The South of Ireland (Illustrated) Up to Date
       Robinson, Son & Co, London, undated, c 1894; an extremely
       rare work, not in the National Library nor the British Library;
       Copied, courtesy, Richard 1 Henchion, Cork historian

230   Showcard advertisement for use in shops and stores, issued
       mid-1890s. This specimen presented to National Museum
       (accession number 33-1978) by Thomas Woods, Dublin, formerly
       of Ballincollig, at the author's request; assistance, Larry Ryan,
       Cork. *ILLUSTRATION 5*

231   *Ballincollig Development Plan*
       Cork County Council, 1973

*   *   *   *   *

PARLIAMENTARY

232   Drainage and Navigation Act, 1715, 2 George I, Chap XII,
       Dublin

233   The Gunpowder Act, 1772, 12 George III, Chapter LXI,
       Westminster

234   The Gunpowder Stores (Liverpool) Exemption Repeal Act,
       1851, 14 and 15 Victoria, Chapter 67

235   The Liverpool Gunpowder Regulation Act, 1865, 28 and 29
       Victoria, Cap 278

236   Mersey (Gunpowder) Act, 1883, 46 and 47 Victoria, Chapter
       184

237   An Act for the Abolition of the Slave Trade, 1807, 47 George
       III, Chapter XXXVI

238   An Act for the Abolition of Slavery throughout the British
       Colonies, 1833, 13 and 14 George IV, Chapter LXXXIII

239   *Copies of Memorials addressed to the Secretary of State
       respecting the Liverpool and Wallasey Magazines; and of the
       Correspondence between the Secretary of State and other Parties
       relating thereto*
       February 1851 (47) LII,359

240   *Copies of Further Correspondence relating to the Liverpool and
       Wallasey Gunpowder magazines*
       February 1851 (78) LIII, 413

241   *Copies of Further Correspondence relating to the Liverpool and
       Wallasey Gunpowder Magazines*
       April 1851 (78-1) 419

242   *Report of an Inquiry into the Suitability of the Gunpowder
       Magazines on the River Mersey (with Minutes of Evidence and
       Appendices)*
       C 6169, 1890

243   Evidence by Thomas Tobin, Senior, pages 1-15:
       *Third Report of the Select Committee appointed to Consider the
       Best Means which Great Britain can adopt for the Final Extinction
       of the Slave Trade*
       1848 : 536

244   Evidence by James Aspinall Tobin, pages 214-21:
       *Report of the Select Committee on Africa (Western Coast) with
       Proceeding and Minutes of Evidence*
       1865 : 412

245   Years 1772-87
      An account of the Value and Amount of the Production of
      Africa imported into Britain
      (573-6) LXXXI

246   Years 1790-1844
      An Account of the Quantity of Palm Oil Annually Imported into
      the United Kingdom from the Western Coast of Africa
      1845 (187) XLVI

247   Years 1844-53
      Return of the Quantities of Tallow, Palm Oil etc imported into
      the United Kingdom
      1854 (296) LXV

248   Entries re Thomas Tobin, Junior and the Company:
      Volume E/18, page 35:
      County of Cork, Barony of East Muskerry, Parish of
      Carrigrohane
      General Valuation of Rateable Property in Ireland
      Richard Griffith, Commissioner of Valuation
      General Valuation Office, Dublin, 1852

249   *Return of Owners of Land of One Acre and Upwards in Ireland*
      Local Government Board, Ireland
      C1492,1876

                                                    INFORMATION SUPPLIED

250   Location of Sir Thomas Tobin's grave:
      Michael Healy, Registrar, Inniscarra Cemetery

251,252   Background data re the Mills:
      Patrick Tobin (no relation of the Liverpool Tobins)
      Ballincollig; Agnes O'Brien, Bishopstown, formerly of
      Ballincollig; both born 1885, neither saw the production
      processes

253   Miscellaneous details:
      William Murphy, caretaker of the Mills, 1930-73

254   Biographical Background:
      Richard Dowden;
      Daniel Meagher;
      Maura Murphy, PhD (Leic), Cork

255   No entry re Sir Thomas Tobin in State Department files of
      "Letters requesting Passes to visit the South" nor in
      "Miscellaneous Correspondence Files"   (CONTINUED)

Milton O Gustafson, Chief,
Diplomatic Branch, National Archives, Washington DC, USA

256 No evidence of Ballincollig sales to Confederacy in several
series of records checked by Elaine C Everly, Chief and Dale
E Floyd and Michael P Musick, Navy and Old Army Branch,
National Archives nor in a number of published works checked
by Virginia JH Cain, the Woodruff Advanced Studies Library,
Emory University, Atlanta, Georgia

257,258 Identification of Tobin companies' depots in West Africa:
Permanent Committee on Geographical names for British
Use,
Royal Geographical Society, London
PEH Hair, History School, Liverpool University

259 The African Association:
PN Davies, Director of Social Studies, Liverpool University

260 No details are available re the Tobin depots and trade,
correspondence with:
AJH Latham, historian of Calabar, University College Swansea;
Ekei Essien Oku, Director, Cross River State Library, Calabar;
JC Enwere, Nigerian National Archives, Ibadan;
EN Arinze, Nigerian National Museum, Lagos;
No replies were received to queries sent to various institutions
in Gambia, Ghana, Liberia and Sierra Leone

261 The Horsfall Gun:
RG Bartelot, Royal Artillery Institution, Woolwich, London

262 Brassey Family:
Archives, Victoria Library, Westminster

263 Biographical details re CP Cotton:
Maeve Condron, Institution of Engineers of Ireland, Dublin

264 A Ruffer and Sons:
J Saunders, Archivist, Institute of Bankers, London

265 J C im Thurn:
Guildhall Library, London

266 Very little information is available on early electrical
installations:
Institution of Electrical Engineers, London

267 The Berchtesgaden Cannoneers:
A Konig, Administrative Manager, Abteilung I, Organisations-
Komitee fur die Spiele der XX Olympiade, Munchen, 1972

Chapter One - The Fenians/Six Thousand Barrels
ORIGINAL MANUSCRIPTS
ROYAL ARCHIVES, WINDSOR CASTLE

Sources 268, 270, 280-84 contain large numbers of letters between Strathnairn, Mayo, Larcom, Campbell, Mackay, the Tobins and others

268   The Papers of George, Second Duke of Cambridge, RA Vic EI:
5693, 5694, 5695, 5696, 5697, 5698
5703, 5704, 5705, 5736, 5741, 5760, 5774
(13 items, 107 folios)

269   Cabinet papers, 1868; no reference to Ballincollig

BRITISH LIBRARY, LONDON

270   The papers of Sir Hugh Henry Rose, First Baron of Strathnairn and Jansi
Additional Manuscripts, 42, 824/5, volumes LIII-LIV
(24 items, 152 folios)

NATIONAL LIBRARY, DUBLIN

271   Minutes, Commissioners of National Education in Ireland
Manuscript 5747

272   Correspondence of Lord Mayo re Ballincollig
Manuscript II, 198
(12 items, 28 folios, minor value)

STATE PAPER OFFICE, DUBLIN

Chief Secretary's Office, Registered Papers

273   Letter, Sir Thomas Tobin re Fenians 1865:9578

274   Strathnairn/Larcom correspondence re guard on Mills 1867:39

275, 276   Robbery at Murray's Magazine
1868:240R and 1868:374R

277   Greek Fire attack, Cork 1868:397R

278, 279   Attacks on Leslie and Newenham houses
1868 :1687R and 1868: 1809R

STATE PAPER OFFICE, DUBLIN
Chief Secretary's Office, Registered Papers

280   Correspondence re conveyance of powder to Queenstown
      1866: 1776R

281   Ballincollig Powder Mills
      1867:22354
      (45 items, 164 folios)

282   Ballincollig Powder Mills
      1868: 18550
      (10 items, 84 folios)

283   Ballincollig Powder Mills
      1869: 7276
      (124 items, 343 folios)

284   Ballincollig Powder Mills
      1870: 16527
      (15 items, 43 folios)

285   Names of Suspected Fenians, Ballincollig District, 1866-71
      Irish Crimes Index, Volume I   (bound)
      (reference, courtesy, Maura Murphy, Cork)

                                                        ORIGINAL PRINTS

NATIONAL LIBRARY, DUBLIN

286   Letter signed "A Ballincollig Man" to editor, *The Irish People*
      2 September 1865, page 652   (See Source 287)

287   Evidence of John J Corydon re Fenianism in Ballincollig, pages
      25-27:
      Cork Special Commission
      Ir 3431 IC8

288   *Rules and Regulations,*
      Commissioners of National Education in Ireland
      Pamphlets 652 no 6

289   Report of Head Inspector John E Sheridan, pages 129-30:
      Twenty-ninth Annual Report,
      Commissioners of National Education in Ireland, 1862
      Ir 374 c 4

PARLIAMENTARY

290   The Gunpowder Act, 1860, 23 and 24 Victoria, Chapter 39

INFORMATION SUPPLIED

291   Opinion of DB Kernahan, Manager, Black Powder and Fuse
       Department, Nobel's Explosive Company, Ardeer, Ayrshire,
       Scotland

292   Thomas Duggan's service in Confederate forces:
       Walter McGrath, Cork

293   No confirmation of Duggan's service in Confederate records:
       Timothy K Nenninger, Navy and Old Army Branch, National
       Archives

294   Jeremiah Donovan; Patrick Blake (grandnephew), Cloghroe,
       Co Cork

Chapter Two - Kynoch

ORIGINAL MANUSCRIPTS

SECRETARY'S DEPARTMENT, IMI, KYNOCH WORKS,
WITTON, BIRMINGHAM
       (Formerly Imperial Metal Industries)

295   Minutes of the Board of Directors, 1884-1929:

       G Kynoch and Company Limited, 1884-

       Kynoch Limited, 1897-
       The Birmingham Committee:
       Explosives Trades Limited, 1918-
       Nobel Industries Limited, 1920-
       Imperial Chemical Industries Limited, 1926-

       (typescript edited from manuscript volumes)

296   Annual Reports, Kynoch Limited, 1897-1922
       (printed with handwritten endorsements)
PUBLIC RELATIONS DEPARTMENT, IMI, KYNOCH
WORKS, WITTON, BIRMINGHAM
       (Formerly Imperial Metal Industries)

297   *Illuminated address*, bound, in box, presented to Arthur
       Chamberlain by the Arklow workers, February 1900

       (After 1976 presented to Arthur Chamberlain the third,
       Birmingham)

298   *The History of Kynoch's*
       Text of a lecture delivered at Kynoch Works about 1937 by an
       unidentifiable individual employed at Witton who had

previously been attached to the Royal Laboratory, Woolwich
9 (c) (typescript)

299 Notes of an interview with FW Beeching, Witton employee,
1903-39
1950 2 (x) c (typescript)

300 View, Explosives Factory, negative 12888/2,
ILLUSTRATION 10

301 Women at work, probably First World War, negative 12888/3
ILLUSTRATION 7

ARCHIVES, ICI MILLBANK, LONDON

302, 303   Nobel's Explosives Company, Ardeer, 1871-1918
The Nobel-Dynamite Trust Company, London, 1886-1915
Records generally (manuscript and typescript)

304 Draft agreement for supply of Cordite Pulp by Nobel's to
Kynoch, November 1894
(Printed Proof, 14 Folios)

305 Correspondence re proposed agreement, letters and telegrams
between Thomas Johnston, Thomas Reid, Edward Kraftmeier
and Arthur Chamberlain Senior, November-December 1894
(mainly typescript, 25 items, 54 folios)

306 Correspondence, Thomas Johnston and Edward Kraftmeier,
1897
Box 22/1 NDT

307 Correspondence, Henry de Mosenthal and Thomas Johnston
on visit of Coleman du Pont re American Agreement
Am Ag volume 1, pages 42-43

308 Indenture of transfer of Arklow, January 1912
(27 folios)

309 Prospectus, Kynoch-Arklow Limited for issue of £210,000,
$5^1/2\%$ mortgage debentures
January 1912
(printed leaflet)

310 Correspondence, FJ Shand and Sir Ralph Anstruther re
possible acquisition of Arklow by Nobel's, December 1912
(3 items, 15 folios, typescript)

311, 312   High Explosives Trade Association
            Safety Explosives Trade Association
            Records Generally

313   Disposal of Arklow, pages 156-64:
       Minutes, Merger Committee, Explosives Trades/Nobel
       Industries

PUBLIC RECORD OFFICE, LONDON

Memoranda of Association, Statutory Returns

314   The Consumer's Dynamite Company Limited
       BT31: 3901/24640

315   Kynoch-Arklow Limited
       BT 31: 20429/119836

HOUSE OF LORDS RECORD OFFICE, LONDON

316   *In the House of Lord*
       Patent Infringement
       Appeal from the Court of Appeal in England between Nobel's
       Explosives Company Limited, Appelants and William Anderson,
       Respondent
       Not Reported

317   *In the House of Lords*
       Petition of Right-Goods sold and delivered -
       English Information - Breach of Contract - Damages
       On Appeal from His Majesty's Court of Appeal (England)
       between Kynoch Limited Appelants and His Majesty's Attorney
       General (on behalf of His Majesty) Respondent

       printed with handwritten endorsements
       (assistance, HC Cobb and D Johnson)

BRITISH LIBRARY, LONDON

318   Correspondence, Henry Campbell-Bannerman, Secretary for
       War with Sir Ralph Thompson, Under Secretary, War Office;
       George Lawson, Director of Army Contracts; John Morley,
       Chief Secretary for Ireland and Captain John Spencer, Assistant
       Private Secretary, War Office, later the first Lord Pentland

       The Pentland Papers, Additional Manuscripts 41, 206-41, 252

DEPARTMENT OF EMPLOYMENT, LONDON

319   *Accident 497/1917, Report on the Circumstances attending an
       Explosion which occured on 21 September 1917 at the Factory
       of Kynoch-Arklow Limited, Arklow, County Wicklow, Ireland,
       Major A Cooper-Key, Chief Inspector of Explosives, Home Office,
       London, October 1917*
       (typescript, not printed, laid before Parliament and published
       as a command paper in the usual way such as Sources 358-60)
       (copy, courtesy, Inspector W McCarthy and GJ Holder,
       Inspectorate of Explosives, Health and Safety at Work
       Executive)

STATE PAPER OFFICE, DUBLIN

320   Correspondence re proposed shipyard, Captain AJC Donelan
       MP with the Commissioners of Public Works, Dublin and Lord
       Pirrie, Comptroller General of Merchant Shipping London
       Registerd Papers 1918:3896

321   Many papers concerning Kynoch, Arklow Harbour
       Commissioners, the Commissioners of Public Works and the
       Department of Agriculture and Technical Instruction are "not
       up"

NATIONAL LIBRARY, DUBLIN

322   Letter from Arthur Chamberlain, Senior to John Redmond
       MP with memo on the Explosives Act, 1875 and copies of
       correspondence.   Manuscript 15,247 (3)

323, 324   Two photographs of John E Redmond MP visiting the
            factory, date not given (copies presented by author,
            1981)

SECRETARY'S OFFICE, CIE, HEUSTON STATION, DUBLIN

325   Minutes, Dublin, Wicklow and Wexford Railway
               *   *   *   *   *

326   Character Reference, February 1919
       (Copied, courtesy, Michael Ryan, Arklow)

327   Inscribed silver snuffbox presented to James Dunphy, 1908 by
       Kynoch (seen courtesy, Catherine Brennan, Kynoch Lodge,
       Arklow)

328   Cloakroom check, thin brass hexagon, given to author by
       Thomas Byrne (Source 374) and presented to National Museum
       (accession 13-1978, Coin & Medal Register)
       ILLUSTRATION 8

LIBRARY, THE CHEMICAL SOCIETY, LONDON

329   Obituary, AT Cocking

    *   *   *   *   *

ORIGINAL PRINTS

330, 331   Lectures by Edmund Davy on new type of explosive and
improved method of making Guncotton 1851

Pages 105-7; 117-18:
Reports of Evening Meetings, Royal Dublin Society

    *   *   *   *   *

BIRMINGHAM LOCAL STUDIES LIBRARY

332   Obituary, George Kynoch; April 1891, pages 177-81:
Birmingham Faces and Places monthly magazine

    *   *   *   *   *

333   "The Arklow Chemical Works Limited"
John Morrison, 1872, pages 3-16

*Transactions of the Newcastle-upon-Tyne Social Chemical
Society*

334   Entry re Walter Morrison and company, page 111:
Tyneside Industries
Historical Publishing Company, London, Newcastle, c 1884
(assistance, JWM Thompson, Newcastle Central Library)

    *   *   *   *   *

BRITISH LIBRARY, SCIENCE REFERENCE, HOLBORN,
LONDON

335   Patent 6,560: 1888, Ballistite to Alfred Nobel
Application May 1888; acceptance March 1889

336   Patent 11,664:1889
Cordite to Frederick Abel and Sir James Dewar
Application, July 1889; acceptance May 1890

INSTITUTION OF CIVIL ENGINEERS, LONDON

Minutes of Proceedings
337   "The Machinery used in the Manufacture of Cordite"
Edward W Anderson
Paper 3075, volume CXXX11, 1897-98, part 2, pages 69-120

338   "Some Properties of Cordite"
The Late Sir William Anderson
Paper 3144, volume CXXXV1, 1898-99, part 1, pages 251-64

339   Obituary, Sir William Anderson
       Volume CXXXV, 1898-99, part 1, pages 320-26;

INSTITUTION OF ELECTRICAL ENGINEERS, LONDON

340   Entry re Kynoch and Arklow Urban District Council
       February 1902, page 629:
       The Electrician, weekly contracts journal, London

NATIONAL LIBRARY, DUBLIN

341   "The Kieselguhr of County Antrim":
       James Holmes Pollok,
       part 1, 1899, pages 33-36
       Scientific Proceedings, Royal Dublin Society

NATIONAL LIBRARY, DUBLIN

342, 343   "Munitions, British Government and Irish Trade"
            full front page article signed by Arthur Griffith:
            '*Nationality*' weekly paper, 31 July 1915

            Editorial headed "England and Arklow" with reprint
            of previous item in issue 23 February 1918

            *   *   *   *   *

344   "The Irish Farmers Union: its Objectives and Achievements"
       EJ Cussen, Cork County Secretary, pages 15-17:
       Official Year Book and Directory, 1926-27
       Cork County Farmers' Union; Irish Annuals Press, Dublin
       (copy in author's possession, photocopy in National Library)

345   *Invitation to Subscribe for £3 million Ordinary Share and Loan
       Stock*
       Cork Co-operative Marts Limited, 1968
       (copy in author's possession)

346   Annual Report, 1977, IMI Limited, formerly Imperial Metal
       Industries

            *   *   *   *   *

ORIGINAL PRINTS

BIRMINGHAM LOCAL STUDIES LIBRARY

The Kynoch Journal
Published in two series. The first, 1899-1907, for public sale, was originally a bi-monthly magazine and later an academic style quarterly. The second, 1918-19, had apparently only three half-yearly issues with technical data solely for internal circulation. The only complete set is in Birmingham Local Studies Library (assistance Dorothy McCulla and Richard Abbot).

347   "Portrait Gallery 1, Arthur Chamberlain, Senior", October 1899, page 1

348   "Portrait Gallery 4, AT Cocking", April 1900, pages 82-83

349   "A Visit to Arklow Factory", October 1900, pages 14-17

350   "The Heat Test of Nitro Explosives", February 1901, pages 57-59

351   "Loading Cordite Cartridges", February 1901, pages 78-79

352   "Portrait Gallery 13, EW Anderson", October 1901, page 2

353   "Glimpses into Kynochland, 1: Arklow", December 1901, pages 26-28

354   "Glimpses into Kynochland, 9: Paper Mills", April 1903, pages 70-72

355   "*The Soap Trust,* by the Chairman", January 1906, pages 161-67

356   View, Chemical Works, frontispiece, January 1919, *ILLUSTRATION 9*

357   "The concentration of Sulpheric Acid in Gaillard Towers" JA Parkes and EG Coleman, June 1919, pages 106-43

PARLIAMENTARY

358   Report CXVI to Home Secretary, Accident at Arklow, 4th October 1895

       Colonel A Ford, Inspector of Explosives
       Cd 7948,1896

359   Report CXCIII to Home Secretary, Accident at Arklow, 1910 Cd 5330, 1910

360   Report to Home Secretary, Accident at Arklow, 1911 Cd 5974, 1911

361, 362   Examination of Arthur Chamberlain, 1900, pages 337-45;
            Conclusions, pages xxiii-xxx;
            'Report from the Select Committee on War Office
            Contracts, Proceedings, Minutes and Appendix'
            Cd 313, 1900

INFORMATION SUPPLIED

363   Mastership of the Buckhounds:
       Sir Robin Mackworth-Young KCVO, Royal Librarian,
       Windsor Castle

364   Spectrum of mercury:
       Shown to instrument of Crookes type by Dean John P Teegan,
       Professor of Chemical Spectroscopy, University College Cork

365   J A Parkes:
       G W Woods, secretary, Goulding Fertilisers, Dublin

366   Arthur Chamberlain, the third, Edgbaston, Birmingham

367   Details of NET operations:
       Roy McMahon, Nitrigin Eireann Teoranta, Arklow

368   Figures of exports:
       Captain Denis Kenny, Harbour Master, Arklow

369   Geology of Whiterock Flint Quarry, Tinahely:
       Ralph R Horne, Geological Survey, Dublin.

370   Sir Stanley Harrington:
       Ronald Harrington (nephew), Cork

371   Munster and Leinster Bank:
       HJ O'Brien, Allied Irish Banks, Regional Office, Cork, former
       Munster and Leinster Head Office

372   Arklow colony, Umbogintwini:
       JG Jenkins, personnel administration manager, African
       Explosives and Chemical Industries, AECI, Umbogintwini,
       Natal, South Africa

373   Dudley W Dolan, Wicklow, former payclerk

FORMER GENERAL WORKERS

374   Thomas Byrne, Templerainey, Arklow

375   Dora Coombs, Dublin

376   James Doherty, Ballinskea, Arklow

377   Marian Murphy, Dublin

378   Thomas Murphy, Shillelagh

Chapter Two - Irish Industrial Explosives

ORIGINAL MANUSCRIPTS

COMPANIES OFFICE, DUBLIN

Memoranda of Agreements, Statutory Returns

379   Irish Industrial Explosives Limited
       File 22132/2

380   Kemek Limited
       File 40004

ORIGINAL PRINTS

381   'Explosives Technical Data'
       series of information bulletins issued by the company

INFORMATION SUPPLIED

382   Terence W Mullan, factory manager, Clonagh, Enfield, Meath.

Chapter Three - Holland

ORIGINAL MANUSCRIPTS

THE PATERSON MUSEUM, PATERSON, NEW JERSEY, USA.

The John P Holland Collection

383   Correspondence, O'Donovan Rossa and Jeremiah Collins, 1876

384   Notes on the Fenian Ram

385   Gunpowder calculations

386   Prospectus, Electric Boat Company, 1899 (printed)

387   Correspondence, Electric Boat Company

388   Correspondence, stockbroker, 1902

389   Correspondence, Fairfield Shipbuilding and Engineering Company, 1904

390   Correspondence, Bethlehem Steel Company, 1904

391   Correspondence, patent agents and attorneys, various dates

392   Plans for amusement submarine
       (Copies, courtesy, Thomas A Peters, Director and John A Herbst, History Curator)

       *   *   *   *   *

*   *   *   *   *

ORIGINAL PRINT

393   Report, "75 Years of British Submarines" Exhibition National
       Maritime Museum Greenwich, London (visited by author)
       National Maritime Museum News, winter, 1976

*   *   *   *   *

INFORMATION SUPPLIED

LIBRARY OF CONGRESS, WASHINGTON, DC, USA
Congress of the USA, Marlene C McGuirl, Chief, Law Library

394   Act of March 3, 1893, ch 212,27 stat 718

395   Act of June 10, 1896, ch 399, 29 stat 379

396   Act of March 3, 1899, ch 421, 30 stat 1039

ROYAL NAVY SUBMARINE MUSEUM, HMS Dolphin,
Gosport, Hampshire

397   Earliest sinking of ship by submarine:
       Sue J Britton

Chapter Three - Grubb and Parsons

ORIGINAL PRINTS

398   "On the Correction of Errors in the Distribution of Time
       Signals"
       Sir Howard Grubb, Vice-President
       volume IX, 1899, Paper VI, pages 37-45:
       Scentific Proceedings, Royal Dublin Society

399   "A New Collimating-Telescope Gun-Sight for Large and Small
       Ordnance"
       Read March 1901, volume VII, Paper X, pages 321-29:
       Scientific Transactions, Royal Dublin Society

400,401   "The Grubb Sight"

           June 1902, page 115;

           April 1903, page 83;

           The Kynoch Journal (See Page 318)

INFORMATION SUPPLIED

402   HE Scrope, Secretary, Vickers Limited, Head Office, London

403   SJ Wornom, Public Affairs Manager, Electric Boat Division,
       General Dynamics Corporation, Connecticut, USA

404   Parsons turbine and Turbinia
       Judith M Blacklaw, Library, Royal Naval College, London
405   Biographical and other details:
       GE Manville, director and David Sinden;
       Sir Howard Grubb Parsons and Company, Newcastle-upon-Tyne

Chapter Three - Blacker

ORIGINAL MANUSCRIPTS

ARCHIVES, ICI MILLBANK, LONDON

406   The ICI War effort; CW James, December 1943
       War Records, Miscellaneous Papers
407   Address by Chairman, Lord McGowan, annual meeting,
       May 1945

       *   *   *   *   *

ORIGINAL PRINTS

408   A History of the Family of Blacker of Carrickblacker in Ireland
       LCM Blacker; Hodges, Figgis; Dublin, 1901
409   "The Hedgehog", Chapter 12, pages 123-40:
       The Secret War, 1939-45
       G Pawle; Harrap, London, 1956
       (copy, courtesy, JM King, Librarian, RAF College, Cranwell,
       Lincoln)

INFORMATION SUPPLIED

NATIONAL ARMY MUSEUM, LONDON

410   Details of AVRE:
       DK Smurthwaite, Keeper of Books and Archives

Chapter Three - Brennan

ORIGINAL MANUSCRIPTS

ROYAL AIRCRAFT ESTABLISHMENT,
FARNBOROUGH, HAMPSHIRE

The Louis Brennan Collection

411   Biographical material
412   Papers re the Torpedo
413   Papers re the Monorail
414   Papers re the Helicopter
415   Correspondence with Winston Churchill's Office, February 1926
       (Courtesy, BC Kervell, Main Library)

ROYAL IRISH ACADEMY, DUBLIN

416   Entry re Louis Brennan:
       Prospectus of proposed "National Academy for Ireland"
       RI Best Papers (printed with numerous handwritten
       annotations)

PUBLIC RECORD OFFICE, LONDON

417   Invention for Removing Barbed Wire Entanglements
       Submitted by Harcourt Lees, Miller, Portarlington, June 1915
       Inventions Department, Ministry of Munitions
       MUN 3/32, specimen of documents destroyed

ROYAL ENGINEERS MUSEUM, CHATHAM, KENT

418   Photo, specimen of Brennan Torpedo
       (copy, courtesy, Lt Col CTP Holland, Curator)

ORIGINAL PRINTS

LIBRARY, NATIONAL MARITIME MUSEUM, GREENWICH, LONDON

419   Drawing of Brennan Winding Engine, Plate LXXI A, Chapter V
       Torpedoes and Torpedo Warfare
       C Sleeman; Griffin & Co, Portsmouth, 1889

420   Section re the Brennan Torpedo, pages 71-88:
       Torpedoes and Torpedo Vessels
       GE Armstrong; George Bell, London, 1896

421   Annual reports, Royal Navy Torpedo School, 1881-
       (Assistance MWB Sanderson and Mary Patrick)

INFORMATION SUPPLIED

422   Development of wire guided missiles in Germany, 1941-45:
       Hans A Maurer, Canoga Park, California
       Application of the Brennan Principle in current weapons
       systems

423   British Aerospace

424   Bofors, Sweden

425   Contraves-Oerlikon, Switzerland

426, 427, 428 Soviet Embassy, Dublin;
            Soviet Weekly, London;
            Soviet Military Review, Moscow;

429   Kawasaki Heavy Industries, Japan

430, 431   Department of the Navy;
              Department of Defence, USA

432   McDonnell Douglas, St Louis, USA

433   Hughes Aircraft Company, California, USA

434   Aerospatiale, France

435   Messerschmitt-Bolkow-Blohm, West Germany

436   Euromissile (French office)

Chapter Four - The World Wars

ORIGINAL MANUSCRIPTS

PUBLIC RECORD OFFICE, LONDON

437   History of the Irish Factories: Dublin, Cork, Waterford, Galway
        (Typescript; includes aircraft components, Dublin, text page 242)
        MUN 5/539

438   Correspondence, Arthur E Porte
        MUN 5/6 specimen of documents destroyed

439   Machinery Audit Book, Waterford National Cartridge Factory
        MUN 3/445 specimen of documents destroyed

440,441   Correspondence re Importation of Irish Labour
             MUN 5/57/320/27
             MUN 5/57/320/31

442   Chart showing Gross Quarterly Expenditure, Ministry of
        Munitions 1916-18
        MUN 5-40, 263, 4/15

443   Diagram showing Indoor Staff, Ministry of Munitions, 1915-18
        MUN 5-24 R 261/11

444   Ministry of Munitions, *Secret Weekly Report*
        MUN 2
        (Printed for private circulation)

445   Article "Shell Making in a Railway Workshop"
        February 1917, page 79:
        Ministry of Munitions Journal
        (printed monthly, restricted circulation)

HOUSE OF LORDS RECORD OFFICE, LONDON

446   Report by Sir Maurice Levy MP to David Lloyd George MP,
      Minister for Munitions, November 1916 (typescript)
      Lloyd George Papers, Series E/Box 1/Folder 7; Ireland 4 and 5
      Collection 10 of the Beaverbrook Papers

ARCHIVES, CITY HALL, BELFAST

447   Committee of the Lord Mayors and Mayors of Ireland re Price
      of Domestic Coal, 1916-18
      Minutes of Miscellaneous Committees
      (Courtesy William J Johnston, Town Clerk, Belfast; assistance,
      Philp Faulkner)

PUBLIC RECORD OFFICE, BELFAST

448   The Belfast Committee
      The Belfast and North of Ireland Employers War Munitions
      Committee
      Minutes, correspondence and accounts, 1915-18
      (photocopied by permission of GL Auret, secretary, Northern
      Ireland Chamber of Commerce and Industry)
      D/1857/3/10

NATIONAL LIBRARY, DUBLIN

449   The All-Ireland Committee
      The All-Ireland Munitions and Government Supplies
      Committee. Statement issued at the War Supplies Conference,
      Dublin 21 February 1916 (typescript, 7 folios)

450   Prospectus of the aims, objects and membership of the
      Committee (printed leaflet)
      The Colonel Maurice Moore Papers, Manuscript 10,579

PUBLIC RECORD OFFICE, DUBLIN

451   Records, Irish Industrial Development Association
      (Lodgement arranged by author, 1978)

PATENT OFFICE, DUBLIN

452   Lapsing of the Irish National Trade Mark
      Registry of Trade Marks

STATE PAPER OFFICE, DUBLIN

453   Chief Secretary's Office, Registered Papers
       Large numbers of letters, reports and other documents passed
       through Dublin Castle concerning munitions production and
       the War generally. Most were apparently removed at the
       transfer of administration in 1922 leaving only a few minor
       items such as requests for the setting up of factories in various
       towns.

SECRETARY'S OFFICE, CIE, HEUSTON STATION, DUBLIN

454   Reports of the Chief Engineer to the Traffic and Works
       Committee, Board minutes, Great Southern and Western
       Railway
       (reference, courtesy, Peter Rigney, Dublin)

CORK ARCHIVES COUNCIL

455   Minutes, Tolls and Markets Committee, Cork Corporation

456   Minutes and correspondence, Cork District Trades Council

LIBRARY, TRADES UNION CONGRESS, LONDON

457   Papers re the National Federation of Women Workers
       Gertrude Tuckwell Collection, Tuc 357

       *   *   *   *   *

ILLUSTRATION 11

458   *On War Service, 1916,* badge; given to author by Florence
       Ross, (Source 473) and lodged with others of different designs
       for 1914 and 1915 in National Museum, 1980

       *   *   *   *   *

                                              ORIGINAL PRINTS

NATIONAL LIBRARY, DUBLIN

459   Annual Reports, Irish Trades Union Congress, 1894-1918
       (microfilm)

       and courtesy, Ruaidhri Roberts, General Secretary
       Irish Congress of Trade Unions, Dublin

NATIONAL LIBRARY, DUBLIN

460   Reference, Pulvertafts and Cork Shell Company, page 6:
       Annual Report, 1917, Cork Industrial Development Association
       Ir 33 80941 c5

       *   *   *   *   *

*   *   *   *   *

ORIGINAL PRINTS

461   Article "Chaos in Cork" by local correspondent:
       July 1916, page 380:
       New Ireland, weekly journal, Dublin
       (Copy, courtesy, Jack Lane, London)

462   "Munitions of War and the Smaller Engineering Workshops"
       FG Thompson, lecture, November 1916; volume XLIII,1918,
       pages 3-22:
       Transactions of the Institution of Civil Engineers of Ireland

463   Jeffcott, HH
       "Munitions Work by the Engineering Department of Royal
       College of Science for Ireland
       (includes aircraft components, text page 242)
       Volume XIX, No 2, 1919, pages 175-79;
       *Journal of the Department of Agriculture and Technical
       Instruction for Ireland*

464   "Modern Armies and Modern Transport: A Review of the
       Irish Railway Companies during the War".
       two part article; unsigned; pages 490-93 and 525-28, March,
       April 1920
       (Includes armoured vehicles; reference, courtesy, Peter Rigney,
       Dublin)
       Railway Gazette, technical weekly, London

465, 466, 467 Writings of EJ Riordan:
       Book;
       Chapter XI, Government Contracts, Pages 196-214:
       Modern Irish Trade and Industry
       Methuen, London, 1920

       Articles;
       "Restraints of Irish Industry",
       pages 306-14, June 1918

       "A Fragment of Irish Industrial History",
       pages 633-43, December 1918
       Studies, Jesuit quarterly, Dublin

PARLIAMENTARY

468   Report, War Cabinet Committee on Women in Industry
       Cmd 135, 1919

469   Memorandum by John O'Neill (Chairman, All-Ireland
       Committee) pages 71-72:
       Final Report, Committee on Industrial and Commercial Policy
       after the War
       Cd 9035,1918

470   Report, Proceedings of the Irish Convention
       Cd 9010, 1918

INFORMATION SUPPLIED

Interviews with Munitions Workers

471   Mary O'Connor, nee Lally (Australia) Galway National Shell
       factory who kindly gave her souvenir shell to author

472   A woman employee, desirous of anonymity, Cork National
       Shell Factory; (interview arranged by David Nolan)

473   Florence Ross, nee Lea, Dublin Dockyard Shell Factory who
       agreed to lodge her souvenir shell, Ministry of Munitions *On
       War Service* badge, ornate employer's reference and set of
       photographs in the National Museum (Accessions 2,3,4,5,6,
       - 1976) See Source 458

              *   *   *   *   *

474   Irish Industrial Development Association:
       C Towers, Dublin, private secretary to EJ Riordan and his
       successor as secretary until dissolution

475   Membership Amalgamated Society of Engineers in munitions
       factories; records not available, Frank Callaghan, District
       Secretary, Amalgamated Union of Engineering Workers, Dublin

476, 477   JP Evans and Company:
            W Scott, manager, Shannon Foundry, Limerick
            Aine Thornhill, Reference Librarian, Limerick City
            Library

478   Gallagher and Company, Strabane:
       Sheila Sinclair JP (through local library)

479   MF Ronayne, sales director,
       Waterford Ironfounders Limited

480   PJ Cowman, sales manager,
       Pierce Wexford Limited

481, 482   Alec G Wilson:
       Deborah Sharkey, Irish and Local Studies Library,
       Belfast
       JW Vitty, Linenhall Library, Belfast

Chapter Four - The World Wars (Second)
                                        ORIGINAL MANUSCRIPTS
PUBLIC RECORD OFFICE, BELFAST

483   Records of the Production Council:
       Ministry of Commerce and Production, Stormont, 1940-45
       COM 66
       (mainly typescript, includes Miles Aircraft wooden house, text
       page 244)
484   Ballylumford Electricity Station
       COM 30

ARCHIVES, CITY HALL, BELFAST

485   Minutes, Police Committee, Belfast Corporation (printed)

PUBLIC RECORD OFFICE, LONDON

486   Recruitment of Irish Workers, minutes and correspondence
       AVIA 15: 1853, 1854, 1855, 1856
       *   *   *   *   *

                                             ORIGINAL PRINTS

487   Operation of conscription, page 18:
       Reminiscences of the Connolly Association, Emerald Jubilee
       C Desmond Greaves; Connolly Association, London, 1978

STATIONERY OFFICE, BELFAST

Ulster Year Book, 1947: Stationery Office, Belfast

488   Air Raids, pages xxxii - xxxviii;

489   War Production, pages xxxviii-xliii;
       From "A Historical Survey, 1939-45" By DA Chart, Deputy
       Keeper of Public Records:

       *   *   *   *   *

INFORMATION SUPPLIED

490   Robert Thompson, trade union member, Production Council

491   John F Kelleher, formerly of the Dairy Disposal Company,
       Limerick

Chapter Four - The World Wars   USA Bases in Ireland
First War   INFORMATION SUPPLIED

492   From Files P and PA; Gibson B Smith:
       Navy and Old Army Branch, National Archives, Washington
       DC

Second War   ORIGINAL PRINT

493   "Bases in the North Atlantic, Londonderry, Lough Erne"
       volume II, pages 61-67:
       *Building the Navy's bases in World War II, History of the Bureau
       of Yards and Docks and the Civil Engineer Corps, 1940-46*
       United States Government Printing Office, Washington DC, 1947

Chapter Five - Guns

ORIGINAL MANUSCRIPTS

BRITISH LIBRARY, LONDON

494   Letter, Roger Boyle to Earl of Cork re Cannon, January 1642
       Additional Manuscript 4227

TRINITY COLLEGE, DUBLIN

Documents of the Irish Board of Ordnance

495   Estimates for the supply of muskets by various Dublin makers,
       1705
       Manuscript 1180, number 52

496   Contract for the supply of muskets by John Van Bylaart, 1706-07
       Manuscript 1181, number 42
       (reference, courtesy, Howard L Blackmore, Tower of London)
       The Southwell Papers

ASSAY OFFICE, DUBLIN
497 Minutes, Goldsmiths' Company, Dublin

STATE PAPER OFFICE, DUBLIN
498 Return of Arms made up and delivered into the Small Arms Stores, Dublin, August 1807
Office of Ordnance, Dublin
Official Papers 1807: 239/13
499 Licences for the Import of Arms and Materials for Making up Arms
Official Papers 1808: 261/20

PUBLIC RECORD OFFICE, LONDON
500 Memoranda of Association, statutory returns
Henrite Explosives Limited
BT31: 18705/11371

RDS LIBRARY, DUBLIN
Minutes, Royal Dublin Society
501 May 1744, Nathaniel Dunn
502 May 1756, Elizabeth Nix and George Kent
503 November 1786, John Gray, page 12 (printed)

BODLEIAN LIBRARY, OXFORD
504 Walloons, 1632
Ms Rawl D 918 (13, 684)

OIREACHTAS LIBRARY, DUBLIN
505 Report by Isaac Corry and Thomas Pakenham re Irish Board of Ordnance 1788 Manuscript 8H3, Oireachtas Library, Leinster House, Dublin.
Microfilm positive 4045, National Library, Dublin

ARMOURIES, TOWER OF LONDON
506 The Maddock Gun:
Catalogue entry XII, 1554
(Courtesy, Howard L Blackmore, Deputy Master and Ruth R Brown)

NATIONAL MUSEUM, DUBLIN

507   The Rigby Gun:
       Accession 32-1944
       ILLUSTRATION 13
       (Courtesy, Oliver Snoddy, Assistant Keeper, Art and Industry)

CORK PUBLIC MUSEUM

508   The Crispin Case of Pistols:
       Catalogue G 232
       (Courtesy Aodh O'Tuama)

CALENDARED MANUSCRIPTS

509   Inventory of stocks of prefirearms artillery:
       entry 1227 of c 1224

       Calendar of Documents, Ireland

510   Richard Sonner:
       entry 12-133, pages 150-51
       Rotulus Clausus de Anno 17 Ric II, Vol I, Pars I:

       Rotulorum Parentium et Clausorum Cancellaire Hiberniae
       Edited by Edward Tresham; His Majesty's Printers, Dublin,
       1828
       (One of the very earliest calendared works)

511, 512, 513, William Cornell:
                Entry 30 of 1462
                Entry 98 of 1454 (sic)
                Entry 107 of 1479
514   Christopher Cornell:
                Entry 114 of 1479
                "Some Ancient Deeds of the Parish of St Werburgh,
                Dublin"
                Henry F Twiss; volume XXXV, Section C, numbers 7,8
                Proceedings of the Royal Irish Academy

515   Entries re various gunmakers:
       The Register of the Parish of St Michan, Dublin, 1636-1700
       Parish Register Society of Dublin, 1909

516   Costs of ironmaking, 1616:
        Volume II, entry CLVI,
        The Lismore Papers (Second Series)
        Selections from the Private and Public (or State) Correspondence
        of Sir Richard Boyle
        First and 'Great' Earl of Cork
        Edited by AB Grossart; printed for private circulation, 1887

517   Roger Boyle's appointment as Master of the Ordnance in
        Ireland:
        Tenth entry, page 16, Report 7, Appendix, Historical Manuscripts
        Commission, London 1879

518   Justin McCarthy's recommendation re muskets, pages 130-31:
        Earl of Dartmouth Manuscripts, Report II, Appendix, Part V
        Historical Manuscripts Commission, London, 1887

519   Establishment of ironworks,
        entry 712 of 1610:
        Calendar of State Papers, Ireland

Proposals for Making Ordnance:

520   Entry 394 of 1618

521   Entry 1222 of 1624

522   Third entry, page 171, of 1632
        Calendar of State Papers, Ireland

523, 524, 525 Wright and Blacknall:
        Pages 74-75 of 1626
        Entry 1979 of 1631
        Entry 2150 of 1632
        Calendar of State Papers, Ireland

526   Requisition for steel, October 1689
        Letter Book of Richard Talbot
        Page 103:
        Analecta Hibernica no 4, 1932

527   Mock gun and *sow* at siege of Ballyaly Castle, 1642
        Pages 17-18:
        Narratives Illustrative of the Conflict in Ireland
        Edited by TC Croker; The Camden Society, London, 1841

ORIGINAL PRINTS

ROYAL IRISH ACADEMY

528   Making of mortar, siege of Castle Coot, page 119:
       The History of the Execrable Irish Rebellion Traced from many
       preceding Acts to the Grand Eruption the 23 October, 1641 and
       thence pursued to the Act of Settlement MDCLXII
       London, printed for R Clavel; sold by J Howes, Dublin
       MDCLXXX

529   Entry re mock guns, page 10
       The Actions of the Enniskillen-Men: from their First Taking up
       Arms in 1688, in Defence of the Protestant Religion, their Lives
       and Liberties to the Landing of Duke Schomberg in Ireland
       Andrew Hamilton; Licenced White-Hall, 1689
       London, printed for Ric Chiswell
       Holiday Collection of Pamphlets

BIRMINGHAM LOCAL STUDIES LIBRARY

530   Reference to orders by the Irish Board of Ordnance, 1790s.
       Page 7:
       Observations on the Manufacture of Fire-Arms, for Military
       Purposes; on the Number supplied from Birmingham, to the
       British Government, during the late War; the Proof to which the
       Barrels are subjected; and on the Birmingham Proof-House;
       together with some Remarks upon the Inexpediency of the
       Ordnance Department Fabricating Small-Arms; and upon the
       Obstacle to the Free Export of Arms
       Anonymous; Longmans, London and James Drake,
       Birmingham, 1829

              *   *   *   *   *

531   Mallet's manufacture of guns, pages 280-1:
       "On the Physical Conditions involved in the Construction of
       Artillery and on some hitherto unexplained Causes of the
       Destruction of Cannon in Service"
       Read June 1855, Robert Mallet; 1856, volume XXIII, Part I,
       Science, pages 144-436
       Transactions of the Royal Irish Academy

532   Paper by John Rigby, 1839, pages xxxvi-xlvii;

533   Description of W & J Rigby's "Improved Mould for Casting
       Solid Balls", 1844, pages 1-4;
       Proceedings, Royal Dublin Society
       (assistance, Mary Kelleher, RDS Library)

534   Reference to gun made from Creevelea iron, page 29:
       Memoirs of the Geological Survey, Sheet 55, Sligo and Leitrim,
       James R Kilroe;
       Stationery Office, Dublin, 1855

535   Harland and Wolff's manufacture of gunmountings, page 126:
       Contracts and Finance
       Second World War, official British history series
       William Ashworth; Stationery Office and Longmans, London,
       1953

                                                    PARLIAMENTARY

536   Report CLXXVI to Home Secretary, Report of Explosion on
       premises of Trulock, Harriss and Richardson, Dublin, 1906
       Cd 2972, xv, 393, 1906

                                                INFORMATION SUPPLIED

537   Charters of the Goldsmith's Company:
       Ronald Le Bas, Assay Master, Assay Office, Dublin

538   Irish Metal Industries Limited:
       A C Norton, secretary, head office, Dublin and L H Coy, former
       managing director, factory, Galway

539   The Birmingham Gun Trade:
       Jim Andrew, Science and Industry Museum, Birmingham

Chapter Five - Guns (Kavanagh)

                                                ORIGINAL MANUSCRIPTS

COMPANIES OFFICE, DUBLIN

Memoranda of Association, Statutory Returns

540   The Fenian Gun Company of Ireland Limited
       File 13547

541   Birr Projects Limited
       File 23132

REGISTRY OF DEATHS, LONDON

542   Death of Kevin Kavanagh:
       Volume 21, p 0208, 1975, Falmouth District, Cornwall

PARLIAMENTARY

543   Firearms (Proofing) Act, 1968, number 20, Dublin

544   Firearms (Shotguns) (Proofing Methods, Marks and Fees)
       Regulations
       Statutory Instrument 65 of 1969, Prl 602

INFORMATION SUPPLIED

545, 546   Operation of the Act
            Department of Industry, Commerce and Tourism
            A H Porter, Director, Standards Division
            Institute for Industrial Research and Standards, Dublin

547   Grants to the Company:
       Maeve Garrett, Information Division
       Industrial Development Authority, Dublin

548   Kevin Kavanagh
       Interviewed in Cork, June 1974

549   Michael Davis
       former factory worker, Birr

550   Buddy Burke
       journalist, Birr

551   John Donnelly, accountant, Dublin
       Chairman, Receiver and Liquidator of the Company

552   An official of the Birmingham Gun Barrel Proof House

Chapter Six - Armoured Vehicles

CALENDARED MANUSCRIPTS

553, 554, 555 Siege Towers: entries 2735, 2736 and 2775 of 1245
                Calendar of Documents, Ireland

556   *Sow* at Kinsale:
       Annals of Kinsale, November 1601, twelfth entry, page xxviii:
       The Council Book of the Corporation of Kinsale
       Edited and published by Richard Caulfield, Cork, 1879

ORIGINAL PRINTS

NATIONAL LIBRARY, DUBLIN

557   Sarsfield's *sow*, siege of Sligo, page 34:
      *A True and Impartial History of the Most Material Occurences
      in the Kingdom of Ireland during the Two Past Years. With the
      Present State of Both Armies*

      *Written by an Eye Witness to the Most Remarkable Passages
      London: Printed for Ric Cheswell, MDCXCI
      White-Hall, let this be printed, 1691*

      J94016

     *   *   *   *   *

558   "Production of Armoured Fighting Vehicles in Ireland"
      Canavan, DA
      January 1976, pages 38-39:

      An Cosantóir, The Irish Army Journal, monthly, Dublin

     *   *   *   *   *

INFORMATION SUPPLIED

559   Snowy Glen:
      A J Armstorng, Reference Librarian, Carrickfergus Library

Chapter Six - Armoured Vehicles (Timoney)

ORIGINAL MANUSCRIPTS

COMPANIES OFFICE, DUBLIN

Memoranda of Association, Statutory Returns

560   Industrial Engineering Designers Limited
      File 16645

561   Technology Investments Limited
      File 51536

562   Ad Tec Teoranta
      File 48368

     *   *   *   *   *

563   Photo Timoney APC, *ILLUSTRATION 14*
      Copyright, Spearman Photographic Services, Drogheda

ORIGINAL PRINT

564   "Development of a High Mobility On/Off Highway Vehicle"
      Eanna Timoney, January 1977, pages 6-10:
      *IRISH ENGINEERS. Journal of the Institution of Engineers of
      Ireland*

INFORMATION SUPPLIED

565   Professor Seamus G Timoney who showed factory to author

566   Department of Defence

567   Michael Foy
      Information Officer, Irish Sugar Company, Dublin

Chapter Seven - Ships

ORIGINAL MANUSCRIPT

BRITISH LIBRARY, LONDON

568   Report, surveyor general of customs; timber in Derry area
      being used for shipbuilding:
      Harleian Manuscript 2138

CALENDARED MANUSCRIPTS

569   Mandate for galleys, entry 1048, 18 July 1222;

570   Mandate re Portsmouth, entry 2558 of 1241;

571   Oars and boards for England, entry 1232 of 1224;

572   Boards for England, entry 3090 of 1250;
      Calendar of Documents, Ireland

573   Proposal re small boats, volume XXXI, 1599-1600, page 461:
      Acts of the Privy Council of England
      (Reference, courtesy, RJ Hunter, New University of Ulster,
      Coleraine)

574   Report, timber suitable for shipbuilding, entry 516 of 1609;
      Calendar of State Papers, Ireland

575   Galleys of c 1632, fourth entry, page 171;
      Calendar of State Papers, Ireland

576   Export of timber, volume I, entry LVII:
      The Lismore Papers (See Source 516)

PARLIAMENTARY

THE EAST INDIA COMPANY

577   An Act for Preserving Timber Trees and Woods
      10 William III, Chap XII, 1698, Dublin

CALENDARED MANUSCRIPTS

578   Petition, entry 705 of 1613
      Calendar of State Papers, Ireland

579   Letter from Whitehall to the Company, 1610, pages 355-56:
      *The Register of Letters of the Governor and Company of
      Merchants of London Trading into the East Indies*
      Edited by Sir George Birdwood; Bernard Quaritch, London
      1893

580, 581, 582 References to timber from Ireland:
      Entries 718 and 735 of 1614 and 892 of 1615
      Calendar of State Papers, Colonial Series, East Indies

Kinsale   **CALENDARED MANUSCRIPTS**

583   Chudleigh and Stacey, pages 34-35:
      *St Multose Church, Kinsale, As It Was, As It Is And As It Ought
      To Be*
      John Lindsey Darling, Rector; Guy and Company, Cork, 1895
      (copy, courtesy, Michael Mulcahy, Honorary Curator, Kinsale
      Regional Museum)

584   Boom:
      Annals of Kinsale, 1667, second entry, page xlix:
      The Council Book of the Corporation of Kinsale (See Source 556)
      Edited and published by Richard Caulifield, Cork, 1879

Verolme   **ORIGINAL MANUSCRIPT**

585   Photo *LE Deirdre*   *ILLUSTRATION 15*
      Robert Bateman, Cork, official photographer to Verolme

                               INFORMATION SUPPLIED

586   Patrick G Martin, naval architect and John Brennan, Verolme

587   Department of Defence
      (Author enabled to see *LE Aoife* under construction, courtesy
      of Department and Company)

ORIGINAL PRINTS

Workman Clark

588   Full list of ships built in:
       Shipbuilding at Belfast
       Published for Workman Clark (1928) Limited by ED J Burrow
       & Co, London, 1934

589   Reference to National Shipbuilders Security Limited, page 4:
       *The Bulletin of the Shipbuilders and Repairers National
       Association*
       London, June 1977 (final issue)

INFORMATION SUPPLIED

Warrenpoint Shipyard

590   John D Pearson, Dublin, former works manager

591   Jim McCart, former employee, Warrenpoint
       (courtesy Elizabeth Dunsmore, Warrenpoint Librarian)

Chapter Seven - Ships (Harland and Wolff)

ORIGINAL MANUSCRIPTS

NAVAL HISTORICAL BRANCH, MINISTRY OF DEFENCE,
LONDON

592   Admiralty List of Ships
       (assistance, JD Brown)

PUBLIC AFFAIRS DEPARTMENT, QUEEN'S ISLAND,
BELFAST. HARLAND AND WOLFF

593   Company List of Ships

594   Letter from Admiralty to London and Glasgow Company, 1885

595   Employment figures

596   Press statement re *Hawk* range of motorcyle accessories
       News from Harland and Wolff, 2/78, January 1978

597   Press statement re Harland-MAN Engines
       News from Harland and Wolff, 3/78 June 1978

ARCHIVES, ICI MILLBANK, LONDON

598 Report by Harry McGowan:
Canadian Merger Series, Guardbook I, 1910

599 Correspondence, Edward Kraftmeier and FJ Shand, 1910
Box 46/I, Nobel-Dynamite Trust

ORIGINAL PRINTS

600 "Shipbuilding at Belfast - its Origins and Progress"
Sir Edward Harland, Engineer and Shipbuilder
Chapter XI, pages 288-323:
Men of Invention and Industry
Edited by Samuel Smiles; John Murray, London, popular
edition, 1897

601 *Record of a Visit to the Belfast Ropework Company*
Reprinted from *The Irish Textile Journal,* 1892

602 "The Shipbuilding Industry in Belfast"
Alec G Wilson (son of WH Wilson, original director)
1915-16 pages 5-29:
Proceedings, Belfast Natural History and Philosophical Society

603 Annual Report
Belfast Harbour Commissioners, 1853

604 *A Short History of the Port of Belfast*
DJ Owen (harbour secretary); Mayne, Boyd & Son, Belfast,
1917

605 "Harland and Wolff's Shipyard & Engine Works, Belfast"
Denis Rebbeck
Paper to section G, British Association at Belfast, September
1952, reprinted from *Engineering,* London, September 1952

Company Publications, Harland and Wolff

606 Annual Reports

607 *P 200,* booklet on expansion plans, 1973

608 *Ship Repairing at Belfast,* leaflet, undated

609 *Marine Engines Spares and Repairs,* booklet, undated

610 *Electrical Products and Services,* booklet, undated

HMS Belfast Museum Publications

611   *HMS Belfast* Photograph *ILLUSTRATION 16*

612   *HMS Belfast*
      Brochure, 1971, ISBN 333 13456 7

613   *HMS Belfast* Guide Book
      revised edition, 1976, ISBN 333 13457 5
      HMS Belfast Trust and Macmillan Press, London

SHEFFIELD CITY LIBRARY

614   *The War Traders: An Exposure*
      George H Perris; National Peace Council, London, 1913,
      pamphlet

615   *The War Trust Exposed*
      JT Walton Newbold
      National Labour Press (publishing arm of the Independent
      Labour Party)
      London 1919, pamphlet
      (these references, courtesy, Clive Trebilcock, Pembroke
      College, Cambridge)

PARLIAMENTARY

616   *Shipbuilding Industry (Loans) Act (Northern Ireland)*
      1966, Chapter 30, Stormont

617   *Shipbuilding Inquiry Committee, 1965-66, Report*
      Chairman RM Geddes, Cmd 2937, 1966, Westminster

618   *Industrial Democracy*
      A Working Paper on Worker Participation in Harland and Wolff
      Introductory Note by Merlyn Rees MP, Secretary of State;
      Foreword by Stanley Orme MP, Minister of State, Northern
      Ireland
      ISBN 0 337 17102 0 Stationery Office, Belfast, March 1975

619   *Harland and Wolff Limited*
      Information Document for Members of Parliament
      Stanley Orme MP
      Debate on the shipbuilding Industry (Northern Ireland) Order,
      1975
      ISBN 0 337 06071 4 Stationery Office, Belfast, September 1975

620   *The Shipbuilding Industry (Northern Ireland) Order, 1975*
      Statutory Instrument 1975 No 815 (NI 5)

621   *The Shipbuilding Industry (no 2) (Northern Ireland) Order, 1975*
      Statutory Instrument 1975 no 1309 (NI 14)

INFORMATION SUPPLIED

622   Denis Rebbeck, Holywood, former Chairman and Managing
      Director

623   Alan Hedgley, Public Affairs Manager, Queen's Island

624   Department of Commerce, Northern Ireland

625   Roger L Facer, Secretary of State's Office,
      Ministry of Defence, London

Chapter Eight - Aerospace

Lillian E Bland: ORIGINAL PRINT
SCIENCE MUSEUM LIBRARY, LONDON
BRITISH LIBRARY, SCIENCE REFERENCE, KEAN
STREET, LONDON

626   Numerous items, by and about, from December 1909 to
      February 1912 in *Flight*, now *Flight International*, Weekly Journal
      London

Harland and Wolff   INFORMATION SUPPLIED

627   Various details of the company's aircraft production during the
      First World War:
      Carl A Beck, formerly of the Company, Belfast

Potez   ORIGINAL MANUSCRIPT
COMPANIES OFFICE, DUBLIN

628   Memorandum of Association, Statutory Returns
      Potez Industries of Ireland Limited
      File 18132

INFORMATION SUPPLIED

INFORMATION DIVISION, INDUSTRIAL DEVELOPMENT
AUTHORITY, DUBLIN

629   Grants paid to the Company:

Garrett   **ORIGINAL MANUSCRIPTS**

COMPANIES OFFICE, DUBLIN

630   Memorandum of Association, Statutory Returns
       Garrett Ireland Limited
       File 63614/2

INDUSTRIAL DEVELOPMENT AUTHORITY, SOUTH
EASTERN REGION, WATERFORD

631   Press Statement, May 1978

Miles Aircraft   **ORIGINAL MANUSCRIPT**

632   AVIA 15: 1968, correspondence, Ministry of Aircraft Production

                                         INFORMATION SUPPLIED

633   Lindsay Martin, Banbridge, Co Down
       (through R Dougan, Craigavon Library)

Short Brothers   **ORIGINAL MANUSCRIPTS**

PUBLIC RECORD OFFICE, LONDON

634   AVIA 9-18 Private Office Ireland
       Papers of the Ministers private office re Ireland
       (includes correspondence on electricity from the South, text page
       197)

635   AVIA 15:21326, minutes, correspondence and memos with and
       about the company

636   AVIA 15:2175, minutes, correspondence and memos with and
       about the company

637   AVIA 15:2266, minutes, correspondence and memos with and
       about the company

PUBLIC RELATIONS DEPARTMENT, SYDENHAM

638   Press statement, change of name, June 1977
639   Press statement, USA subsidiary, November 1977
640   Press statement, development plans, December 1978

Chapter Eight - Aerospace /Shorts   ORIGINAL PRINTS
PUBLIC RELATIONS DEPARTMENT, SYDENHAM
641   Photograph, *SD3-30*, negative 74625-24; *ILLUSTRATION 17*

642   Photograph, *Seacat*, nagative 69565: *ILLUSTRATION 18*

643   Photograph, *Tigercat*, nagative 69215-26: *ILLUSTRATION 19*

644   Photograph, *Blowpipe*, nagative 77428-41: *ILLUSTRATION 20*

645, 646, 647, 648 Sales Brochures for *SD3-30, Seacat, Tigercat* and
          Blowpipe

          *   *   *   *   *

649   *Burntollet*
       Bowes Egan and Vincent McCormick; LRS Publishers,
       London, 1969

                                              PARLIAMENTARY
650   Loans (Belfast Air Freighter) Act (Northern Ireland), 1961
       Chapter 2, Stormont
651   Aid to Aircraft Industry Act (Northern Ireland), 1963
       Chapter 16, Stormont
652   Aid to Aircraft Industry Act (Northern Ireland), 1965
       Chapter 7, Stormont
653   Aircraft Industry (Loans) Act (Northern Ireland), 1969
       Chapter 2, Stormont
                                         INFORMATION SUPPLIED
654   JP Samuel, Deputy Librarian, Labour Party, London
655   Jim White, Publicity Officer, Sydenham
656   Hugh Murphy, employee from 1937, former full-time shop
       steward
657   Sales literature and details of *Shillelagh:*
       Don Flamm, Director, Public Affairs
       Ford Aerospace & Communications Corporation, California,
       USA

Epilogue

ORIGINAL MANUSCRIPT

DWIGHT D EISENHOWER LIBRARY, ABILENE, KANSAS, USA

658   Final Presidential broadcast, January 1961, box 38, speeches; known as the *"military - industrial complex speech"* (typescript, copy, courtesy, John E Wickman, Director)

       *   *   *   *   *

ORIGINAL PRINTS

659   Details of armoured cars collated from:
The Military Balance 1978-79
International Institute for Strategic Studies, London

660   Details of missiles collated from:
Missiles of the World
Micheal JH Taylor and John WR Taylor; Ian Allen, London, 1976

661   *NATO Handbook*, 1978
North Atlantic Treaty Organisation, Brussels

662   Assembly, European Economic Community
debate, 13 June 1978

663   *Report on European Armaments Procurement Cooperation*
on behalf of the Political Affairs Committee
May 1978,83/78, PE50, 944 fin

664   Commission, European Economic Community,
Action Programme for Aeronautical Research
(Communication from the Commission to the Council)
COM (77) 362 fin

665   *Commission Communication to the Council with a View to*
Concerted Action on Aircraft Programmes
COM (78) 211 fin

PARLIAMENTARY

666   Aircraft and Shipbuilding Industries Act, 1977
Elizabeth 11, Chapter 3

667   Northern Ireland Act, 1974, Elizabeth 11, Chapter 28

668   Aircraft and Shipbuilding Industries (Northern Ireland) Order
1979, no 294 (NI 1) ISBN O 11 093294 3

669   Defence (Amendment) Act, 1979 number 1, Dublin

INFORMATION SUPPLIED

DEPARTMENT OF FOREIGN AFFAIRS, DUBLIN

670   Ireland's ratifications of international agreements

INFORMATION DIVISION, INDUSTRIAL DEVELOPMENT
AUTHORITY, DUBLIN

671   Policy on potentially polluting and high risk industries

UNITED AUTO WORKERS, DETRIOT, USA

672   Details re Walter Reuther and Charles Wilson:
        Jerry Dale, Assistant Director, Public Relations

Multiple Reference   ORIGINAL MANUSCRIPTS

STATE PAPER OFFICE, DUBLIN

673   *The Case of Richard Spear*
        Accounts and correspondence concerning purchases of supplies
        for the Irish Board of Ordnance
        (49 folios, 2 printed)
        Official Papers 1797: 23/32

NATIONAL LIBRARY, DUBLIN

674   Membership Census, 1918,
        Irish Transport and General Workes Union
        The William O'Brien Papers, Manuscript 13, 948

        *   *   *   *   *

675   *Alphabetical Index of Companies registered under the Companies
        Acts in London, Edinburgh, Dublin and Truro, 1856-1920*
        Stationery Office, London
        The copy in the Companies Office, Dubl.   ⌐en courtesy, P
        Brown, contains various handwritten endorsements, now the only
        surviving details as all the individual files were lost in the
        Custom House fire, 1921

348 SOURCES

ORIGINAL PRINTS
GILBERT LIBRARY, PEARSE STREET, DUBLIN

676 *A Chronological Table of the Pedigree and Lineall Descent down from Adam, of the Right Honourable Justin Lord Viscount Mountcashell, Ld Barron of Castle Hinchy, Lievt Generall of his Majeties, Army, Ld Lievt of the County of Corke, Governour of the Province of Munster, Master Generall of the Ordinance, and one of his Majties most Honoble, Privy Council.* Dermot MacCarthy; Cork, printed by William Smith for the Author; No date, c 1690

NATIONAL LIBRARY, DUBLIN

677 References, powdermaking and gunmaking:
An Account of the present State Ireland is in, under King James: and the deplorable Condition of the Protestants

Licens'd, February 1690; printed for R Baldwin, London
Two page broadsheet, semi-newspaper

Thorpe Pamphlets, XI, no 99

*   *   *   *   *

678, 679 Memoir, William Dargan pages ix-xiv;
Entry re Rigbys, page 194;
The Irish Industrial Exhibition of 1853: A Detailed catalogue of its Contents with Critical Dissertations, Statistical Information and Accounts of Manufacturing Processes
Edited by James Sproule;
James McGlashan, Dublin; William S Orr & Co, London; 1854

680, 681 "War Work for the Admiralty and the Ministry of Shipping"
(including shell factory and proposed aircraft plant, text pages 183 and 242)
Chapter IX pages 139-50:
Photograph 86, Dublin Dockyard Shell Factory:
ILLUSTRATION 12

Shipbuilding and Repairing in Dublin; A Record of Work carried out by the Dublin Dockyard Co, 1901-1923
John Smellie (managing director); McCorquodale & Co, Glasgow; no date, accessioned 1935, National Library (Reference, courtesy, John de Courcy Ireland, Dublin)

PARLIAMENTARY

682   Irish Parliament *Journals*:
       Text Pages 4, 5, 7-8, 13-19, 27, 223-224

683   Westminster Parliament *Hansard*:
       Commons. Text Pages 3, 12, 13, 17-18, 34, 42, 57, 74, 74, 82, 86
       94, 96, 127, 132, 134, 146, 154, 170, 174, 183, 187, 195, 210,
       235-238, 242, 243, 261
       Lords. Text Pages 94, 102, 128, 130, 131, 144, 247-248,
       Sources 316, 317, 446

684   Oireachtas Eireann, *Debates*
       Text Pages 158, 209, 213, 219-220, 268

685   Northern Ireland Parliament, *Stormont Hansard:*
       Text Pages 179, 191, 210, 211, 227, 232, 234-235, 257-258

686   *Report of the Select Committee on Explosive Substances, 1874*
       IX,I; Text Page 74

687   Explosives Act, 1875, 38 Victoria, Chapter 17
       Text Pages 74-75, 97, 133

688   Dangerous Substances Act, 1972, number 10, Dublin
       Text Page 74

689   *Annual Reports, Inspectors of Explosives*
       published as command papers
       Text Pages 59, 74-75, 113, 120-121, 133-134, 151-152

DIRECTORIES

690   *The Gentleman's and Citizen's Almanack;* Dublin
       1790's;   text page 10
       1812;   text page 207

691   *Irish Manufacturers' Directory*; Dublin
       1916;   text page 181

692   *Gores Liverpool Directory*
       1830-1870;   text pages 45-46
       1870-1900;   text page 81

693   *Birmingham Directory*
       1830s';   text page 208

694   *Who's Who*; London
       1950s;   text page 255

NEWSPAPERS

695   *Dublin Evening Post*; text page 9; text page 10 (separate series)
696   *Faulkner's Journal*; Dublin; text page 204
697   *Freeman's Journal*; Dublin; text pages 17, 68, 121, 205, 205
698   *Irish Times*; Dublin; text page 121
699   *Dublin Evening Mail*; text page 242
700   *Evening Telegraph*; Dublin; text page 241
701   *Northern Star*; Belfast; text pages 19, 206
702   *Belfast Telegraph*; text pages 192, 195
703   *Cork Gazette;* text page 21
704   *Cork Constitution*; text pages 30, 48, 57, 63
705   *Cork Southern Reporter;* text pages 51-52
706   *Cork Examiner;* text page 84. Also Source 203(8)
707   *Birmingham Daily Post*; text page 95
708   *Wicklow People;* text pages 111, 145, 150, 275
709   *Wicklow News-Letter*; text pages 97, 98, 102, 106, 112, 115, 117, 149, 151, 152, 154, 155

INFORMATION SUPPLIED

710   Details of Ballincollig Mills and the Murray shotgun:
John O'Connell, principal, TW Murray and Company, Cork

711   Details of munitions, aircraft components and instruments;
First World War;
Ashenhurst Williams, Dublin:
WJ Stuart, director

712   Details of munitions and aircraft components; First World War:
Thomas Thompson & Sons, Carlow:
PW Thomas, Secretary

713   Details of munitions and aircraft components; First World War:
Thomas Dockrell, Sons and Company, Dublin:
Maurice E Dockrell, former chairman

714   Particulars of barge for Kynoch, *Asgard 11* and miscellaneous details re Arklow:
Jack Tyrrell, chairman, John Tyrrell and Sons

715   Relationship of British Shipbuilders with Harland and Wolff:
Sheila McNair, Information Officer, British Shipbuilders, Newcastle-upon-Tyne

716   Relationship of British Aerospace with Short Brothers:
       Dagmar Heller, Publicity Officer, British Aerospace, London

LATE SOURCES
PARLIAMENTARY
Chapter Two - High Explosives
717   Submission by NET to the Joint Oireachtas Committee on
       State Sponsored Bodies, July 1980

Cheddite Production   INFORMATION SUPPLIED
718   Colonel RW Shaw, Dublin

Chapter Four - The World Wars
Antrim Torpedo Factory
PARLIAMENTARY
PRESS OFFICE, ROYAL NAVY, MINISTRY OF DEFENCE,
LONDON
719   White Paper
       Defence Cuts 1976-77 to 1979-80
       (HC 236-iv) ISBN O 10 291376 5

INFORMATION SUPPLIED

720   Various details:
       Chris York-Edwards,

ORIGINAL MANUSCRIPT
DEFENCE HEADQUARTERS, DUBLIN
German bombing in South

721   *Chronological Statement of Events from the Outbreak of War on
       3 September 1939 to 1 October 1944*
       uncatalogued document
       (assistance, Captain Peter Young, Archivist, Army Press Office)

Chapter Four - The World Wars
Production in The South

ORIGINAL PRINTS

722   The Emergency Scientific Research Bureau and the Industrial
       Research Council:
       Various annual and other reports published by the Stationery
       Office in the 1940s

723   Article by Colonel JG McDonald, former Director of Ordnance,
       additional details verbally
       "The Army Ordnance Corps"
       March 1977, pages 84-87:
       An Cosantóir, the Irish Defence Journal
       (Reference, courtesy, Denis McCarthy, Dublin)

724   Article by Desmond Reilly, formerly of the ESRB
       additional details in correspondence
       "Production of War-Short Materials in Eire"
       August 1947, pages 2426-28
       Chemical and Engineering News
       American Chemical Society, Washington DC
       (copy, courtesy, Engineering Librarian, UCD)

INFORMATION SUPPLIED

725   Daniel Barry, former commercial manager, Metal Products
       (Cork)

726   Colonel RG Mew, Dublin, former Director of Engineering

Chapter Five - Guns   **CALENDARED MANUSCRIPTS**

727, 728   References to Robert McCormick, gunmaker, Belfast:
                Entries 245 and 247 in the *Drennan Letters*
                (AS SOURCES 107-110)

State Ammunition Project   **ORIGINAL MANUSCRIPTS**
STATE PAPER OFFICE, DUBLIN

729   Cabinet Minutes, 1923-1939

730   File S 6627, Department of the Taoiseach
       Sgeul: Ammunition Factory
ARCHIVES, ICI MILLBANK, LONDON

731   Files:
       Eire: Proposed Small Arms Ammunition Factory

ORIGINAL PRINT

732   "Award of the Boyle Medal to Professor Jospeh Reilly"
       Volume XII, 1938-1942, page 287
       Scientific Proceedings, Royal Dublin Society

INFORMATION SUPPLIED

733   The late Eamon de h-Óir, placenames officer, Ordnance
       Survey, Dublin told the author in June 1973, while making
       available Sources 207-09, that there had been a proposal for
       some form of armament plant in Clare during the Second War.
       It was not until June 1980, after extensive enquiries, that Sources
       729 and 730 were found

Chapter Six - Armoured Vehicles
Short Brothers

ORIGINAL MANUSCRIPT

PUBLIC RELATIONS DEPARTMENT, SYDENHAM

734   Shorland Anti-Hijack Vehicle; Statement, June 1980

ORIGINAL PRINT

735   Brochure, *Shorland* Mark 4 and *SB 401*; June 1980

Ashbourne Project   **ORIGINAL MANUSCRIPTS**

736   Statement by Industrial Development Authority, Dublin; July
       1979

COMPANIES OFFICE, DUBLIN

737   LJ Warnants & Co Limited
       File 14827

738   Cournil Ireland Limited
       File 67527

ORIGINAL PRINT

739   Brochure, Cournil vehicle

INFORMATION SUPPLIED

740   Various details:
       John D Hamill, director

PARLIAMENTARY

741   Evidence re Timoney APC, paragraphs 450-465:
      Dail Eireann Committee of Public Accounts, Report
      (Appropriations Accounts, 1976)
      prl 8014; typescript circulated April 1979; printed February
      1980 (assistance, Ken O'Brien, *Irish Times*, Dublin; copy,
      courtesy, Seamus Phelan, Committee Secretary)

Chapter Seven - Ships

ORIGINAL MANUSCRIPTS

742   Records of construction at Warrenpoint Shipyard,
      In course of transfer to National Maritime Museum, Greenwich,
      full details not available; DJ Lyon

743   Closure of Belfast Ropework Co. Ltd.
      Statement by McLeery L'Amie Group; July 1979

744,745   Statements by Parliamentary Under Secretary,
          Department of Commerce:
          Northern Ireland Information Service
          IIOB/79, 23 July 1979
          164/79,4 October 1979

INFORMATION SUPPLIED

746   Ross Company:
      Aiden Kent, company office, New Ross

ORIGINAL PRINTS

747   Ringsend Dockyard;
      Entry, page 292,
      Irish Industrial Year Book, 1939; McEvoy Publishing Co, Dublin

748   "Royal Navy Disposals, 1945"
      Series by George Ransome in *QUARTERDECK, International*
      Naval Magazine, Liverpool, bi-montly, October 1979-

Chapter Eight - Aerospace

Potez

INFORMATION SUPPLIED

749   Various details re Baldonnel plant from Aer Lingus

ORIGINAL MANUSCRIPT

Cross and Jackson

750   File 694/67
      Planning Department, Cork County Council

INFORMATION SUPPLIED

751 Dominic J Daly, auctioneer, Cork

752 SJ Robinson, public relations,
British Hovercraft Corporation, Isle of Wight

753 Information Division. Industrial Development Authority,
Dublin

Garrett Ireland   **INFORMATION SUPPLIED**

754 RV Coveney, personnel manager

Ernst Grob   **ORIGINAL MANUSCRIPTS**

755, 756   Ernst Grob
Statements by the Industrial Development Authority,
Waterford,
July 1979
November 1979

McCandless   **INFORMATION SUPPLIED**

757 WS Gibson, managing director, WAC McCandless (Engineers),
Belfast

758 Alfred Montgomery, Ulster Museum

759 Robert Galbraith, Ulster Folk and Transport Museum

Lear Fan   **ORIGINAL MANUSCRIPT**

760 Statement by Department of Commerce; Northern Ireland
Information Service, 18/80, February 1980

ORIGINAL PRINT

761 Brochure, *LearFan*
Learavia Corporation, Reno, Nevada

Gulfstream/Zwaam project   **INFORMATION SUPPLIED**

762 Details from Department of Commerce

PARLIAMENTARY

781   Defence (Amendment) (no 2) Act, 1979, no 28

Nuclear Defences Limited

ORIGINAL MANUSCRIPT

COMPANIES OFFICE, DUBLIN

782   File 74990/2

ORIGINAL PRINT

783   Sales Literature issued by the company

INFORMATION SUPPLIED

784   Various details,
       Patrick Prendergast, Director

ORIGINAL PRINTS

785   *How to survive the Nuclear War*
       Published by the Ecology Party on behalf of itself, the World
       Disarmament Campaign, the Campaign for Nuclear
       Disarmament and the International Civil Defence Organisation;
       London 1980

786   *Protect and Survive*
       ISBN O II 340728 9
       Official handbook for nuclear warfare
       Home Office; Stationery Office; London, new edition, 1980

787   *Armaments or Disarmament? The Crucial Choice*
       Stockholm International Peace Research Institute, Sweden,
       1979

QUANTIFICATION OF SOURCES
Table One Disposition

	ORIGINAL MANUSCRIPTS	CALENDARED MANUSCRIPTS	ORIGINAL PRINTS	PARLIA-MENTARY	INFOR-MATION SUPPLIED
ONE Gunpowder 1-294	1-27 51-102 139-213 268-285	28-39 103-112	40 41 113-119 214-231 286-289	42-46 120-136 232-249 290	47-50 137 138 250-267 291-294
TWO High Explosives 295-382	295-329 379 380		330-357 381	358-362	363-378 382
THREE Inventors 383-436	383 -392 406 407 411-418 (444)		393 398-401 408 409 419-421		394-397 402-405 410 422-436
FOUR World Wars 437-493	437-458 483-486 (634)		459-467 487-489 493	468-470	471-482 490-492 (565)
FIVE Guns 494-552	494-508 540-552 (295)	509-527	528-535	536 543 544	537-539 545-552
SIX Armoureed Vehicles 553-567	560-563	553-556	557 558 564 (464)		559 565-567
SEVEN Ships 568-625	568 585 592-599	569-576 578-584	588 589 600-615	577 616-621	586 587 590 591 622-625
EIGHT Aerospace 626-657	628 630-632 634-640 (444)		626 641-649 (463) (483)	650-653	627 629 633 654-657
EPILOGUE 658-672	658		659-665	666-669	670-672
MULTIPLE REFERENCE 673-716	673-675		676-681 690-709	682-689	710-716
LATE SOURCES 717-787	721 729-731 734 736-738 742-745 750 755 756 760 763-774 777-780 782	727 728	722-724 732 735 739 747 748 761 775 776 783 785-787	717 719 741 781	718 720 725 726 733 740 746 749 751-754 757-759 762 784

QUANTIFICATION OF SOURCES
Table Two Aggregation

	ORIGINAL MANUSCRIPTS	CALENDARED MANUSCRIPTS	ORIGINAL PRINTS	PARLIA-MENTARY	INFOR-MATION SUPPLIED
ONE Gunpowder 294	172	22	31	41	28
TWO High Explosives 89	37		30	5	17
THREE Inventors 53	20		10		23
FOUR World Wars 57	26	13		3	15
FIVE Guns 59	18	19	8	3	11
SIX Armoured Vehicles 15	4	4	3		4
SEVEN Ships 58	10	15	18	7	8
EIGHT Aerospace 32	11		10	4	7
EPILOGUE 15	1		7	4	3
MULTIPLE REFERENCE 44	3		26	8	7
LATE RESOURCES 71	33	2	15	4	17
787	335	62	171	79	140

Table Three
Multiple Reference crossreferenced to text including directories 690-694 and newspapers 695-709

	ORIGINAL MANUSCRIPTS	CALENDARED MANUSCRIPTS	ORIGINAL PRINTS	PARLIA-MENTARY	INFOR-MATION SUPPLIED
ONE	673		676-678	682 686-684	710
TWO	674 675			683 687 689	714
THREE				683	
FOUR	674		680 681	683 685	711-713
FIVE	673		676 677 679	683-685 689	710
SIX					
SEVEN			680	682 683 685	714 715
EIGHT			680	683 685	711-713 716
EPILOGUE				683 684	715 716

Table Four
Late Sources

	ORIGINAL MANUSCRIPTS	CALENDARED MANUSCRIPTS	ORIGINAL PRINTS	PARLIA-MENTARY	INFOR-MATION SUPPLIED
ONE					
TWO	729			717	718
THREE					
FOUR	721		722-724	719	720 725 726
FIVE	729-731	727 728	732		733
SIX	734 736-738		735 739	741	740
SEVEN	742-745		747 748		746
EIGHT	750 755 756 760 763-774		761 775 776		749 751-754 757-759 762
EPILOGUE	777-780 782		783 785-787	781	784

INDEX TO INSTITUTIONS IN SOURCES

INDEX TO INDIVIDUALS IN SOURCES

INDEX

M

P

O

S

T

EDITOR'S NOTES

In preparing this work for the press my guiding principle has been to avoid as far as possible making changes in the character of what is essentially a thesis.

Such small changes as I have made will, I hope, clear up an occasional obscure reference.

My thanks are due to various persons who have generously helped me by discussing aspects of the subject with which I was unfamiliar, or who have been helpful in other ways. In particular I must mention

Professor Alan Crocker: University of Surrey

Glenys Crocker of Guildford

The Registrar: University of Surrey

Arthur Percival MBE BA FSA: Civic Trust, London

Professor John Butt: Strathclyde University

Professor Michael Wilks: Birkbeck College, London

The Gunpowder Mills Study Group, London

Association for Industrial Archaeology, Shropshire

Jack Lane: Department of Trade & Industry, London

Michael Mulcahy: Kinsale Regional Museum

Dr Michael Mortell, President: University College, Cork

Con O'Brien, Assistant Registrar: University College, Cork

Michael Monk: Archaeology Department, University College, Cork

Professor John Maguire: Social Theory and Institutions, University College, Cork

Senator Professor John A Murphy: History Department, University College, Cork (Examiner of Thesis)

Tom Widger: *The Sunday Tribune,* Dublin

Dan Kelleher, Superintendent: Killarney National Park

Donal Musgrave: *The Cork Examiner*

Jack Fitzsimons: Kells, Co Meath

Tim Cadogan: Cork County Library

Niall P O'Siochain: Munich, Germany

(CONTINUED)

Joe Noonan BCL: Executor of Estate

Councillor Brian Bermingham, Cork

Finally, my thanks go to everyone in DATAPLUS, Belfast who have patiently accommodated all my suggestions.   With special mention of

The Proprietor, Diane Forsythe and family.

Print Manager, Adrian Glenn.

Printer, David McAlpine and staff.

The Computer Staff:

Michelle Aggett
Jessie Taylor
Jennifer Aicken

and Susan Kerr who designed the cover of this book.

Also my gratitude

to everyone I met during my many pleasant visits to Northern Ireland.

JOHN F KELLEHER
22 FEBRUARY 1993

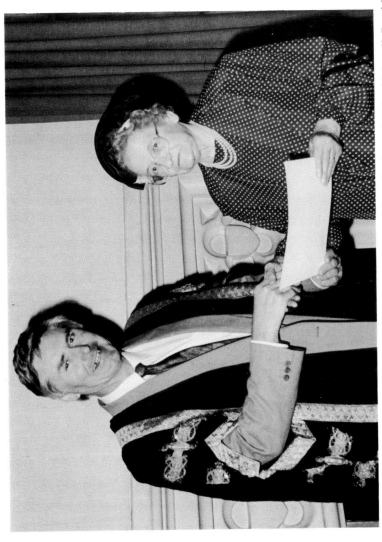

Mrs Joan Kelleher being presented with a posthumous M.A. award from Professor Michael Mortell, President of University College, Cork, on behalf of her son, Mr George D. Kelleher on 1st September 1989.

Ruth Kelleher, John A Kelleher, Ted Kelleher, Mrs Jack Lane, Professor John A. Murphy (Examiner of Thesis), Rev. Finbarr Kelleher, John F Kelleher (Publisher), Dr Michael Mortell (President of U.C.C.), Dan Kelleher, Mrs Joan Kelleher (Mother), Rev. Jerome O'Hanlon, Andrew V. Kelleher, Michael A. Monk (Archaeology, U.C.C.), Mrs Andrew V. Kelleher, Michael Mulcahy, Rosalind Kelleher, Joan Kelleher B.A., Jack Lane, Yvonne Kelleher, Con O'Brien (Assistant Registrar, U.C.C.), Professor John M. Maguire (Sociology, U.C.C.).

400